# Reason
## and
## Faith

**PAUL MARSTON AND
ROGER FORSTER**

**MONARCH PUBLICATIONS**
Eastbourne

Biblical quotations are from the
New International Version © International Bible Society
1973, 1978, 1984, unless otherwise marked.

*Front cover photo: Tony Stone Photolibrary — London*

**British Library Cataloguing in Publication Data**

Marston, V. Paul (Victor Paul), *1946–*
Reason and faith.
1. Christian doctrine.  Faith
I. Title  II. Forster, Roger
234'.2

ISBN 1–85424–054–4 (Monarch)
0–7324–0437–1 (Albatross)

Co-published in Australia by
Albatross Books, PO Box 320, Sutherland, NSW 2232

Printed in Great Britain for
MONARCH PUBLICATIONS LTD
1 St Anne's Road, Eastbourne, E Sussex BN21 3UN by
Courier International Ltd, Tiptree, Essex
Typeset by J&L Composition Ltd, Filey, North Yorkshire

# REASON AND FAITH

# CONTENTS

# ABOUT THE AUTHORS

## Roger T Forster MA

ROGER FORSTER COMPLETED STUDIES IN theology and mathematics at Cambridge University. After Cambridge, he did national service as an officer in the RAF, then entered teaching. In 1957 he entered full-time Christian work as an evangelist and teacher, ministering in numerous conferences and meetings of many denominations and student bodies at home and abroad since that time. For some while he and his wife, Faith, ran their home as an extended family for the socially maladjusted. He has served on councils of various interdenominational bodies, such as the Evangelical Alliance, and as a vice-president of the UCCF. Currently, he leads the fellowship, training programme and ministry team of the South London based Ichthus Christian Fellowship, one of the fastest growing churches in the UK. Faith is also involved in a preaching and counselling ministry, and they have three children. Roger's other writings include: *Saving Faith, Saturday Night, Sunday Morning ...*, *Ten New Churches (ed), That's a Good Question* (with V Paul Marston) and *God's Strategy in Human History* (with V Paul Marston).

## V Paul Marston BSc (Econ), MSc (OR), MSc (History and Philosophy of Science) PhD

V Paul Marston studied economics, politics and statistical and scientific methodology at London University's LSE, and he has also completed a further London MSc in the history and philosophy of science, and a PhD which concerned interactions between science, Christianity and scientific methodology. As a senior lecturer in Lancashire Polytechnic's Faculty of Science, he has been involved in design and teaching on degree-level courses on scientific method, history of science, and science and religion in Western culture. He has also been involved as a speaker in various conferences of Christian and secular academic bodies on these issues. Paul is involved with his wife, Janice, and their two children in the evangelical Free Methodist Church, in which he is a lay minister and the chairman of the denominational Social and Moral Issues Committee. Apart from a book on statistical theory, Paul's Christian writings include: *God and the Family, That's a Good Question* (with Roger T Forster) and *God's Strategy in Human History* (with Roger T Forster).

# ACKNOWLEDGEMENTS

Although we alone are, of course, responsible for anything said in this book, we gratefully acknowledge the help and encouragement of many friends in its preparation. In particular we would thank Mr W Baker, Professor R J Berry, Mr D Boulton, Professor F F Bruce, Dr Norma Emerton, Dr A G Fraser, Rev Steve Gaukroger, Mr M Poole, Professor C A Russell and Professor D C Spanner who, from positions of particular expertise, have been kind enough to offer comment (some in great detail) and encouragement on material which has gone into it. We thank friends amongst scientific colleagues at the Polytechnic who advised on some of the technical points, and the long-suffering librarian who had to keep sending overdue notices! We thank those who, for our section on miracles, wrote out their own personal experience of healing.

# FOREWORD

The authors of this work between them cover a wide range of expertise, and are well qualified to answer questions which are posed today about the compatibility of scientific knowledge and Christian faith.

With many of the areas of study dealt with here, I have no first-hand acquaintance. However, during a long academic career I have come to know colleagues and friends who are leading authorities in a variety of sciences — from astrophysics to microbiology to psychology — and who find no difficulty in maintaining a firm and intelligent Christian faith, not keeping their faith and knowledge in watertight compartments, but allowing them to interact constructively, to the strengthening of both. From this, I have concluded that there is nothing in those sciences which is at variance with Christian faith.

I can speak more positively when I come to my own special studies. As a student of history and a practitioner and teacher of biblical criticism, without qualification or apology, I can confidently affirm that I am aware of nothing in historical research or in the critical study of the Bible which in any way diminishes the authority of the Bible or of the witness which it bears to Christ. The trouble very often is that young people have received their faith as part of a package deal, in which the truth of the gospel is wrapped up with a good deal of expendable material. It is sometimes difficult for them to distinguish what is expendable from what is essential — or, to use the old metaphor, to distinguish the baby from the bath water. If a Bible-class leader assures boys and girls that a consistent Christian faith requires them to believe that the world was made in 144 hours between 6,000 and 10,000 years ago, they will find it difficult to square that with what they are taught in school, and may conclude that Christian faith has been undermined by scientific knowledge. What Christian faith actually teaches is quite different — namely, that no matter how far out in space, no matter how far back in time, no matter how far into the constitution of human nature scientists may press their researches, whatever they discover will throw further light on the universe, which God has created and maintains in existence.

One of the merits of this book is that it helps the reader to distinguish clearly between what is of the essence of Christian faith and what is not. It makes fascinating reading; I have found particularly informative the section on the relation through the centuries between Christianity and scientific study. The suggestion that for most of the time they have been allies, not opponents, may be new to many readers, but it is a well-established fact.

I have great pleasure in recommending this work to all who have an interest in the relation between reason and faith.

F F BRUCE
Emeritus Professor,
University of Manchester.

# INTRODUCTION

## Dealing with a God Who Answers

### Our standpoint

THE AUTHORS OF THIS BOOK are Christians. We stand in what might be called the mainstream evangelical movement, having a personal relationship with the risen Jesus Christ. We believe in the historic teaching of Jesus and Christianity, accepting the Christian Scriptures (ie the Bible) as an authoritative revelation of God in his dealings with mankind.

Our claim in this present volume is that biblical or Bible believing Christianity (ie Christianity which takes the Bible as authoritative) 'makes sense' and is consistent with modern science and historical study.

This question, of course, may be of interest both to committed Christians and to those who are not yet believers but who wish to consider seriously whether or not Christianity is true. In either case it will obviously be necessary to ensure that what we are considering IS the Christianity of the Bible. Thus we will, without assuming that all our readers share our acceptance of the inspiration of the Bible, cite or quote the Bible as a definitive source for biblical Christianity. We generally use the New International Version of the Bible, though we may sometimes refer to the Hebrew or Greek originals.

Now, if 'biblical Christianity' is, indeed, to be defined as the Christianity taught in the Bible, it must also be recognised that there may be variations in the way in which people interpret it. How, then, can one decide the true meaning? Can Christians simply reinterpret it to mean whatever they like? We would emphatically deny this. As Christians, of course, we seek the inner witness of the Holy Spirit that our understanding is correct. On an objective level, however, any interpretation of integrity should: (i) make sense of the actual text and fit the words used; (ii) be in line with its literary form (poetry, history, etc); (iii) be in harmony with other biblical passages and (iv) be consistent with the interpretation taken by spiritual Christians throughout history. This last point is not to suggest any infallibility of the church, but that one should be suspicious of identifying as a valid Christian belief any novel modern theology which has no support in previous Christian history. Thus, though this is very much a book about today's thinking on issues of faith, history and science, we often cite earlier Christian teaching — in particular from early church periods. To simplify the latter, we have used (wherever possible) the standard American edition of the *Writings of the Fathers*, edited by A Roberts and J Donaldson (1985 printing). References are made as follows:

The Ante-Nicene Fathers, vol ii, p 314 (*Ant Nic Fath*, ii, 314)
The Nicene and Post-Nicene Fathers, series 2, vol iii, p 212 (*Nic & Pos Nic Fath*, 2, iii, 212).

We have conscientiously tried to check all our references and citations for content and context, being conscious that some Christians have been justifiably criticised on this account in recent years.

### God and the honest questioner

So what is the attitude of the Christian God, the God of the Bible, towards those who ask the kind of questions we consider together in this book? The evidence is that he likes people who are prepared to be real and honest with him. Abraham, for example, is presented in the Bible as a friend of God (Gen 12–25). Yet when God told him about his intentions to judge Sodom, Abraham was far from un-questioning and subservient. He reminded God about aspects of divine character which were inconsistent with certain courses of action! (Gen 18:20–5) Again, the Bible shows Job as unable to understand his own suffering and convinced that there has been a slip up in the divine admini-stration; yet God commends him for 'speaking rightly', and his honesty leads him to an encounter with God (Job 8:20, 9:24, 13:15, 38:1, 42:7). The prophet Habakkuk is shown questioning God's providence, taking his stand on a watch-tower to wait for God's answer — and he gets it! (Hab 1:2,5,2:1–2). To the self-righteous, inflated with their own importance in the order of things, God may say, 'Who are you to answer back to your maker?' (eg Rom 9:20).[1] But the God of the Bible responds to the honest searcher after truth, for Jesus himself said, 'Seek and you will find' (Mt 7:7–8).

## Answers which make sense

What kind of answers should be looked for? Should we expect the Christian's faith to make sense in a rational way? Is reason opposed to faith? It must be emphasised, of course, that Christian faith is a relationship of trust in God — not just a reasoned set of beliefs. God's kingdom is entered in a childlike way, through a response of the will to the message of the cross (Mt 18:3–4; Lk 18:17; Jn 1:12; 1 Cor 1:17). Neither reason, nor knowledge, nor intellectual belief in God can substitute for this kind of faith which involves response (1 Cor 8:1; Jas 2:18–23). Paul argues that worldly wisdom, if it actually begins by ruling out the message of the cross and Resurrection, is not true wisdom but folly, and is spiritually barren (1 Cor 1:18–25).[2] Spiritual understanding and power, moreover, depend on the Holy Spirit — not merely on correct logic (Jn 16:13; 1 Cor 2:4).

Nevertheless, having said all this, it is clear that neither Jesus nor his apostles rejected knowledge or reason. They argued logically about doctrines, expecting their teachings to make sense (eg Jesus in Mt 5:46, 6:30, 7:11, 16. Paul's whole approach is structured and logical, but see eg Rom 2:1; 1 Cor 6:2; Gal 2:14). Jesus appreciated the value of eye-witness accounts (Jn 15:27). In dealing with unbelievers, the apostles continually argued and disputed, starting from whatever assumptions their listeners shared (Acts 9:22,29, 17:2–4,17, 18:4,19,28).[3] It is, moreover, the non-intellectual fisherman Peter who instructs Christians to: 'Always be prepared to give an answer to everyone who asks you to give the reason for the hope that you have. But do this with gentleness and respect' (1 Pet 3:15). It is in this spirit that this book has been written.

This book, then, is intended to help honest questioners — both within and outside the Christian church. It does not present pat answers, for to many of the most important questions in life these simply do not exist. But it does try to help others to go some way to thinking through their own answers — even where mysteries of life still remain. Being a Christian does not mean sacrificing intellectual honesty. Rather it means becoming a whole person in body, mind and spirit.

## Meaning, history and faith

In considering whether or not Christianity makes sense of our world, the first issues we take up are those of meaning and history.

We start by considering Christianity in the twentieth century, and asking how distinctive are its claims about the world. This leads to looking at the uniqueness of Jesus, and the historical evidence for his life and teaching. The

Resurrection is identified as a key issue in the assessment of the Christian claims about Jesus, which leads to assessing how well the different accounts of this fit together as historical accounts should, and whether or not any alternative explanations to the Resurrection are plausible. Finally, having argued that the basic historical evidence for biblical Christianity is good, Chapter 7 asks why this is not better known.

## Implications of science

Chapters 8–16 consider key issues raised by modern science for Bible-based Christian faith. These include general issues, such as the approach to the Bible on issues of science, the meaning of personhood, and the possibility of miracles. They also include issues of specific interpretation of biblical passages such as Genesis 1–3. The treatment is aimed both at Christians, and at those who are not believers but who have an interest in the rationality of Christian belief. Though written unashamedly from an evangelical viewpoint, we have attempted in it to maintain proper standards of citation and the careful objective checking of any 'facts' given.

## The 'creationism' issue

In the last quarter of a century a new movement has arisen among evangelical Christians, usually termed 'scientific creationism' or, more descriptively, 'young-earth creationism'. The tenets of this may briefly be summarised as follows:

1. The world is not much more than about 6–10,000 years old.
2. It came into being during a period of 144 hours, by a series of instantaneous miraculous fiat creations.
3. Genesis 1 describes these events literally, and the Bible is itself a source of high-quality scientific information,

which enables it to set a framework of basic scientific truth which may be elaborated by observation.

4. Before the first human sin there was no animal death, and scientific laws were radically different.

5. Evolution cannot account for any basic change in animal structures, but 'degenerative' evolution has — since Adam's sin — caused the production of present habits and organs of predatory life within basic animal kinds.

6. The Flood of Noah was a worldwide cataclysm, during which most of the present geological strata were laid down.

Today this movement has a high profile among evangelicals and in evangelical bookshops, and also in some secular circles since in a few American States they have tried to enforce teaching of 'creation science' in schools. Sometimes it is simply presumed that these young-earth creationists are carrying on the historic Bible-believing approach of evangelicals and fundamentalists. The present authors believe that this is an error with serious consequences — whether it is made by evangelicals (who, therefore, adopt the system) or by secular opponents (who, therefore, reject biblical Christianity altogether).

It is because of the serious nature of this error that what might seem a disproportionate amount of space in this volume is spent demonstrating that the distinctive tenets of young-earth creationism have never been those of mainstream Bible-believing Christianity. No support can be found for the young-earth creationist approach in the early church, classical evangelicalism, or the roots of early fundamentalism. As we show this in some sections from Chapter 11 onwards, reference is made to a number of specific young-earth creationists. In particular, we refer to Henry M Morris, the co-author of *The Genesis Flood* and the key scientific figure in the rise of the movement. Our assertion is that young-earth creationism is presently internally inconsistent, out of harmony with a New Testament approach to understanding Scripture, and presents a factually inaccurate picture of the history of science, theology, and the perceived relationships between them. To demonstrate this properly has required more space on it than we would have wished to spend.

It must be said that it saddens us to be forced to make such assertions against fellow evangelicals, who, although they are theologically unorthodox on issues of the relationship between the Bible and science, may be entirely orthodox on central doctrines of God's love, the Incarnation, and the Atonement. We may share with them in our common love of Jesus, and in many of their spiritual hopes and aspirations. Yet we do regard it as important to establish, both for Christians and for interested non-believers, just what *is* truly representative of classic Bible-based Christianity on scientific issues.

Because of this controversy, parts of our book may, sadly, seem to come over as negative. Our real aim, however, is to positively present the Christian faith as one which is both rational and makes sense of the world in the last quarter of the twentieth century.

## Notes

1. In Romans 9:20 the questioner denies God's right to use some people, who have themselves chosen paths of rebellion or faith, as special demonstrations of the effects of such choices.
2. See also 1 Corinthians 2:6 and 2 Corinthians 11:6, where it is clear that fancy oratory rather than knowledge is what Paul criticises.
3. Also note the approach in Acts 14:16–17 and 17:22–8.

For full details of books referred to in the Notes of this and all other chapters, please see the Bibliography.

# I

# WHY SHOULD WE BOTHER ABOUT RELIGION?

## Looking for meaning in life

THE PSYCHIATRIST DR PAUL TOURNIER writes:

> Let us be the first to discover what modern man is seeking. He is thirsting for God ... Everybody today is searching for an answer to those problems to which science pays no attention, the problem of their destiny, the mystery of evil, the question of death.[1]

But if we all are, in some way, searching for answers, how does an awareness of this come home to us?

Most of us, at least at one time or other, wonder what life — and death — is all about. On a world level there is seldom a time when terrorist acts and war in some part of the globe do not remind us of human hatred and its associated suffering. The superpowers continue in mutual suspicion, threatening each other with ever increasing expenditure on more sophisticated means to destroy us all. In contrast to the resources and sophistication given to destruction, governments seem largely indifferent to the massive suffering of famine which continues in this last quarter of the twentieth century — and that in spite of its having been highlighted by the fund-raising activities of some famous entertainers.

On a national level, high unemployment seems here to

stay. Though politicians argue about how much can be done to minimise it, and rightly work to do so, its persistence throughout Western Europe in countries of differing political allegiance leads many to believe that it will not easily be removed. The various polarisations in society which develop may stimulate periodic flare-ups of violence and frustration.

But many people may feel that all this, even though continually in the news, is remote from them in their individual day-to-day lives. Yet it is on this level that there are the biggest questions of all; for the meaning and destiny of the human species is reflected in each individual member of it. Does humanity have a design and purpose? Or are we all a kind of cosmic accident — with all human achievement destined to an eventual oblivion of destruction in an unthinking universe? Do we as individuals have any meaning, or are we accidental little flickers of consciousness in an eternity of nothingness? More practically, can our lives have any real purpose? How can we manage our relationships in a culture in which, for example, that relationship of marriage, which should be the closest, so often ends in divorce?

Most of us, at one time or another, ask these sorts of question. There may be times — such as the death of a loved one or some personal crisis — when they are the most acute; but the questions are always there.

## Philosophers and meaning

Throughout the past century, many works of art and literature, eg those of Gauguin, Kafka and Beckett, have reflected this search for meaning, portraying man as trying to make sense of a puzzling and pointless universe.

Some major philosophers, eg Nietzsche in Germany and Sartre in France, have understood well the connection between meaninglessness and the fading of God from our beliefs. Both tried, in different ways, to suggest that man could create his own meaning. Nietzsche could not stand the idea of God always watching him and loving him even in his evil; he determined therefore, that God had to die![2] Man was then supposed to laugh in the face of the emptiness of the universe, and rise above it to become superman.[3] Nietzsche himself, however, was unable to do this; his mind snapped under the strain (we say this with compassion) and for the last years of his life he was insane. Jean-Paul Sartre wrote in 1946: 'The existentialist finds it extremely embarrassing that God does not exist, for there disappears with him all possibility of finding values in an intelligible heaven.'[4] Sartre was wrestling with the problem that if (as his atheism implied) mankind is a product of chance, then there is no 'truly human nature' or 'human essence' which defines for us how we should live. Neither human purpose nor morality have any logical basis. Nevertheless, at that time Sartre was hopeful that man could create meanings for himself. Writing later about that earlier part of his life, he was less optimistic; comparing himself to a traveller without any meaning or vocation, he lamented: 'Atheism is a cruel long-term business.'[5] He then tried to solve his problem by plunging into a commitment to a cause: the communist philosophy of Karl Marx.

Ironically, however, Marx's own thought showed Sartre's problem even more clearly. Marx's works of the 1840s, which set the framework for all his thinking, introduced the idea of a 'truly human essence' from which man was alienated.[6] Yet Marx claimed that man was simply a product of material forces. Who or what, therefore, determined this 'truly human essence'? Marx claimed that the fundamental 'realities' were material and economic, and that moral codes were just a kind of side product 'projection' of these realities; they were a part of the 'ideologies' used by the dominant classes in societies. But we might then ask Marx in what sense of the word his promised classless society would be 'better'. And if it is not 'better', then why should we work for it? Marxism really had no answers to the problems of human identity, morality and meaning which Sartre had asked. Where did Sartre himself finally arrive in his quest for meaning? A story is circulating that, right at the end of his life, he admitted in an interview that he had finally come to want to testify to the existence of God.[7] Perhaps this is only rumour, but whether or not he himself found an answer, he had clearly laid out the questions.

## Purpose in life

Where can we look, then, for purpose in life? On the level of society, a hundred years ago there were many who believed that mankind, aided by science, would soon reach a golden age of peace, meaning and prosperity, ie a Utopia. Successive generations throughout the twentieth century have seen this prospect become less and less likely. It is now over forty years since one famous prophet of the coming Utopia, H G Wells, died in disillusion and despair, concluding that life was a huge ugly joke:

> Our universe is not merely bankrupt; ... it is going clean out of existence ... The attempt to trace a pattern of any sort is absolutely futile ... the present writer has no compelling argument to convince the reader that he should not be cruel or mean or cowardly.[8]

Dr C E M Joad is described in *Encyclopaedia Britannica* as 'one of Britain's most colourful and intellectual figures of the 1940s'. In the introduction to Joad's *Returning to the Church*, published in 1984, E P Smith said of him: 'He never missed an opportunity to declare his atheism and his contempt for the church.' Militantly anti-church, he shared in an 'atmosphere of left-wing politics and rationalist philosophy' with what he later came to see as a 'shallow optimism' about human nature.[9] Unlike Wells, however, his later disillusion had a more positive effect. By the 1950s, he could write:

> The rationalist-optimist philosophy, by the light of which I had hitherto done my best to live, came to seem intolerably trivial and superficial — a shallow-rooted plant which, growing to maturity amid the lush and leisured optimism of the nineteenth century, was quite unfitted to withstand the bleaker winds that blow through ours. I abandoned it, and in abandoning it found myself a Christian.[10]

Is the answer found in science? Albert Einstein, probably the most revered scientist of the twentieth century, wrote:

> The scientific method can teach us nothing else beyond how facts are related to, and conditioned by, each other. The aspiration toward such objective knowledge belongs to the highest of which man is capable, and you will certainly not suspect me of wishing to belittle the achievements and heroic efforts of man in this sphere. Yet it is equally clear that knowledge of what *is* does not open the door directly to what *should be*. One can have the clearest and most complete knowledge of what *is*, and yet not be able to deduce from that what should be the *goal* of our human aspirations ... the ultimate goal itself and the longing to reach it must come from another source.[11]

Science may, indeed, offer potential benefits — though today we are all too aware of the equal dangers of its misuse (Einstein's own theory making possible the modern weapons of extreme destruction). But science answers questions of how, not the more crucial ones of why.

On an individual level, these questions of meaning and purpose are, of course, deep in the psychology of men and women as thinking beings. Nearly 3,000 years ago the writer of the biblical book of Ecclesiastes wrestled with them, and looked at many of the ways in which people try to avoid facing them. He tried living for pleasure (2:1), sex (2:8), or simply 'drowning his sorrows' with alcohol (2:3). He tried undertaking great building projects, doing on a grander scale what many of us do with our houses and gardens! (2:4–6). He tried amassing wealth (2:8). His conclusion was: 'Everything was meaningless, a chasing after wind' (2:11). How remarkably this prefigures the words of the twentieth-century writer and broadcaster Malcolm Muggeridge. A former Utopian and agnostic, as a Christian he writes: 'I never met a man made happy by worldly success or sensual indulgence, still less by the stupefaction of drugs or alcohol. Yet we all, in one way or another, pursue these ends, as the advertiser well knows.'[12]

Even worthy undertakings, such as the arts, knowledge, or justice, can enhance but not in themselves create a meaning for life. The writer of the Ecclesiastes also knew this. He tried the arts, focusing on choral work (2:8). He saw that 'wisdom is better than folly' and turned to the academic world for fulfilment (2:13). His conclusion could face many academics today as they throw themselves into the round of research, conferences, and published papers: '"The fate of the fool will overtake me also. What then do I gain by being wise?" I said in my heart, "This too is meaningless"' (2:15). What, finally, about throwing oneself into a 'good cause'? Alas, he concludes that even this seems pointless if 'all share a common destiny — the righteous and the wicked, the good and the bad' (9:2).

On their own, none of these things found, in the words of Ecclesiastes, 'under the sun' can pretend to give us a purpose or meaning; without anything more, they act at best as sedatives or distractions to avoid facing the basic questions (2:17). Answers cannot be found if we look only on the physical level of space-time, so what can we do?

This question arises in the work of one of the most influential figures in twentieth-century philosophy, Ludwig Wittgenstein (1889–1951). In his acclaimed 1921 work *Tractatus*, having admitted that 'the solution of the riddle of space and time lies *outside* space and time', he went on to argue that actually there was no riddle at all – or at least not one which could be expressed and answered in language.[13] To most of us, however, this is a hollow 'solution'.[14] If we cannot find a meaning within the purely physical space-time, then it makes sense to see if it can be found on another level — through a different but related reality.

## The Christian claim

The Christian claim is that this other 'reality' *can* be recognised, *can* be described in language (at least to no *less* an extent than we can describe fundamental physical realities in the light of modern physics) and *is* both described and experienced in Christianity. Christianity claims to give men and women a real meaning and purpose for the fullest development of their beings in all their potentialities: mental, spiritual and aesthetic. It presents mankind, male and female, as a product of divine design, made in the image of a personal God, and capable of receiving eternal life — becoming God's children through faith. In this way, mankind may find its true place in the universe, beginning to live in God's way in his world, relating to others as God intended.

Christianity claims, moreover, to solve mankind's universal problem of death (which seems to deny any meaning to the individual), for in the historical Resurrection of the man Jesus Christ, death has both been defeated and been shown to be defeated. Now, all this may be mistaken, it may be a lie, it may be raising false hopes, it may be a wishful dream; but the one thing which it certainly is *not* is irrelevant to contemporary mankind. If we are talking about the authentic message of Jesus, and not some anaemic version of Christianity, then it is certainly worth bothering to find out what it says and whether or not it is true.

# Notes

1.  Paul Tournier, *The Whole Person in a Broken World* (1965), p 149.
2.  See for example, F Nietzsche, *Thus Spoke Zarathustra*, (1883–4) in the words of the Ugliest Man, (Translated by R J Hollingdale) p 278.
3.  See, for example, *ibid*, p 298, Zarathustra's words to the Higher Man: 'He who sees the abyss, but with an eagle's eyes — he who grasps the abyss with an eagle's claws; he possesses courage.' We are, of course, aware of the difficulty of being certain of Nietzsche's exact meaning, caused by his comparatively unsystematic approach.
4.  Jean-Paul Sartre, *Existentialism and Humanism* (1946; English translation by Philip Mairet, 1948), p 33. Sartre's plays, above all, show what a great understanding he had at that time of the significance of disbelief in God's existence.
5.  Jean-Paul Sartre, *Words* (1964), p 157. First English edition: Hamish Hamilton (1964). Edition used: Penguin (1967).
6.  See especially his *1844 Manuscripts* and *The German Ideology* (written 1845–6), where these phrases occur. Later notebooks *(The Grundrisse*, written 1857–8) mention alienation, but in the still later works like *Das Kapital* (1867) the concern is too narrowly technical.
7.  This story was referred to by the philosopher Jean Guitton in an interview in *Paris Match*, 12th December 1986. He suggested Sartre's long-time companion (the feminist writer Simone de Beauvoir) had suppressed the publication of Sartre's interview.
8.  H G Wells, *Mind at the End of its Tether* (1945), chap 3.
9.  C E M Joad, *Returning to the Church* (1984).
10. C E M Joad, *Recovery of Belief* (1952), p 82. Joad refers, of course, to left-wing Utopianism rather than any realistic Christian Socialism.
11. Albert Einstein, *Ideas and Opinions* (1973; first published 1954), p 41.
12. Malcolm Muggeridge, *Another King* (1968), p 96.
13. L Wittgenstein, *Tractatus Logico-Philosophicus* (1921: translated 1922), 6.521; see also Max Black, *A Companion to Wittgenstein's Tractatus* (1971), p 375. The early Wittgenstein combined a kind of mysticism with the paradoxical assertion that 'the riddle [of life] does not exist' (6.5). This made him a father-figure both to logical empiricists (who denied meaning to metaphysics) and to some existentialists (who thought metaphysical phenomena real but incommunicable). Both these two great systems of atheistic twentieth-century philosophy ran into blind alleys, and are now largely dead.
14. Wittgenstein himself moved away from the *Tractatus*, and in his *Lectures on Religious Belief* a few years later found a place for religious language. Such language still seems, however, to refer to a

life-directing frame of reference rather than allowing us to ask whether or not God really exists — reflecting the insistence in his later works that language is used differently in different spheres. Derek Stanesby, in *Science, Reason & Religion* (1985), chap 3, helpfully analyses from a Christian viewpoint Wittgenstein and some of his philosophical offspring.

# 2

# WHEN THERE ARE SO MANY RELIGIONS, WHY CONSIDER CHRISTIANITY IN PARTICULAR?

## Religious pluralism today

THE QUESTION RAISED IN THIS chapter has always been asked, but at one time it was fairly abstract. People were aware that in their world there were many people of other religious faiths, and vaguely felt that consideration of 'religion' should include them. Today, however, it is a more immediate question. Not only has television brought home to us the large numbers of Muslims, for example, in the world, but many societies are themselves increasingly pluralistic. In the United Kingdom, for example, by the mid-1980s mosques were becoming an increasingly familiar sight. School religious education too had become more interested in non-Christian faiths, and the media more concerned with 'ethnic minority' groups.

With this increased awareness has come a commendable desire to avoid prejudice against those of other cultures and beliefs. Those of us who are Christians will certainly approve this. Where a person's religious or moral lifestyle has no effect on their potential as an employee, tenant or 'good neighbour', then it should in no way affect their selection for any of these. Equally, we must reject any sweeping critical generalisations about other lifestyles, based on hearsay and ignorance rather than evidence. If we reject state religion, and believe in toleration, we will regard as 'prejudice' any avoidance of normal social intercourse with those whose beliefs or lifestyles differ from our own.[1]

But we must be careful here. Cultural toleration is not the same thing as cultural relativism. We may, for example, be quite prepared to employ or live next to members of the Flat Earth Society, provided that their beliefs do not affect their work or 'good neighbourliness'. But this does not imply that we accept their beliefs as 'just as true and valid as our own'. It is neither sensible nor practical to suggest that any and every belief about the physical world can be equally true. If there is more than one belief, then on points where they differ we need to weigh the evidence and make our decision. The same, we suggest, applies to the moral and spiritual world. The fact that there are different beliefs about this, is all the more reason to take seriously the examination of 'evidence' in deciding between them.[2]

## Main types of belief system

Are there, in practice, so many different belief systems that deciding between them becomes an impossible and overwhelming task? There may, in fact, be helpful ways to categorise them into main types, such as this:

1. 'Godless' philosophical systems, eg Epicureanism, Marxism, humanism and existentialism.
2. Animism.
3. Religions of the 'Way', eg Hinduism, Taoism, Buddhism.
4. 'Mixed' religions, eg Sikhs, Bahai.
5. Monotheistic or 'One-God' religions, which worship a single personal Creator-God, eg Judaism, Christianity, Islam.

These are not, of course, watertight categories, but they do give a useful schema. Let us now look at them each in turn.

*Godless philosophical systems*

Godless philosophical systems (such as humanism, Marxism or existentialism) are generally attempts by men or women to reach up, using observation and reason independently of any 'religious sense', and grasp the truth about our world. Interestingly, where they actually get much following outside narrowly academic circles, they often seem to 'borrow' from the religious ways of thinking which they deny.

Now 'humanism', for example, in its original sense meant the assertion of human values in a Christian framework.[3] It was entirely rational to assert such values for a being designed and made in the image of a personal Creator. In the modern atheistic and negative sense, however, the term 'humanism' means an attempt to assert similar values for a mankind viewed as a result of chance material forces. But why should human actions, if there were no design or purpose behind being human, have any more significance than those of apes or ants? Modern humanism's values are 'borrowed' from Christianity without the philosophical basis which gave them validity.

By 'Marxism' here we refer not just to the socio-economic analysis (which actually some Christians have accepted),[4] but the whole system which Marx tried to erect of human meaning without God. It has, indeed, been argued that for his system, Marx borrowed from the Jewish Moral fervour of his culture,[5] but in any event we have already touched on some of the contradictions he faced in trying to reach a human essence without God.[6]

Finally, 'existentialism' too has its original roots in an emphasis on deep religious experience in a world where meaning derives from God.[7] In its more usual modern atheistic sense, however, it means a quest for meaning in human experience in a world where there is believed to be no God. In our last chapter we saw how one of its leading figures, Sartre, struggled against the obvious fact that this led to nothingness.

The fervour, then, of many such Godless systems can be traced to religious roots. But in their own terms, there is no God and so no Designer. Mankind is left meaningless, purposeless and destined for oblivion, and they preserve their values only because of continued borrowing from the roots they have come to deny. They leave us, anyway, asking the rather obvious question as to whether or not there IS a personal God.

## Animism

Animism is a belief in innumerable spiritual beings concerned with human affairs and capable of helping or harming our interests. It undertakes to communicate with these supernatural beings, not about ultimate truth or the dilemmas of moral life, but about everyday urgent practicalities like obtaining food, curing illness and escaping danger. Animism does not have any particular creed, and a genuine worship of the supernatural is hardly present. Though it often has creator-gods appearing in myth, or even forms a part of a nominal allegiance to one of the great world credal religions, any such gods or God remain distant. Of more immediate concern are the animistic 'spirits', which may punish men for ritual neglect or breaking taboos, but are not usually concerned with moral issues.

Science challenges animism by offering alternative answers to the two basic issues animism addresses. Firstly, it offers answers for reasons behind individual physical events, eg drought or epidemic. Secondly, it offers alternative (and more effective) procedures for manipulating the everyday world to secure food, health, etc. But neither science nor animism offer any help on the ultimate questions of the meaning of life. We are still left wondering if there is, in fact, a Creator-God, and a design and identity for mankind.

*Religions of the 'Way'*

There are, of course, profound differences between the respective 'Ways' of Hinduism (Dharma), Buddhism (the Eightfold Path) and Taoism (Tao). Some, for example (the *Bhagavad-Gītā* of Hinduism), emphasise devotion to deities in a way foreign to others (Buddhism or Taoism). Yet there are similarities. There is generally a lack of strong identity of a personal Creator-God. Coupled with this, there is a lack of emphasis on the identity of the individual. The ultimate goal for the individual is not that of having a righteous standing before a moral God. Rather, it concerns the individual achieving 'enlightenment', which generally implies either personal extinction or reabsorption into the monistic 'universal'. It ultimately aims at perceiving the harmony in the 'good' and 'bad' in the universe rather than looking for 'good' to triumph. Even in that Hindu element which comes closest to recognising a personal God, the warrior is told: 'Realise that pleasure and pain, gain and loss, victory and defeat are all one and the same.'[8]

It would be foolish to attempt to sum up and write off such great religions in a few paragraphs (though we do hope to look in a little more detail at them in a later volume). Certainly, any geuine seeker may well wish to read more of some of these for himself or herself. Yet they all leave some questions still to be asked. Are 'justice' and 'right and wrong' meaningful? Is there some ultimate meaning for the human individual? And, above all, *is there*, in fact, a personal Creator-God who is concerned with the world he (or she) has created, and who wants to enter into relationships with individual men and women? The claims of the Jews, Christians and Muslims are that the answers to each of these questions is 'yes'. Though they need not deny that the followers of various 'Way' religions have amazing experiences through their religious practices, these central questions still remain to be asked. Does 'God', in this transcendent and personal sense, exist?

### 'Mixed' religions

The Sikh religion is a blend of Islam and elements of 'Way' religion, whilst Bahai tries to fuse together all the major religions since it sees all as true. There is, clearly, a major problem here in that Islam and Christianity say quite different things about Jesus. To Christians, his death was a central purpose in his coming, prophesied in the Old Testament and testified to in his teaching. Old Testament sacrifice was, according to Christians, a 'picture' of the coming true sacrifice of Jesus for sin. To Islam, however, Jesus was a holy prophet whom God would not allow to die in this way, and the biblical accounts are seen as distortions. At this point, however, we are not considering so much whether or not such 'mixed' religions are consistent, but the remarkable fact that since Judaism, Islam and Christianity would *all* point to a *consideration* of Jesus, then religions which are derived from combinations of these must point the same way.

### 'One-God' religions

As we know, there are three major world religions which claim to possess revelations from a unique Creator-God: Judaism, Christianity and Islam. Any serious seeker after truth could in a short time read through the sacred books of all three; though proper study would, of course, take longer. There would be, however, one very interesting point to emerge, and this concerns the place of Jesus.

The Jewish sacred writings (sometimes called the Torah) are in the Hebrew Bible, which is the Old Testament part of the Christian Bible.[9] One strong theme which emerges in these is the expectancy of a coming 'Messiah' (the very word is a Hebrew one), who is to be a central figure in God's dealings with his people. But what kind of Messiah was expected? A number of different lines of prophecy are involved in this, but in Isaiah 40–66 occur a remarkable series of passages looking forward to a coming 'chosen servant' of God. Reference to a coming Messiah is shown in many verses, such as 42:1–4; 50:4–11 and 61:1. A key passage is found in Isaiah 53:

Who has believed our message and to whom has the arm of the Lord been revealed? He grew up before him like a tender shoot, and like a root out of dry ground. He had no beauty or majesty to attract us to him, nothing in his appearance that we should desire him. He was despised and rejected by men, a man of sorrows and familiar with suffering. Like one from whom men hide their faces he was despised, and we esteemed him not. Surely he took up our infirmities and carried our sorrows, yet we considered him stricken by God, smitten by him and afflicted. But he was pierced for our transgressions, he was crushed for our iniquities; the punishment that brought us peace was upon him, and by his wounds we are healed. We all, like sheep, have gone astray, each of us has turned to his own way; and the Lord has laid on him the iniquity of us all. He was oppressed and afflicted, yet he did not open his mouth; he was led like a lamb to the slaughter, and as a sheep before her shearers is silent, so he did not open his mouth. By oppression and judgement he was taken away. And who can speak of his descendants? For he was cut off from the land of the living; for the transgression of my people he was stricken. He was assigned a grave with the wicked, and with the rich in his death, though he had done no violence, nor was there any deceit in his mouth. Yet it was the Lord's will to crush him and cause him to suffer, and though the Lord makes his life a guilt offering, he will see his offspring and prolong his days, and the will of the Lord will prosper in his hand. After the suffering of his soul, he will see the light of life and be satisfied; by his knowledge my righteous servant will justify many, and he will bear their iniquities (Is 53:1–11).

In its context, this must obviously have a level of meaning which refers to the expected Messiah.[10] How remarkable, then, is its application to Jesus of Nazareth, who claimed to be that Messiah. He was a man rejected by men — believed by the leaders of his own country to be 'stricken' by God for blasphemy. He was 'pierced' for others' sins, silent as he was led before 'judgement', cut off, and with a death associated both with the rich and the wicked. Yet, although he had been 'cut off', paradoxically he would 'see the light of life and be satisfied' — as Jesus claimed through resurrection.

In view, then, of such striking similarities, a most obvious question in the study of Judaism would be: 'Was Jesus the promised Messiah?'

Suppose that we turn now to the holy Qur'an (sometimes written Koran), the sacred book of Islam and accepted by all the main groups of Muslims. The Qur'an refers to both Jews and Christians, and itself repeats many of the stories from both Old and New Testaments. The Qur'an says that the Torah was given to Moses 'as a clear testimony, and guide and a blessing for men'.[11] The Qur'an, moreover, pictures Jesus as coming in fulfilment and confirmation of God's words and prophecies given to the Old Testament prophets such as Moses. It says,

> We sent forth Jesus, the son of Mary, confirming the Torah already revealed, and gave him the gospel in which there is guidance and light, corroborating what was before revealed in the Torah, a guide and an admonition to the righteous.[12]

Jesus' own words too, then, are the 'gospel' or 'good news', and we should listen to them if we accept the Qur'an.

What we find, then, is the amazing fact that all the three major religions which claim to have a revelation from God, seem to indicate that we need to look seriously at the man Jesus of Nazareth and what he had to tell us about God. Coupled with his unique position in major religions, there is, as we shall see, a uniqueness in his words and character which sets him apart from other 'holy men' of history. All this indicates that the Jesus of the New Testament is a logical place to begin any consideration of whether or not a Creator-God has communicated with humanity.

# Notes

1.  We hope to consider in a later volume the issues of Christian attitudes to minority groups in Western Society, ie of other religions or moral systems.

2.  We hope to consider in more detail in a later volume the issues of whether or not all religions may lead to God.

3.  This refers, for example, to followers of Desiderius Erasmus (1467–1536).

4.  Christian Marxists include, for example, Jose M Bonino (see his *Christians and Marxists*, 1976).

5.  A seminal work in this (though it remains controversial) was *Philosophy and Myth in Karl Marx* (1961), by R A Tucker, which views Marxism as a religion; but there is a whole wealth of literature on it.

6.  See Chapter 1.

7.  We refer here to ideas of, for example, Dostoyevsky and Kierkegaard.

8.  From the *Bhagavad-Gītā* (c 1st or 2nd centuries AD).

9.  The Hebrew word 'Torah' is sometimes used more restrictively of the first five books of the Bible, and sometimes more generally to include the oral traditions which interpret the Hebrew Bible.

10. The reference to being 'cut off' in Isaiah 53:8 was associated in Daniel 9:26 with the Messiah long before Jesus' birth.

11. Qur'an, 'The Story' (translated N J Dawood), p 77.

12. Qur'an, 'The Table' (translated N J Dawood), p 382.

# 3

# HOW RELIABLE ARE OUR RECORDS ABOUT JESUS?

## Assessing reliability

THE JESUS OF CHRISTIANITY IS the Jesus of the New Testament — but are the accounts of the New Testament historically reliable?

Obviously, no historical account of anything can be absolutely 'proved' to be accurate in all details. But we can ask certain questions about it. In particular, we can ask:

1. What date was it originally written?
2. If it refers incidentally to facts now known from other sources, does the writer reveal a general accuracy and reliability of observation?
3. How textually reliable are the copies we now have as reflecting what was originally written?
4. Are the particular events it claims to record corroborated by independent accounts?

The last of these is a rather different question, which we examine in the next chapter, but the first three may now be considered together.

## Manuscripts

Various museums today have the actual physical earliest copies of the New Testament books. Experts can accurately determine the dates at which those copies were made. This can be done by comparing them with styles of handwriting and production known from archaeology to have existed at particular dates. These copies are in common Greek, and there are literally thousands of them. Many, including some which are the earliest and date from the first few centuries, have come to light only in the present century. Here are some of the most notable:[1]

| Approx Date Published/ Discovered | Date or Century Written | Title | Contents |
|---|---|---|---|
| 1480 | 4th C | Codex Vaticanus | Almost complete NT |
| 1562 | 6th C | Codex Bezae | Gospels & Acts |
| 1562 | 6th C | Codex Claromontanus | Paul's letters |
| 1624 | 5th C | Codex Alexandrinus | Almost complete NT |
| 1843–5 | 5th C | Codex Ephraemi | Excerpts of whole NT |
| 1844 | 4th C | Codex Siniaticus | Complete NT |
| 1896 | 6th C | Codex Purpureus Petr | About half of Gospels |
| 1896 | 3rd C | BM Papyrus 782 | Parts of Jn |
| 1904 | 3rd C | BM Pap 1532 | Parts of Heb |
| 1906 | 4–5th C | Codex Washington 1 | Gospels |
| 1927 | 4th C | Michigan Pap 1571 | Parts of Acts |
| 1931 | Early 3rd | Chester Beatty Pap 1 | Parts of Gospels & Acts |
| 1931 | Early 3rd | Chester Beatty Pap 2 | Most of Paul's letters |
| 1931 | Later 3rd | Chester Beatty Pap 3 | Rev 9–17 |
| 1932 | 3rd C | PSI Pap 1165 | Parts of Acts |
| 1935 | Early 2nd | John Rylands Pap 457 | Jn 18:31–33, 37–8 |
| 1953 | Late 2nd | Magdalen MS Gk 18 | Mt 18 — 9 verses |
| 1955 | 50 | 7Q5–7, 7Q15[2] | Fragment of Mk (?) |
| 1955 | 100 | 7Q4 | Fragment of 1 Tim (?) |
| 1955 | 60–70 | 7Q8–7Q9 | Fragments of Rom & Jas (?) |
| 1956 | 150–200 | Bodmer Pap P66 | Jn 1–14 + fragments |
| 1956 | 150–200 | Bodmer P75 | Parts of Lk & Jn |
| 1956 | 159–200 | Bodmer P72 | Pet & Jude |

Three important points may be made about these. Firstly, it may be noted that some of the very earliest parts or fragments have become known to scholars only in the twentieth century. Secondly, we may see what an enormous wealth of material this represents, compared with any other ancient work.[3] Caesar's *Gallic Wars*, for example, has been based on a single ninth-century manuscript, ie one dating from five centuries after the earliest copies now available of the complete New Testament, and a millennium after it was first written. Thirdly, it may be added that the variations between the different New Testament manuscripts are small. One expert puts it:

> When everything has been taken into account, the number of variants that make any difference (let alone any important difference) to the meaning is extremely small . . . The other thing that needs to be said is that almost certainly the original meaning is in the vast majority of cases to be found somewhere in the existing manuscript tradition.[4]

Apart from the manuscript copies of the original New Testament books, there is the second corroborating evidence for the text of the very early translations. The most significant of these may be summarised thus:

| Language | Version | Original Date | Earliest Manuscripts | Contents |
|---|---|---|---|---|
| Syriac | Old Syriac | c 200 | 4–5th C | Most of Gospels |
| Syriac | Peshitta | c 430 | 5th C | NT except 2 Pet, 2–3 Jn & Rev |
| Syriac | Harkleian | 508/616 | 7th C | Complete NT |
| Coptic | Bohairic | Early 3rd | 4th C | All but Rev |
| Coptic | Sahidic | 2–3rd C | 4th C | All (in fragments) |
| Armenian | Armenian | 400/433 | 9th C | Gospels |
| Gothic | Gothic | 4th C | 5–6th C | About half of Gospels |
| Latin | Old Latin | 2nd C | 4th C | Gospels/Acts/Paul's letters |
| Latin | Vulgate | 4th C | 6th C | Complete (very numerous manuscripts) |

Finally, New Testament quotations are used by early church writers. These writers (like some modern preachers) often quote from memory and are not word-perfect, so they are obviously less useful than actual texts or versions of the Bible. Nevertheless, it is noteworthy that virtually all the New Testament is quoted somewhere (albeit loosely) in the various writings of the second or third centuries. The following are some of the most important writers, together with one modern estimate of the extent of their quotations:[5]

| Name | Dates | Books Quoted (if restricted) |
| --- | --- | --- |
| Clement of Rome | ?–c 101 | Mt, Mk, Lk, Acts, 1 Cor, Tit, Heb, 1 Pet |
| Ignatius | ?–c 110 | Mt, Jn, Acts, Rom, 1 Cor, Gal, Eph, Phil, Col, Thess, Tim, Jas, 1 Pet |
| Justin Martyr | c 100–c 165 | (over 300 quotes) |
| Irenaeus | c 130–c 200 | (over 1,800 quotes) |
| Clement of Alexandria | c 150–c 215 | (about 2,400 quotes) |
| Tertullian | c 155–c 225 | (over 7,000 quotes) |
| Hippolytus | c 170–c 235 | (over 1,300 quotes) |
| Origen | c 185–c 254 | (over 18,000 quotes) |
| Cyprian | ?–258 | (about 100 quotes) |

In summary, we now have:

1. some fragments dating to within twenty years of Jesus' death which seem to be from the New Testament
2. some long sections of John's Gospel from the early second century
3. most of the New Testament in an early third-century text, and more numerous third-century fragments than we could list
4. increasing numbers of fairly complete New Testament texts from the fourth century onwards
5. early manuscripts (some as early as the fourth century) of versions in Syriac, Coptic, Armenian, Gothic and Latin which were first translated from the original language in the second to fourth centuries
6. references to and 'quotes' from the New Testament in the early Christian fathers, going back to the later first century.

In short, the textual evidence for the wording of the New Testament is early, diverse, and based on a whole wealth of material incomparably better than that for any other work of antiquity.

## The views of archaeologists

The second kind of relevant evidence is that of background archaeology. This can be used to check historical details recorded incidentally in the New Testament. Verified historical details can show us two things. They can show that the writer was an accurate observer, and they can show an early date for authorship if details are contained which would not be known in a later age. A whole wealth of such details have now been verified, but, as an example, consider Luke's correct reference to no less than fifteen different titles for different Roman governors.[6] Not only does this show his habit of careful observation, but it simply could not have been composed at a date after the time of the events he claims to record.

On the dating and general reliability of the New Testament documents, an increasing pressure of manuscript and archaeological evidence has caused a steady change in situation in the last 150 years. In the 1830s a group of German abstract philosophers, the Tübingen School, taught that the New Testament was a later second-century composition and Jesus largely a myth. We have already seen how earlier and earlier actual manuscripts have made this view untenable. Some of the views of leading archaeologists show how there was a parallel build-up of archaeological evidence for New Testament early dating and accuracy.

First, there is the great archaeologist Sir William Ramsay. One study puts it:

When Ramsay first set out on his archaeological work, in the late seventies of last century, he was firmly convinced of the truth of the then fashionable Tübingen theory, that Acts was a late production of the middle of the second century AD, and he was only gradually compelled to a complete reversal of his views by the inescapable evidence of the facts uncovered in the course of his research.[7]

Ramsay first doubted his previous views when he noticed that Luke gave a geographical detail which would not have been known after the time of Paul. By 1895, he could describe Luke as 'among the historians of the front rank'.[8] His mature judgement in 1915 was: 'Luke is a historian of the first rank: not merely are his statements of fact trustworthy; he is possessed of the true historic sense.'[9]

Archaeological evidence has continued to build up, and one of the greatest of twentieth-century experts in this area, W F Albright, summarised:

The sensational finds among the Dead Sea Scrolls since 1948 bring an even more complete revaluation of what has passed for historic-literary criticism of the New Testament. At long last we possess original Hebrew and Aramaic religious books from the century and a half before the crucifixion ... There is no longer any concrete evidence for dating a single New Testament book after the seventies or eighties of the first century AD ... To sum up, we can now again treat the Bible from beginning to end as an authentic document of religious history.[10]

Known personally to both the present authors is archaeologist William Baker, who has worked extensively in the Middle East and Israel. He gives his own testimony that, starting his archaeological career as a religious sceptic, he became compelled by the evidence he found to face up to the reality of the challenge of the Jesus of the New Testament. He is today a committed Christian, fully accepting the historicity of the New Testament and still actively involved in archaeological work.

## The views of manuscript experts on dating

John Romer, an archaeologist who recently mounted a TV series but who speaks from no evangelical viewpoint, wrote in 1988:

> There are also very many details in the Gospels, both historical and topographical, that are circumstantially correct, and have a ring of truth about them.[11]

There are interesting parallels among those who specialise in the study of New Testament manuscripts. In the 1939 edition of his work *Our Bible and the Ancient Manuscripts*, Sir Frederick Kenyon wrote: 'During the forty-three years that have elapsed since the first publication of this work, great additions have been made to the evidence bearing on the history of the Bible text.'

In the new edition Kenyon (a leading scholar and ex-director of the British Museum) stated baldly: 'The books of the New Testament were written between the years AD 50 and 100.'[12] Around the same time he added in a different work:

> The interval, then, between the dates of the original composition and the earliest extant evidence becomes so small as to be in fact negligible, and the least foundation of any doubt that the Scriptures have come down to us substantially as they were written has now been removed. Both the authenticity and the general integrity of the books of the New Testament may be regarded as finally established.[13]

In 1943 another expert on biblical manuscripts, Professor F F Bruce, first published his book *The New Testament Documents. Are they Reliable?* This condensed and invaluable work is available today in a revised form and with a more recent bibliography. In it the professor examines and vindicates the accuracy of the New Testament writers in some detail. His conclusion is that the works are authentic, and he confidently asserts: 'A first-century date for most of the New Testament writings cannot reasonably be denied, no matter what our philosophical presuppositions may be.'[14] He himself would date the first three Gospels, for example: 'Mark shortly after AD 60, Luke between 60 and 70, and Matthew shortly after 70.'[15] This would imply that the records about Jesus were set down from thirty to forty years after his death.

The layman may sometimes suspect that scholars who assert the early date and authenticity of the New Testament may be biased by a 'traditional theology'. But one scholar whom surely no one could suspect of such motives would be Dr John A T Robinson, whose book *Honest to God* in 1963 caused an outcry because of its attack on well-accepted Christian views of God. We ourselves disagree with his radical theology, but believe that this springs from his stated desire to reinterpret the New Testament message in terms which he believes will suit 'modern man'; it does not affect his undoubted literary scholarship of the New Testament documents themselves. What is interesting is that this man, whom no one could suspect of 'traditionalist' motives, wrote in 1977:

The time span over which the New Testament documents have been held to come into being ... having been stretched to its greatest lengths by the extremer German critics of the nineteenth century, has been contracting fairly steadily ever since. At the turn of this century, the span extended from about AD 50 to about AD 150 — and that was already a good deal shorter than it had been on some reckonings. By the middle of this century, with the isolated exception of one book, it was halved, from about AD 50 to about AD 100. I am personally of the opinion that it should be halved, or more than halved, again, from about AD 47 to just before AD 70 ... The first draft of St Mark's Gospel could be as early as AD 45.[16]

Of the New Testament writers he asserts: 'There seems to have been a reverence for the remembered speech and acts of Jesus, which provided an in-built resistance to the temptation to make him merely their mouthpiece or puppet.'[17] Dr Robinson is not, of course, saying that the Gospels record Jesus' sayings word-perfect (in any case he would have spoken Aramaic and the New Testament is written in Greek), but that we can rely on the substantial accuracy of their reports of what he said.

As a final example, we may take the testimony of classicist Professor E M Blaiklock. In 1983 he suggests that Mark may date from around AD 55, Matthew from before AD 70, Luke before AD 67. Far from theologians introducing theological bias towards an earlier date than warranted, Professor Blaiklock asserts:

> Classical historians have been a little ironical in recent decades over the calculated scepticism of New Testament scholars who refuse to see what the classicists so naturally see — a record of life in the first century, if no more than that, which must at least be accorded its unique value as historical material.[18]

## Are present texts authentic?

Do we have, then, in the present New Testament texts, substantially what was written by eye-witnesses of the historical Jesus and the early church? Muslims, atheistic sceptics, and sceptical theologians would all deny that we do, and claim that any original texts have been 'corrupted'. But let us review the actual evidence:

1. Archaeological evidence shows general accuracy and first-century authorship.
2. New Testament manuscripts are numerous, with significant fragments going back to early second century and near complete texts to the early third.

3.  We have other early sources, including the quotations in the early Christian writers (going back to the end of the first century) and other translations (going back to the second century).
4.  All these sources show very little variation in the text.

Now all the various different texts, since they show so little variation, must presumably go back in each case to one original. We might picture the 'corruption' theory like this:

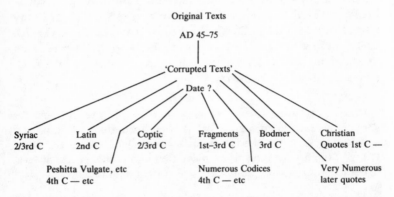

Original Texts

AD 45–75

'Corrupted Texts'

Date ?

Syriac          Latin          Coptic        Fragments      Bodmer        Christian
2/3rd C         2nd C          2/3rd C       1st–3rd C      3rd C         Quotes 1st C —

        Peshitta Vulgate, etc              Numerous Codices          Very Numerous
        4th C — etc                        4th C — etc               later quotes

As we consider the plausibility of this, we must remember that the New Testament is not a single book but a collection of books. Where a work (eg the Book of Mormon) is the product of one single writer, then there may be much more room for that writer's imagination to operate. But in this case there is a collection of books, all agreed on such essentials as Jesus' teaching of love and devotion to God, his miracles, the crucifixion and Resurrection. If this agreement is not based on truth, then there are only three ways it could have come about. The first would be by deliberate collusion — an agreed hoax. This is frankly incredible, as it would ignore the moral teaching brought by those very books, and the fact of the early church and its dedication (even to death) to its faith. The second would be that all the writers based their books on myths built up and commonly accepted by a later date. This is impossible, as archaeology has now shown those books to date from the first century — there was no time for myth to build up. The third would be that a single copy of all the books was 'corrupted' by a single person or small group of people, this corrupted version, being the one from which all the later versions derive. Is this third alternative plausible?

The problem with this is to find a time when the supposed 'corruption' could have taken place. We must remember that the books were originally written separately, probably on scrolls. There then had to be time for the (apparently innovative) collection of them into a codex book.[19] On the other hand (even if, for now, we ignore the controversial 7Q first-century fragments), there are undisputed early second-century fragments of John's Gospel, and a near complete New Testament by the early third. Moreover, the single 'corrupted' version would have to have become widespread enough to form the basis of the divergent second-century Syriac and Coptic translations — as well as the version quoted by Christian leaders from the late first century and throughout the second. There simply is no time into which the supposed single corrupted version could be put.

What does this mean? In, say, the early nineteenth century the 'corruption' theory might just have been plausible. Today, however, our present wealth of discovered manuscript material and archaeological evidence makes it impossible.

## The canon of scripture

There is one final point. People sometimes wonder if the Gospel writers took a particular view of Jesus, and the church later selected these particular writings and rejected the 'equally authentic' different views in others, eg the gnostics.[20] Two points here are important. Firstly, the extant gnostic writings, such as the famous Nag Hammadi finds, are mostly fourth-century translations where even the originals were not written until AD 130.[21] Unlike the Gospels, then, they are later, show little familiarity with the actual milieu in which the historical Jesus lived, and present supposed secret teachings of Jesus rather than any historical detail.[22] Our commitment today is to the *historic* Jesus, who lived, taught, and worked as a Jew in Israel. Gnostic writings do not offer an alternative historical Jesus to that of the Gospels — but only a set of mystic, often highly immoral, teachings which stand in opposition to the whole dealing of a holy God with Israel in history.[23]

## Summary

The clear objective evidence, then, is this. The original New Testament books were mostly written between about AD 45–70, and all before the end of the first century. In terms of general background observation the writers were reliable observers, presenting a picture of a historical figure. The copies we now have are early, numerous, and very unlikely to differ in any significant way from what was originally written.

Professor F F Bruce, who is certainly one of the most distinguished scholars today on such issues, concluded in 1988 that:

> The New Testament writings provide incontrovertibly our earliest witness to Christ, presenting him as one in whom the history of salvation recorded in the Old Testament, reached its climax.[24]

Very early church figures, like Clement and Ignatius, clearly held there to be a gap between the authority of writings sanctioned by the apostles, and their own.[25] The early church showed wisdom in their decisions on authority and inspiration which have given us the collection of books in the New Testament, and no alternative writings could today be taken as having serious claims to present an alternative Jesus of any authenticity.

## Notes

1. Further details of these are in: F Kenyon, *Our Bible and the Ancient Manuscripts* (1939) or *The Text of the Greek Bible* (revised by A W Adams, 1975); Bruce Metzger, *The Text of the New Testament* (1968); F F Bruce, *The Books and the Parchments* (1984, revised edition) and *The New Testament Documents: Are They Reliable?* (1961); E M Blaiklock, *Man or Myth* (1983). J H Greenlee, *Scribes, Scrolls and Scriptures* (1985), chap 3, gives a particularly early date for the Bodmer papyri. Metzger gives the total number of manuscripts as 5366 (*Manuscripts of the Greek Bible*, 1981) and more than 30 distinct papyrus sources or fragments are third century or earlier.

2. These 7Q fragments were found in caves near where the Dead Sea Scrolls were found. They are small fragments, but Prof E M Blaiklock in *Man or Myth* (p 39) argues that the statistical chances of them fitting as they do the New Testament books would be small if they were from other books. Definitive publication of Dead Sea material fragments is suffering some delay: see G Vermes, 'Biblical Studies and the Dead Sea Scrolls 1947–1987', in *Journal for the Study of the Old Testament*, Vol 38 (1987): pp 113–128.

3. Kenyon, Metzger, Bruce and others (see books in note 1) all make this point forcibly. J A T Robinson, in *Can We Trust the New Testament?* (1977), calls the New Testament: 'by far the best attested text of any ancient writing in the world' (p 36).

4. *Can We Trust the New Testament?* p 37.

5. These details are given by Josh McDowell, *Evidence that Demands a Verdict* (1979), and we have not otherwise verified them. It is, of course, not entirely meaningful to count separate quotations, but the numbers may give some idea.

6. Historian Paul Barnett, in *Is the New Testament History?* (1986), usefully lists (p 159–63) many such points made incidentally in the New Testament and corroborated elsewhere. Professor Bruce lists Luke's governors (eg proconsuls, Asiarchs, praetors, lictors, politarchs, first man, tetrarch and procurator) and other details in chap 7 of F F Bruce, *The New Testament Documents*.

7. *The New Testament Documents*, p 90.

8. William Ramsay, *St Paul the Traveller and the Roman Citizen* (1895), p 4.

9. William Ramsay, *The Bearing of Recent Discovery* (1915), p 222.

10. W F Albright, *The Christian Century* (November 1958).

11. John Romer, *Testament* (1988), p 177.

12. Frederick Kenyon, *Our Bible and the Ancient Manuscripts*, p 98.

13. Frederick Kenyon, *The Bible and Archaeology* (1940), p 288.

14. F F Bruce, *The New Testament Documents*, p 15; also of interest is Bruce's *The Books and the Parchments*.

15. *The New Testament Documents*, p 12. Later editions repeat the same point.

16. J A T Robinson, *Can We Trust the New Testament?* pp 53, 73; see also his *Redating the New Testament* (1976).

17. *Can We Trust the New Testament?*, p 101.

18. E M Blaiklock, *Man or Myth*, p 34.

19. See, for example, J H Greenlee, *Introduction to New Testament Textual Criticism* (1964), p 24 or *Scribes, Scrolls and Scripture*, p 15, or works of Kenyon or Metzger on this.

20. Thus archaeologist John Romer, in his 1988 television programmes and book *Testament*, accepted the archaeological evidence for early dating and accuracy of historical background of the Gospels. Though he made no similar claims for the gnostic writings, however, he seemed to overestimate the real element of 'choice' for the second-century church in deciding which books represented authentic Christianity.

21. See, for example, B Walker, *Gnosticism* (1983), p 27.

22. Even the *Gospel of Thomas*, the nearest to a historical approach, has very little biographical detail or historical background. See also C Blomberg, *The Historical Reliability of the Gospels* (1987), p 208, etc.

23. See also, for example, F F Bruce, *The Canon of Scripture* (1988) or B M Metzger, *The Canon of the New Testament* (1987).

24. Bruce, *op cit,* p 278.

25. 1 Clem 47.1–3, Ignatius to the Romans 4.3.

# 4
# IS THERE ANY MENTION OF JESUS OUTSIDE THE BIBLE?

## Background

WE HAVE SEEN THE EARLY dating and general historical accuracy of the New Testament documents, but now we consider whether or not outside sources bear witness to the particular events recorded. What can archaeology, Roman historians and Jewish historians tell us about Jesus and his early followers?

Let us first remind ourselves of the basic facts which we might hope to find reflected. Non-Christian sources cannot be expected to record Jesus' miracles and Resurrection, but might reflect his followers' claims about these. They might also record that he lived in Israel and was executed under Pilate's procuratorship. His followers were at first few in numbers, but sometimes stimulated riots, particularly among Jews, and by the sixties were being persecuted by Rome.

## Inscriptions

Could these facts be corroborated by monuments or inscriptions? The obvious difficulty here is that neither the Roman nor the Jewish authorities would have had any reason to raise such monuments. The first-century Christians had neither motive nor inclination — their meetings were held in homes not in 'church' buildings. One incidental piece of evidence may come from an inscription found in Galilee dating from around AD 49. This threatened a death penalty for the removal of bodies from tombs. What motive would Jewish people have to steal bodies? Perhaps rather this reflects the arrival in Rome of a garbled version of the story that Jesus' body had been stolen (Mt 28:11–15).

In the understandable absence, then, of monuments, we might expect that the only 'direct' evidence would be likely to come from tombs. Some have suggested that the tombs found in Jerusalem in 1945 by Professor Sukenik inscribed 'Jesus help' and, it seems, 'Jesus let him arise' have a Christian origin. Unfortunately, one cannot be certain, for the name 'Jesus' was not unique to Jesus of Nazareth at that time — though to which other Jesus might such apparent appeals be made in Jerusalem around AD 50?

More clear are the Christian symbols found in the cities of Pompeii and Herculaneum — which must predate AD 79, as they were covered in a Vesuvius volcanic eruption about that year.[1]

Two other tombs provide other interesting evidence. Around AD 95 the Emperor Domitian banished or executed several people for 'atheism and Judaism', including his own cousin Flavius Clemens, his cousin's wife Flavia Domitilla, and an ex-consul named Acilius Glabrio. In view of the later trials of Christians for 'atheism', and the connection with Judaism it would seem likely that they were Christians. Some remarkable evidence for this comes from inscriptions found at the sites of two early second-century Christian cemeteries in Rome. In one, an inscription was found, indicating that the land's owner was 'Flavia Domitilla'. In the other, a crypt was found under it belonging to 'Acilius Glabrio'. It seems likely, therefore, that by the end of the first century some highly placed Romans had become Christians.[2]

## Roman writers

What then of Roman writers and historians? In actual fact, as Professor Blaiklock bears witness, there is little such material at all in the fifty years following Jesus' death. Basically, it includes: some fables of Phaedrus (AD 15–50); some satirical lines by Persius (AD 34–62); the writings of philosopher-statesman Seneca (c4 BC–AD 65); a poem on a much earlier war by Lucan (c AD 39–65); a racy novel by Petronius (d AD 66); and the anthologies on nature by Pliny the Elder (AD 23–79). Blaiklock asks: 'Of this handful of writers, would any have been likely to mention Christ?'[3] The only serious possibility would have been in the writings of Seneca. Yet, even then, we must remember two important points.

Firstly, as later Roman writings bear testimony, Christianity was often regarded as a superstitious sect of Judaism, and Seneca's lack of reference to Jesus is hardly surprising.

Secondly, Christians only really came to important public notice in Rome after the fire of AD 64 — by which time Seneca was a distracted and tormented man within a year of his death. His *Epistulae Morales* were written in this period, and number XIV 'On the Reasons for Withdrawing from the World' contains a description of tortures very like those which later Roman writers tell us Nero inflicted on the Christians.[4] Seneca closes the description with the words: 'Let us therefore avoid giving offence ... the wise man will never provoke the anger of those in power.' Since it was his one-time pupil but now insanely cruel Emperor Nero who was in power at the time, Seneca follows his own advice by making very little reference to actual contemporary political events in his *Epistulae Morales* (a precaution which failed, as Nero ordered his suicide in AD 65). His failure to mention the Christians is, therefore, not surprising.

When we consider the next generation of Roman writers, the situation is changed. The writings include books on oratory by Quintillian (c AD 35–96); the epigrams of Martial (c AD 40–104); the letters of Pliny the Younger (c AD 62–113); the historical works of Tacitus (c AD 55–120); the satire of Juvenal (c AD 60–140) and the biographical writings of Suetonius (c AD 120). Here we do find mention both of the Christians and of Jesus.

Suetonius, in his *Life of Claudius*, writes that around AD 49 (as we would reckon it) the Emperor Claudius 'expelled the Jews from Rome on account of the riots in which they were constantly indulging at the instigation of Chrestus'.[5] We know how often there was rioting among Jews when Jesus was preached (Acts 14:1–6), and it would be natural enough for a later pagan historian to mistake such accounts to be saying that 'Chrestus' was there in person. This seems the more likely because 'Christ', unlike 'Jesus', is not a name but a title that a Jew would not normally take to himself. Suetonius' reference also confirms Luke's account that when Paul arrived in Corinth (c AD 50), he found there 'a Jew named Aquila, a native of Pontus, who had recently come from Italy with his wife Priscilla, because Claudius had ordered all the Jews to leave Rome' (Acts 18:2; see also Rom 16:3).

Suetonius also mentions in his *Life of Nero* that: 'Punishment was inflicted on the Christians, a body of people addicted to a novel and mischievous superstition.'[6]

This had been described in the slightly earlier historical accounts of Tacitus. He describes how the Roman populace suspected Nero himself of starting the great fire in Rome, and:

> To put an end to this rumour, he shifted the charge on to others, and inflicted the most cruel tortures on a group of people detested for their abominations and popularly known as 'Christians'. They got their name from Christ, who was executed by sentence of the procurator Pontius Pilate in the reign of Tiberius. That checked the pernicious superstition for a short time, but it broke out afresh — not only in Judaea, where the

plague first arose, but in Rome itself, where all the horrible and shameful things in the world collect and find a home.[7]

Obviously, the most important thing here is that Tacitus places Jesus correctly in location, time and the manner of his death. But it also confirms that, by AD 64, not only were Christians fairly numerous in Rome, but also that educated Romans regarded Christianity as primitive superstition. The intellectual Seneca probably shared this contempt, not deigning to mention them before AD 64, and, as we have seen, too cautious to make reference when they became a 'political' issue after that date.

Attitudes towards the Christians do not seem generally to have improved in the half century after Seneca and Nero. Pliny the Younger was governor of Bithynia between about AD 110–113, and wrote a number of letters to the Emperor Trajan. He describes the execution of people simply for being Christians, but adds the testimony of some who had left the faith:

> They were in the habit of meeting on a certain fixed day before it was light, when they sang in alternate verses a hymn to Christ, as to a god, and bound themselves by a solemn oath, not to perform any wicked deed, but never to commit any fraud, theft or adultery, never to falsify their word, nor deny a trust when they could be called upon to make it good.[8]

All this is much what we would expect from such a person without much understanding looking at Christian practices.

### Jewish writers

Roman writers, then, say much what we would expect about Jesus and his followers. What of Jewish writers? Firstly, there are the various Jewish legal traditions handed down. These were embodied in the written *Talmud*, which consists of the *Mishnah*, which was compiled between AD 100–200, and the *Gemara*, which are commentaries on these written in the ensuing 300 years. Though they are primarily legal rather than historical, Jesus is mentioned much in terms that we might expect. One passage reads:

> Jesus was hanged on the Passover Eve. Forty days previously the herald had cried, 'He is being led out for stoning, because he has practised sorcery and led Israel astray and enticed them into apostasy. Whoever has anything to say in his defence, let him come and declare it.' As nothing was brought forward in his defence, he was hanged on Passover Eve.[9]

This is interesting in that it recognises that, although as a Jew he was expected to be stoned, he was in fact 'hanged',[10] and on the eve of the Passover, as John 19:14 states. The charge of sorcery presumably relates to his miracles and was made in Jesus' lifetime (Mt 9:34; Mk 3:22). Elsewhere Jesus is referred to as the 'Son of Pantera' (perhaps a corruption of the Greek *parthenos* or virgin), is said to have claimed to come not to destroy but add to the Jewish Law, and his disciples (five of whom are named) healed the sick in his name.[11]

Little actual first-century Jewish writings remain. There are important works of Philo, the Jewish philosopher from Alexandria in Egypt (c 20 BC– c AD 50), but these were philosophical not historical and would have no reason to refer to Jesus.

Virtually the only other significant first-century work is that of the Jewish historian known as Flavius Josephus. Born in AD 37, he completed in Greek his great work *Antiquities of the Jews* around AD 93. We should not exaggerate Josephus' accuracy in writing of the times of Jesus, for — unlike the New Testament writers — he was writing of a period just before he was born. Nevertheless, he does describe and give valuable background to many of the characters mentioned in the Gospels, such as Pilate, Herod, Caiaphas, John the

Baptist and even Jesus' brother James.[12] In the present Greek versions of his work there is the following passage:

> Now there was about this time, Jesus, a wise man, if it be lawful to call him a man, for he was a doer of wonderful works, a teacher of such men as receive the truth with pleasure. He drew over to him both many of the Jews and many of the Gentiles. He was (the) Christ; and when Pilate, at the suggestion of the principal men amongst us, had condemned him to the cross, those who loved him at the first did not forsake him, for he appeared to them alive again the third day, as the divine prophets had foretold these and ten thousand other wonderful things concerning him: and the tribe of Christians so named from him, are not extinct at this day.[13]

We can note a number of points about this:

1. There is no textual indication that this is any different from the rest of Josephus' work, and it appears thus in all available Greek texts.
2. It was in this form by the time it was quoted by the Christian historian Eusebius in his *Ecclesiastical History* (about AD 325), and by later Christian writers.
3. It seems obvious, however, that Josephus was not a Christian, and he shows little other interest in church development.
4. Origen (writing in AD 230 and 250) refers to Josephus' passage on James, and adds: 'It is wonderful that, while he did not receive Jesus as the Christ, he did nevertheless bear witness that James was so righteous a man.'[14]
5. In 1971 there was published a version of this passage preserved in the writings of Agapius, a tenth-century Bishop of Hieropolis:

> At this time there was a wise man called Jesus, and his conduct was good, and he was known to be virtuous. And many people

from among the Jews and other nations became his disciples.
Pilate condemned him to be crucified and to die. And those who
had become his disciples did not abandon their discipleship.
They reported that he had appeared to them three days after his
crucifixion and that he was alive. Accordingly, he was thought to
be the Messiah concerning whom the prophets have recounted
wonders.[15]

What do all these points add up to? It would have been very
odd for Josephus not to have mentioned Jesus at all; on the
other hand, it seems most unlikely that a non-Christian Jew
would have written what is said in the present Greek
versions. The most probable view among modern scholars is
that Josephus wrote something similar to the Arabic version,
and the latter has been translated from an early Greek text.
Some time in the last part of the third century, an over-
enthusiastic Christian copyist made a few subtle additions as
'improvements' to the Greek original. This 'improved'
Greek version passed into use in the church, and — as we
now lack any very early texts of Josephus — it is this which
has come down to us today. In fact scholars had widely
accepted something like this before the discovery of the
Arabic version, and the latter, therefore, stands as corroborating evidence for it.[16]

## Conclusion

What may be concluded from all this? Do we find mention of
Jesus and his followers in those contemporary sources which
we might expect? The short answer is 'Yes'.

Secondly, what do such references confirm? They confirm that Jesus lived in Judaea (Tacitus, Josephus and the
Jewish *Talmud*); he kept and taught high moral standards
(Pliny and Josephus); miracles were ascribed to him and
his followers (the *Talmud*), who saw him as a Messiah or
divine figure (Pliny and Josephus). He was put to death
under Pilate (Tacitus and Josephus), by crucifixion (Josephus

and the *Talmud*). By AD 64, Jesus' followers were numerous enough in Rome to be blamed by Nero for a great fire, for which they were persecuted (Suetonius and Tacitus).

All this offers considerable corroboration for the New Testament picture of the historical Jesus.

## Notes

1. A description of the inscriptions discovered is contained in Michael Green's *Evangelism in the Early Church* (1984), pp 214–18.
2. For fuller details see F F Bruce, *The New Testament Documents*, pp 114–5 and *The Spreading Flame* (1982), pp 162–3, Michael Green, *op cit*, p 213.
3. E M Blaiklock, *Man or Myth* (1983), p 16.
4. In particular Tacitus' descriptions (see note 7).
5. Suetonius, *Life of Claudius* (written around AD 120; this edition translated by J C Rolfe, 1914) section xxv.
6. Suetonius, *Life of Nero* section xvi.
7. Tacitus, *Annals* vol xv, p 44.
8. Pliny, *Epistles* vol x, pp 96–7.
9. Talmudic *Babylonia Sanhedrin* 43a (cited, for example, in F F Bruce, *Jesus and Christian Origins Outside the New Testament* (1974), p 56.
10. That this would be the natural Jewish way to refer to crucifixion is shown in Acts 5:30 and 10:39.
11. See F F Bruce, *Jesus and Christian Origins Outside the New Testament*, chap 4; also the classic J Klausner, *Jesus of Nazareth* (1925).
12. Josephus, *Antiquities* (W Whiston translation, 1960), vol xviii, 5,2; vol xx, 9,1.
13. Josephus, *Antiquities*, vol xviii, 3, 3.
14. Origen, *Commentary on Matthew* 17 (Ant Nic Fath x.424) and also *Against Celsus* i.xlvii (Ant Nic Fath iv.416).
15. The passage is quoted, for example, in E M Blaiklock's *Man or Myth* (pp 27–31) and the 1984 edition of F F Bruce's *Jesus and Christian Origins* (p 49).
16. See, for example, earlier editions of Bruce's *Jesus and Christian Origins* or *The New Testament Documents*, or the footnote in R Marcus' Loeb translation of Josephus.

# 5

# WHAT IS SO SPECIAL ABOUT JESUS?

## Jesus and prophecy

WE HAVE SEEN HOW BOTH internal and external corroborating evidence confirms the early date and general accuracy of the New Testament portrayal of Jesus. But why is the Jesus it portrays so special?

We saw in Chapter 2 how Jesus Christ stands in a unique relationship to all three major religions which claim a direct revelation from a Creator-God. In regard to the Jewish Old Testament writings this brings the striking witness of prophecy. Many details of Jesus' life were prophesied centuries before his birth. How remarkable are these? It must, first, be admitted that some Christians have overstated the case from prophecy.[1] Many 'prophecies' identified by theologians are small snippets of larger passages, where these larger passages do not relate to Jesus. Although these may validly be taken by the mind of faith as prophetic, they are no use as 'evidence' for sceptics, because too much has to be 'read in'.[2] Others were obviously purposely fulfilled by Jesus, as part of his claim to that messiahship.[3] The fact that Jesus did so may give cause for thought to Jews (for not all men could have fulfilled them), but are less compelling for sceptics. Other prophecies, such as his birth place, he could not have purposely fulfilled (Mt 2:6 quoting Mic 5:2). Sceptics may allege that some of these fulfilments were made up by later New Testament writers. But is this really plausible? Would writers committed to such high moral standards have falsified accounts at a time when many would have still been alive to tell them the truth?

Some points of prophecy are, moreover, impossible to explain away even on this basis. In particular, there are two passages which (i) contain a number of precise details all together, and (ii) relate to no incidents or even customs known in the lives of the writers. The first is Psalm 22, which contains the following:

> My God, my God, why have you forsaken me? Why are you so far from saving me, so far from the words of my groaning? . . . In you our fathers put their trust; they trusted and you delivered them . . . But I am a worm and not a man, scorned by men and despised by the people. All who see me mock me; they hurl insults, shaking their heads: 'He trusts in the Lord; let the Lord rescue him . . . since he delights in him.' Yet you brought me out of the womb; you made me trust in you even at my mother's breast . . . I am poured out like water, and all my bones are out of joint. My heart has turned to wax; it has melted away within me. My strength is dried up like a potsherd, and my tongue sticks to the roof of my mouth; you lay me in the dust of death. Dogs have surrounded me; a band of evil men has encircled me, they have pierced my hands and my feet. I can count all my bones; people stare and gloat over me. They divide my garments among them and cast lots for my clothing (Ps 22:1,4,6–9,14–18).

The traditional New Testament picture of crucifixion was confirmed in 1968 when archaeologists discovered near Jerusalem the bones of a young contemporary of Jesus who had been crucified between AD 7–66.[4] An iron nail had pierced each wrist and both heels, and both legs had been broken (Jn 19:32,20:24–7). The piercing of Jesus' heels, incidentally, would have fulfilled an even older prophecy in Genesis 3:15. But what about David's Psalm?

It may be seen that details of it graphically and prophetically describe the crucifixion of Jesus. Yet, when David wrote, nearly a thousand years earlier, crucifixion was not known in Israel — and neither Rome nor Carthage (where it was common) had even been founded. Why should David write in this way — when he himself had no such experience? What makes it all even more remarkable is that Jesus had committed no crime against the Roman state. The usual Jewish method of execution was by stoning (Deut 17:5–7). Why was he crucified and not stoned to death?

As we consider this, we need to look at John 18:31–2:

> Pilate said, 'Take him yourselves and judge him by your own law.' 'But we have no right to execute anyone,' the Jews objected. This happened so that the words Jesus had spoken indicating the kind of death he was going to die would be fulfilled.

Do the words of the Jews mean that it was Roman law which stopped them from executing Jesus by stoning?

Now there is a single much later reference in Jewish tradition to the loss of right to the death penalty about this time.[5] Josephus also indicates (in connection with the execution of James in AD 61) that the procurator's consent was necessary to assemble the Jewish High Court or Sanhedrin to try a capital offence.[6] But with Pilate's express permission for them to judge Jesus according to their law, it seems most unlikely that this would have stopped them judging and executing him. There are, moreover, four further reasons for doubting that it was any Roman law which prevented them doing so.

Firstly, Jesus' own prophecy (ie in Jn 3:14, 12:32–3) would have been unremarkable if John's readers knew that the only execution he *could* have faced was a Roman crucifixion. Secondly, if the crucial factor were Roman law, then it seems strange that Pilate himself shortly afterwards suggested that the Jews themselves execute him (Jn 19:6).

Thirdly, the reference to Jesus' death in the later Jewish *Talmud* (looked at in our previous chapter) seems to expect Jesus to be stoned, but then unexpectedly says he was, in fact, crucified. Fourthly, it was not much later that Stephen was executed by stoning after a Jewish court had tried him (Acts 7:58).[7]

For these reasons, it seems very likely that it was not Roman but their own laws of trial and execution during the Passover, which stopped the Jewish court from executing Jesus by stoning.[8] This is why John saw Jesus' own prophecy as remarkable — but even more remarkable is the much earlier Psalm 22 prophecy.

A final point about the Psalm 22 prophecy is the part about the gambling for Jesus' clothes. Obviously, Jesus himself had no way to control such events. Had he been executed in the Jewish manner, it would not have happened, but it is entirely in character with the Roman soldiers. This adds to an already amazing passage of prophecy.

The other equally remarkable passage is Isaiah 53, already quoted in Chapter 2. As we have noted, this passage occurs right in the middle of a whole series on the coming Messiah, and can only be assumed to be intended as prophecy. Looking again at the passage, we remember how Jesus was rejected by his own people, who thought him stricken by God for blasphemy. He was silent before his accusers and was 'led away' by a judicial act ('by judgement'). In his death he was associated with the wicked (by crucifixion) and the rich (in a private tomb). Yet — and this makes sense only by a resurrection — the prophecy goes on to predict a satisfaction for him after his death.

### Jesus' character

Jesus, though, was remarkable not only for his fulfilment of prophecy, but for his personal life and character. He was someone who led a life of self-sacrificial service, helping and reputedly healing others. Yet, on a human level, there were great paradoxes in all he taught and did. He claimed to be humble, yet he claimed to be able to forgive sins and to be the unique way for man to be right with God and achieve eternal life (Mk 2:5; Lk 5:20; Jn 14:6). He clearly believed in only one God, yet himself accepted the worship due only to God on numerous occasions (Mt 8:2,9:18).[9] He taught one of the highest moral codes of love and righteousness in history, yet claimed himself to be sinless by its standards (Jn 8:46). In the words of historian K S Latourette:

> It is highly significant that in one as sensitive morally as was Jesus and who taught his followers to ask for the forgiveness of their sins there is no hint of any need for forgiveness for himself, no asking of pardon, either from those about him or of God.[10]

Amazingly, those men, who had travelled with Jesus for several years, actually gave their assent to his explicit and implied claims to sinlessness (1 Pet 2:22; 1 Jn 3:5).

We must, of course, remember that Jesus did not come from any of those 'Way' religions (mentioned in Chapter 2), where divinity is a rather diffuse idea and the sharp consciousness of sin is absent. Indeed, his own teaching reinforced the Jewish belief in the oneness of God and the reality and serious nature of sin.

His claims for himself, then, stand in marked contrast to the attitudes of those in history whom we might generally regard as remarkable 'holy' people. The most remarkable and famous of such people were usually loud in acknowledging their own unworthiness. St Francis of Assisi, for example, is seen by many as the epitome of humble, loving, service. Yet he claimed that God used him so much because there was nowhere a greater sinner or more miserable creature than he![11]

M K Ghandi was politically controversial, yet remains for

many a twentieth-century symbol of non-violence, whose title 'Mahatma' ('Great Soul') indicates his spiritual reputation. In his autobiography, however, he wrote:

> It is an unbroken torture to me that I am still so far from him, who, as I fully know, governs every breath of my life, and whose offspring I am. I know that it is the evil passions within that keep me so far from him, and yet I cannot get away from them.[12]

Finally, in our own generation, Mother Teresa and her Sisters of Mercy have become world renowned for their lives of humble poverty and self-sacrificial love. Yet daily they proclaim their own feelings of unworthiness in praying: 'Make us worthy, Lord, to serve our fellow-men throughout the world who live and die in poverty and hunger.'[13]

Why was Jesus so different? He was surely not just a 'good man' — for he was so unlike others we would call 'good'. How could he be so similar in his life of love, but so different in his view of himself? It might be suggested that he was mad, though his elevated view of his own nature seems to bear none of the usual marks of psychological delusion or illness. C S Lewis well sums up for us, however, the central dilemma:

> A man who was merely a man and said the sort of things Jesus said would not be a great moral teacher. He would either be a lunatic — on a level with the man who says he is a poached egg – or else he would be the Devil of Hell. You must make your choice. Either this man was, and is, the Son of God: or else a madman or something worse.[14]

Could it be that the accounts are touched with later legend? Interestingly, third-century legendary accounts of Jesus' life are available. The New Testament differs from them not only in its accuracy in incidental historical detail, but in the vivid portrait it paints. One of our leading New Testament scholars has written:

It is difficult enough for anyone, even a consumate master of imaginative writing, to create a picture of a deeply pure, good person moving about in an impure environment, without making him a prig, or a prude or a 'plaster saint'. How comes it that, through all the Gospel traditions without exception, there comes a remarkably finely drawn portrait of an attractive young man moving freely about among women of all sorts, including the decidedly disreputable, without a trace of sentimentality, unnaturalness, or prudery, and yet, at every point, maintaining a simple integrity of character? Is it because the environments in which the traditions were preserved and through which they were transmitted were peculiarly favourable to such a portrait? On the contrary, it seems that they were rather hostile to it.[15]

Another example of this atmosphere of veracity surrounding the Jesus of the Gospels, is his capacity for doing what is at first sight unexpected, and yet what, when one thinks about it, seems inevitable (Mk 9:36,12:17; Jn 8:7). In legends, leading figures tend to be more conventionally heroic. Many, moreover, have testified to the realistic, 'unmythlike' feeling in the accounts. J B Phillips, for example, whose translating involved detailed work on the New Testament text, wrote: 'I have read in Greek and Latin scores of myths, but I did not find the slightest flavour of myth here.'[16]

The character of Jesus stands forth vividly, and others have questioned, both from a literary and a moral standpoint, whether or not it is credible to suggest that someone could have made up a set of accounts like the Gospels. The famous nineteenth-century non-Christian philosopher John Stuart Mill asked:

Who among [Jesus'] disciples or among their proselytes was capable of inventing the sayings ascribed to Jesus or of imagining the life and character revealed in the Gospels? Certainly not the fishermen of Galilee; and certainly not St Paul, whose character and idiosyncracies were of a totally different sort.[17]

Some sceptics have, indeed, questioned some points of Jesus' morality, but usually these turn out to be fairly straightforward misunderstandings.[18] Many, however, even among non-Christians, would accept the further words of John Stuart Mill:

> About the life and sayings of Jesus there is a stamp of personal originality combined with profundity of insight, which ... must place the Prophet of Nazareth, even in the estimation of those who have no belief in his inspiration, in the very first rank of men of sublime genius of whom our species can boast. When this pre-eminent genius is combined with the qualities of probably the greatest moral reformer, and martyr to that mission, who ever existed upon earth, religion cannot be said to have made a bad choice in pitching upon this man as the ideal representative and guide of humanity.[19]

So what are we to make of Jesus? What are the alternatives if he were actually other than he claimed to be? Let us summarise them and their problems:

1. *Just a good man?*
Problems: (a) egocentricity: Jesus' claims to divinity in the context of his monotheist society are incompatible with normal goodness.
(b) sin: a merely human Jesus, however good, must surely have been conscious of *some* failure to meet his own very high moral standards — yet Jesus shows no such consciousness.
2. *A liar and fraud?*
Problems: (a) moral inconsistency: how could the founder of so high a moral system himself be a great fraud?
(b) motive: surely a fraud would not be prepared to suffer crucifixion for his lie, with no possible personal gain (unless he were also mad).
(c) success: how would a fraud convince several men who travelled with him for three years of his own sinlessness? If

they were part of the conspiracy, then why would they too be prepared to die for it?

3. *A madman?*

Problems: (a) morality: it would be an incredible irony were one of the highest moral codes in history to be the product of an insane mind.

(b) psychology: Jesus seems not to bear the usual marks of insanity.

(c) success: how could a madman command the following that Jesus did, and has done ever since, in people who seem themselves so balanced?

By any standing, Jesus is an enigma. Obviously if one begins from the presumption that his claims are utterly impossible, then one of the above improbable theories will have to do. But suppose that we recognise that there is a coherence and consistency in the whole supranaturalistic framework of Christian beliefs in which Jesus' claims are accepted? Then the improbability of alternative theories should cause us to look very seriously at those claims.

## Conclusion

The writings of all three major world religions which believe in a single Creator-God point towards Jesus. The passages of detailed prophecy about his life, and his unique character, all mark Jesus out as someone who was very special, and whose words bear careful study. His effect on his followers is also remarkable. In this connection we will turn, in the next chapter, to look at one even more amazing fact about him. This is that serious contemporary witnesses testified to seeing him alive after he had been crucified and buried.

## Notes

1. Though sympathising with their intentions, we feel that uncritical inclusion of vague or purposely fulfilled 'prophecies' is unhelpful to

their case in the treatments like those of P Stoner, *Science Speaks* (1963) or Josh McDowell, *Evidence that Demands a Verdict*.

2. Eg Zechariah 13:6, where verses 3–5 have no obvious reference to Jesus. Jesus himself took verse 7 to refer to him (Mt 26:31), but he spoke to his disciples and not to offer evidence to those sceptical of his claims.

3. Eg Luke 19:35–7 in fulfilment of Zechariah 9:9; Jesus deliberately rode a donkey into Jerusalem in fulfilment of the prophecy.

4. See under 'Cross, Crucifixion' in *The Illustrated Bible Dictionary* (ed J D Douglas, 1980).

5. See Alfred Edersheim in *The Life and Times of Jesus the Messiah* (1900), vol ii, bk 5, chap 13.

6. Josephus, *Antiquities*, xx.9.

7. Thus Edersheim, whilst believing that formally the Sanhedrin had by then ceased to give capital sentence (*op cit*, vol ii, p 556), later adds (p 570 n3) that John 18:32 seems to imply that they 'might have found a mode of putting Jesus to death in the same informal manner in which Stephen was killed'.

8. Edersheim (*op cit*, vol ii, p 556) lists the many ways in which such a sudden, night-time trial, during the Passover period, would be illegal under Jewish law.

9. Other examples include Matthew 14:33, 15:25, 18:26, 20:20, 28:9, 17; Mark 5:6, 15:19; Luke 24:52; John 9:38. The restriction of worship to God is asserted, using the same word, in Matthew 4:10 and Luke 4:8.

10. Kenneth Scott Latourette, *A History of Christianity* (1976), p 47. It is this that is more telling than the single (arguably ambiguous) verse John 8:46.

11. St Francis' attitude is given in any biography, eg L Cunningham, *St Francis of Assisi* (1977); M Habig, *St Francis of Assisi* (1983).

12. M K Gandhi, *An Autobiography* (1972), p xvi.

13. This is from section 10 of the *Constitution of the International Association of Co-Workers of Mother Teresa*.

14. C S Lewis, *Mere Christianity* (Fontana 1962 edition), p 52.

15. C F D Moule, *The Phenomenon of the New Testament* (1967), p 63.

16. J B Phillips, *Ring of Truth* (1970), pp 47–48. See also E M Blaiklock, *Man or Myth*.

17. John Stuart Mill, *Essay on Theism*, part v.

18. See, for example, E M Blaiklock, *op cit*, chap 7.

19. John Stuart Mill, *op cit*, part v.

# 6

# IS THERE REALLY EVIDENCE FOR JESUS' RESURRECTION?

## Introduction

As RECORDED IN THE NEW Testament, the Resurrection of Jesus Christ must be seen as a supernatural or miraculous event; there seems not even a remote prospect that it could be 'scientifically explained'. Now to some people this will automatically mean that the New Testament accounts are false. These are people who feel (either on religious grounds or on what they think are scientific ones) that *whatever the evidence*, the miraculous simply cannot happen.[1] Now, clearly, if someone has decided in advance that to rise from the dead is literally impossible, then no amount of evidence will convince them. But is there any historical evidence which might convince the more open minded?

There are five passages claiming to be historical accounts of the Resurrection: the four Gospels (Mt 28:1–8; Mk 16:1–8; Lk 24:1–10; Jn 20:1–8) and 1 Corinthians 15. What would mark these out as genuine independent (or semi-independent) historical reports of actual events?

We must first note some general points about the nature of eye-witness accounts and historical writing:

1. *Selection and 'Contradiction'* Firstly, we must recognise that historians select which details about events to

include, depending on their particular purposes in writing.[2] Secondly, eye-witnesses of events not only remember different points, but actually see those events differently. Accounts which fail to show differences of selection and perspective are, therefore, likely to be a result of fraudulent collusion or copying. On the other hand, it should be possible to see ways to reconcile apparent contradictions.

2. *Incidental Corroboration* In two genuine but independent accounts details given in one may make sense only in the light of the other. This is because the accounts are true but incomplete. It is virtually impossible to fabricate these kinds of details unless one writer has the other's account in front of his eyes and deliberately sets out to do so.

3. *Historical Credibility* Details of the events described should be in harmony with known practices and background of the period in question.

4. *Coherence* Most historians now recognise that historical study is inherently interpretive, and does not provide 'absolute truth'. But historical accounts should be coherent, self-consistent, and make better overall sense than alternative ones.[3]

Do the New Testament accounts of the crucifixion and Resurrection of Jesus bear these marks of historical coherence and truth? The analysis which follows lists the people and places involved, then looks scene by scene at a comparison of the accounts, and finally considers briefly what ways (other than an actual resurrection) critics have sought to explain the evidence. In Appendixes 1 and 2 is contained some further brief details of the people involved, and also a comparative tabulation of the actual Gospel accounts. Readers will obviously want to refer to this and/or the Gospels themselves in following the analysis.

In our reconstruction we shall (as with any historical

reconstruction) suggest some details which cannot be known with certainty. However, our object is not to show that these details are the only possible ones, rather that with such (or similar) suggested details, the accounts fit together as a powerfully coherent whole. The evidence is that something very like this happened. Reference will be made in our account to the diagrams given.

## People

The main characters in the story are as follows:[4]

1. Joseph of Arimathea: secret disciple, member of Jewish High Council
2. Nicodemus: secret disciple, scholarly member of Jewish High Council
3. Simon Peter: apostle
4. John: apostle, Jesus' cousin, also called 'the beloved disciple'
5. Mary: mother of Jesus (relating to others as shown below)
6. Cleopas (also called 'Clopas' or 'Alphaeus'): brother of Joseph and so Jesus' uncle
7. Other apostles and disciples
8. Mary (also called 'the other Mary'): wife of Jesus' uncle Cleopas (therefore aunt to Jesus and sister-in-law to his mother), mother of Joses and of the disciple James the Younger
9. Salome: wife of Zebedee and mother of James and John. Also sister of Jesus' mother Mary, and so Jesus' aunt
10. Mary Magdalene (probably to be identified with Mary of Bethany, sister of Martha and Lazarus)[5]
11. Joanna: wife of Herod Antipas' steward Chuza
12. At least one other woman (Susanna of Lk 8:3 perhaps?).

Jesus' immediate relationships can, therefore, be represented thus:

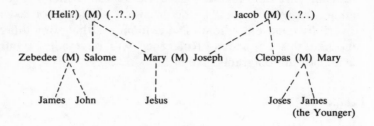

## Scale map of locations

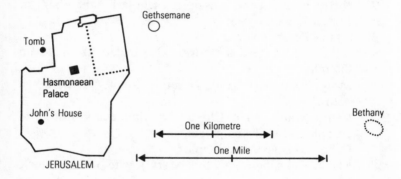

## Places

Known places are:

1. Hasmonaean Palace: probable Jerusalem residence during Passover (rather than the newer Herodian Palace) of Joanna, wife of Antipas' steward
2. The tomb: to the north of the city, outside its walls

3.   Bethany: home of Martha, Lazarus and the Mary who is
     probably the one also called Magdalene. About 1.5
     miles from Jerusalem's city walls

Probable places are: [6]

4.   The house of John the apostle: situated in Jerusalem
5.   John Mark's house: in Jerusalem, probably 'the upper
     room'.

## Writers [7]

1.   Matthew: there is no real reason to doubt that the
     authority behind this Gospel was that of Matthew Levi,
     the ex tax-collector.
2.   Mark: written by John Mark, much from the preaching
     of Peter, but some possibly also from first-hand experi-
     ence as a young man.
3.   Luke: a Greek, Paul's travelling companion on later
     journeys. His viewpoint is that of presenting an accurate
     historical account for the general non-Jewish reader (Lk
     1:1–4).
4.   John: archaeology has demolished all bases of previous
     objections to the source of this as the apostle John,
     though actually set down by one of his disciples (Jn
     21:24). His perspective is one of deliberate selection of
     facts in order to promote belief (Jn 20:31).

## Presuppositions

*Two basic principles* are evident in the way the Gospel
writers treated their material, both of which can be clearly
demonstrated. The first is *incompleteness* in reporting the
presence of personnel. John, for example, mentions Mary
Magdalene, Salome, and Mary the wife of Cleopas at the
cross (Jn 19:25), but only Mary Magdalene going to the

tomb. He can, of course, hardly have expected his readers to take it that a young woman set out alone in the dark for a tomb outside the city. Moreover, when she arrived back, she panted out the words seared on his own memory: 'They have taken the Lord out of the tomb, and WE don't know where they have put him' (Jn 20:2). The plural indicated clearly that others had been with Mary, though John has not mentioned them. Luke shows the same principle. In 24:12 he names only Peter as going to the tomb, but 24:24 refers to 'some' who went there. Clearly, to the Gospel writers, to mention only one name does NOT imply that the writer was unaware that others were also present. We shall later see that this same principle may be applied to the number of 'angels' present.

The second principle is that of telescoping. This may be shown clearly from Luke. Just reading Luke's Gospel, one would get the impression that all Jesus' appearances AND Jesus' Ascension took place on the same day. Yet in the Acts (which no scholar doubts was also written by Luke) it is clearly stated (1:3) that the appearances went on over forty days. In the Gospel he has telescoped events — to bring out a particular perspective. Now Matthew similarly telescopes the events of the Angel's spectacular initial descent (not recorded by other Gospels), and his later conversation with the women. Such telescoping is not uncommon in historical accounts.

### The scene is set (A–B)

After Jesus' arrest, his disciples scattered: Peter and John followed him to Jerusalem, the others ran off. The most obvious place to run to was Bethany: it was in the opposite direction to the city, only a mile or so away from Gethsemane, and they had loyal friends there. They are mentioned no more until the evening of his day of Resurrection. Thomas, alone, may have gone further afield.

Among those watching Jesus on the cross were Mary Magdalene, his aunts Salome and Mary (wife of Cleopas), his mother and his beloved cousin John (Mt 27:56; Jn 19:25–6). Jesus gave his mother into the care of her nephew John, who took her home 'from that hour' to his house in south Jerusalem. Her sister Salome probably went to be with her. John had already taken Peter there, a heartbroken man after his denials during their visit to the house of Caiaphas.

Jesus' body was taken down from the cross by Joseph and Nicodemus, with Pilate's permission, and taken to Joseph's nearby tomb. The Jewish burial custom of wrapping with linen and spices was begun but unfinished owing to the coming high Sabbath. Several women, including the two Marys, watched this. As the Sabbath drew on, they too went back to John's house and 'rested on the Sabbath' (Lk 23:56).

On this Sabbath, though, there was understandably some anxiety on the part of the authorities, and a Roman guard on the tomb was obtained from Pilate (Mt 28:11–15). Jesus' friends, however, quietly passing the Sabbath, knew nothing of this at that time.

*Diagram A* shows locations on that Sabbath. But Salome and Mary (wife of Cleopas) both had sons at Bethany, and Mary Magdalene a sister and brother, so all were anxious to give and receive news. Towards sunset, then, the two Marys and Cleopas went a 'Sabbath day's journey' to the Mount of Olives, completing their walk to Bethany as the Sabbath ended with nightfall. Salome remained in Jerusalem to purchase ointments and return to be with her sister Mary, the mother of Jesus.

*Diagram B*, then, shows their locations during that night. Joanna was at home in the Hasmonaean Palace, probably with her friend Susanna, having arranged a rendezvous with the Galilean women to go to the tomb with spices early next morning and complete the burial rites.

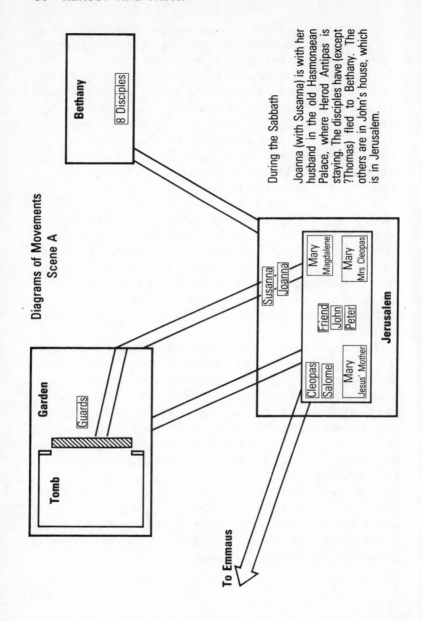

Diagrams of Movements
Scene A

Bethany

8 Disciples

During the Sabbath

Joanna (with Susanna) is with her husband in the old Hasmonaean Palace, where Herod Antipas is staying. The disciples have fled to Bethany. The others are in John's house, which is in Jerusalem.

Garden

Guards

Tomb

Jerusalem

Susanna
Joanna

Mary Magdalene

Mary Mrs Cleopas

Friend
John
Peter

Cleopas
Salome

Mary Jesus' Mother

To Emmaus

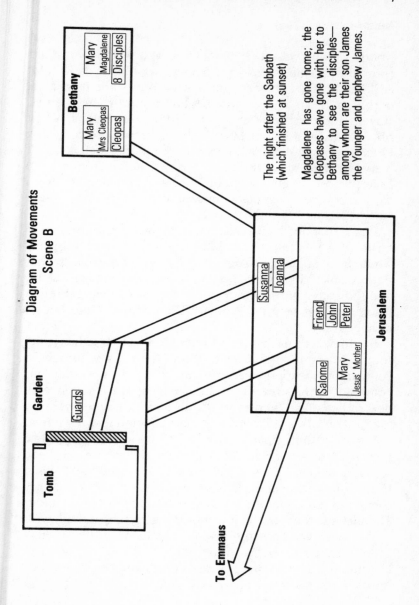

Diagram of Movements
Scene B

**Bethany**

| Mary Mrs Cleopas | Mary Magdalene |
| Cleopas | 8 Disciples |

The night after the Sabbath (which finished at sunset)

Magdalene has gone home; the Cleopases have gone with her to Bethany to see the disciples—among whom are their son James the Younger and nephew James.

**Garden**

Guards

**Tomb**

Susanna
Joanna

**Jerusalem**

Friend
John
Peter

Salome
Mary Jesus' Mother

**To Emmaus**

## Initial events (C–D)

Matthew, who was at Bethany, reports how the two Marys (probably accompanied by Cleopas) set off 'at dawn' (Mt 28:1); John says Mary Magdalene set out 'while it was still dark' (Jn 20:1). They reached John's house where Cleopas stayed, and the two Marys — joined now by Salome — set off to call for Joanna. Mark, who is recognised as giving Peter's version of events, says that the three women set off 'very early' to reach the tomb 'just after sunrise' (16:1–2). Luke, whose account was not first-hand but compiled from various sources, includes Joanna and gives the time as 'very early' (24:1).

Luke, therefore, gives the most comprehensive version in terms of who was present; Matthew records events as they would have appeared to him at Bethany, Mark records what Peter would have experienced at John's house in Jerusalem; and John has a particular focus on Mary Magdalene, through whom he first heard the breathtaking news of the body's disappearance.

Matthew tells us that after the two Marys left Bethany, the four soldiers in the Roman guard (perhaps with Jewish companions) experienced an earth-tremor, not that uncommon in the area. They briefly glimpsed a vision of a descending angel before, wild with terror, they temporarily blacked out. It is an interesting mark of truth that *not one* of the four accounts claims anyone actually saw the moment of resurrection — for in a *fabricated* account who could have resisted making up a story about someone who had? When the soldiers recovered consciousness, they saw the empty tomb and ran off in terror. Guilty of a capital offence under Roman law, they saw their only hope as resting in the Jewish authorities, who agreed to use their influence if the soldiers followed their story. No bribe, though, could stop soldiers blurting out so awesome an experience, and Matthew (with his old contacts with collaborators and tax-collectors) would

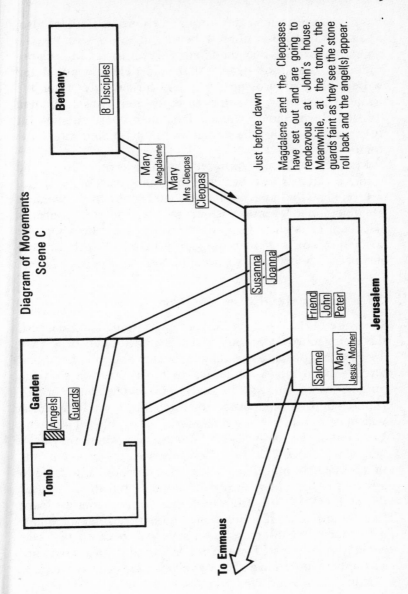

Diagram of Movements
Scene C

Bethany

8 Disciples

Mary Magdalene

Mary Mrs Cleopas

Cleopas

Just before dawn

Magdalene and the Cleopases have set out and are going to rendezvous at John's house. Meanwhile, at the tomb, the guards faint as they see the stone roll back and the angel(s) appear.

Garden

Tomb

Angels

Guards

Jerusalem

Susanna

Joanna

Friend

John

Peter

Salome

Mary Jesus' Mother

To Emmaus

have later got to hear the story and record it. Perhaps also, as an ex-collaborator himself, he saw an especial irony in the abject failure of this humiliating Jewish-Roman collaboration to 'keep Jesus dead'. As the most Hebrew orientated writer, he may also have been concerned to counter the 'stolen body' story, which, even years later,[8] was a common 'official' Jewish line. The soldiers, then, were running off *(Diagram D)*, whilst the women were still on their way to the tomb.

Matthew naturally surmised that the angel seen by the soldiers as the only witnesses of the rolling back of the stone, was one and the same as that who later spoke to the women. He telescoped events, wishing to draw out the contrasts between the soldiers hurrying off to concoct a lie whilst the women ran off to spread the glorious truth. But there is no inconsistency between his account and the others.

## The women arrive (E)

Unaware of the events at the tomb, the women approached, discussing how they would get the stone rolled back (Mk 16:3). Some distance off, they looked up and saw that it had already been moved. Jumping to the conclusion that the authorities had moved the body, Mary Magdalene turned, running in panic and despair to gasp out to John those words which he would always remember: 'They have taken the Lord out of the tomb, and *WE* don't know where they have laid him' (Jn 20:2). Here there are two important points of cross-corroboration. As we have already noted, John apparently has Mary setting off alone — but then she uses the plural 'WE'. It is from the other Gospels that we learn that the other women mentioned earlier by John were also with Mary that morning. John says 'we' because that was actually what she said and he remembered it. In a 'made up' account it would have seemed inconsistent with the earlier part and the writer would have said 'I'.

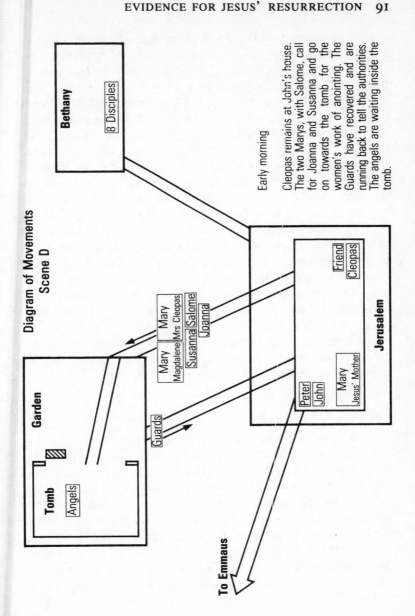

Diagram of Movements
Scene D

Bethany

8 Disciples

Garden

Tomb

Angels

Mary
Magdalene
Susanna

Mrs Cleopas
Salome

Mary

Joanna

Guards

Jerusalem

Friend
Cleopas

Peter
John

Mary
Jesus' Mother

To Emmaus

Early morning

Cleopas remains at John's house.
The two Marys, with Salome, call
for Joanna and Susanna and go
on towards the tomb for the
women's work of anointing. The
Guards have recovered and are
running back to tell the authorities.
The angels are waiting inside the
tomb.

But why, then, did Mary not tell him about the angels? Details in the other Gospels explain this. Matthew reports the initial descent of the angel — seen only by the guards. Mark and Luke show that when the women arrived, the angels were *INSIDE* the tomb. *When*, then, did Mary turn back? John says, when she 'saw that the stone had been removed from the entrance' (Jn 20:1). When was that? Mark tells us: 'When they looked up, they saw that the stone, which was very large, had been rolled away' (16:4). With all the Gospel accounts, we have the whole picture. Arriving at the edge of the Garden after the guards had left and the angels gone inside, the women looked up from some distance off and saw the stone rolled back. Jumping to the obvious conclusion, Mary turned immediately and ran back to Peter and John (see *Diagram* E). The other women then went on to enter the tomb and encounter the angels. Not only do these accounts fit perfectly, but we can understand why from John's perspective it was vital that Mary did turn back — for it led to him personally visiting the tomb and experiencing rebirth of faith. To the other writers it was an unimportant detail, since later she, like the other women, could report seeing both angels and the Lord.

### The angels (F)

At first sight there seem to be contradictions in the accounts over the angels. Matthew mentions only one angel (28:2), Mark a man dressed in white (16:5), Luke two men (24:4), and John two angels (20:12). Is this really inconsistent?

We must first note that the Bible nowhere portrays angels as winged, but always simply as men. There is no contradiction when Luke reports 'men' (24:4), and later has Cleopas speak about 'a vision of angels' (24:23). There is no contradiction between Gospels which speak of 'men in white' and those which speak of 'angels'.

The number of angels is also not a problem. Insofar as

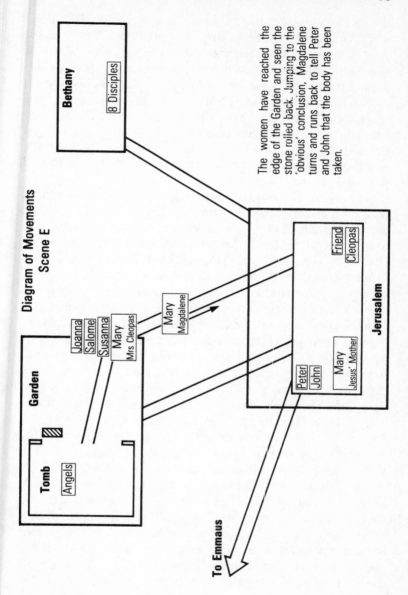

Diagram of Movements
Scene E

Bethany

8 Disciples

Garden

Tomb

Angels

Joanna
Salome
Susanna
Mary
Mrs Cleopas

Mary
Magdalene

Jerusalem

Friend
Cleopas

Mary
Jesus' Mother

Peter
John

To Emmaus

The women have reached the edge of the Garden and seen the stone rolled back. Jumping to the 'obvious' conclusion, Magdalene turns and runs back to tell Peter and John that the body has been taken.

angels in visions are 'really there' (and who can tell?), there were 'really' two of them. But, unless the two angels spoke in unison, one was presumably the spokesperson. Matthew and Mark may very well have been aware that the spokesperson angel they describe had a companion. All historians (secular or sacred) select which details to record, and what secular historian would be pronounced unreliable for speaking of a 'messenger' without happening to mention that he had a companion? It is not really important to the account, and whether or not to mention it is a matter of personal choice.

Now Mark is explicit that at least one angel was sitting, whilst Luke appears to say that the angels 'stood'. But this contradiction is illusory. The three other places in which Luke uses an identical Greek word the NIV renders it 'came up to' (Lk 20:1; Acts 4:1) and 'stopped at' (Acts 11:11). In two other references to angels a similar word in Luke is simply rendered 'appeared to' (Lk 2:9; Acts 12:7). There is no strong implication of standing as against sitting. It simply implies a sudden appearance — which it surely must have seemed to women unsuspectingly entering the tomb. Mark implies as much when he says, 'they were alarmed' (16:5). There would have been nothing particularly alarming in finding a perfectly ordinary young man in white in a tomb from which (as they may have thought) the authorities had taken Jesus' body. Their alarm (Mk 16:5) or fright (Mt 28:4; Lk 24:5) arose because, unsuspectingly entering the tomb, they suddenly came upon what they recognised to be supernatural.

Again, whilst the different writers report different parts of the angel's speech, those words fit together remarkably well. More remarkably, Luke and Mark seem fairly parallel on the parts up to the angel's speech which Matthew omits, but on the speech itself it is Luke who differs and Matthew and Mark are parallel. This is just what one might expect of three accounts which were compiled independently, but drew on some of the same eye-witness accounts.

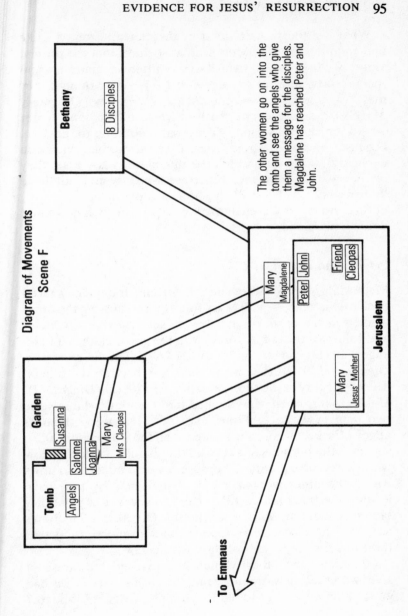

Diagram of Movements
Scene F

Bethany
8 Disciples

The other women go on into the tomb and see the angels who give them a message for the disciples. Magdalene has reached Peter and John.

Garden
Susanna
Salome
Joanna
Mary Mrs Cleopas

Tomb
Angels

Mary Magdalene
Peter John
Friend Cleopas
Mary Jesus' Mother

Jerusalem

To Emmaus

What did the women do after they left the tomb? Luke and John tell us little. Most scholars believe that the present verses 9–20 of Mark (which are omitted in many ancient manuscripts) are not the actual original ones, though they may, of course, have been added very early. Obviously Mark's original did not finish at verse 8. No sane writer would finish by saying, 'They said nothing to anyone, because they were afraid,' just after the women had been explicitly told to go and tell the disciples. In any case, they obviously told *someone*, otherwise Mark would not have known about it. Most likely, Mark simply meant that they bottled up their secret until they were safe behind closed doors with friends.

### Peter, John and Mary (G–I)

Meanwhile, Mary had reached Peter and John. They raced back to the tomb — with Mary following — missing the other women in the maze of city streets (see *Diagram G*). Peter and John saw the empty tomb, with the grave-clothes, but no angels or body (Lk 24:24; Jn 20:2–9). This is shown in *Diagram H*. Then they made their way back to the others. They left Mary at the tomb, weeping (Jn 20:11) (*Diagram I*). Unlike them, when Mary looked into the tomb, she saw the two men in white — though not yet recognising them as angels. Earlier, where she spoke for all the women (Jn 20:2), she used the plural; she now uses the singular, '*I* don't know where they have put him,' because she now no longer knows where the other women are or if they may by now have located the body (Jn 20:13). Then, however, Mary had her famous encounter with Jesus himself (Jn 20:14–17). John's account, therefore, corroborates Mark's report (16:9) that the Lord *first* appeared to Mary Magdalene.

Meantime, the other women had reached the house of John with their news about seeing the angels. The angels had given them a message to tell the disciples (Mt 28:7; Mk 16:7

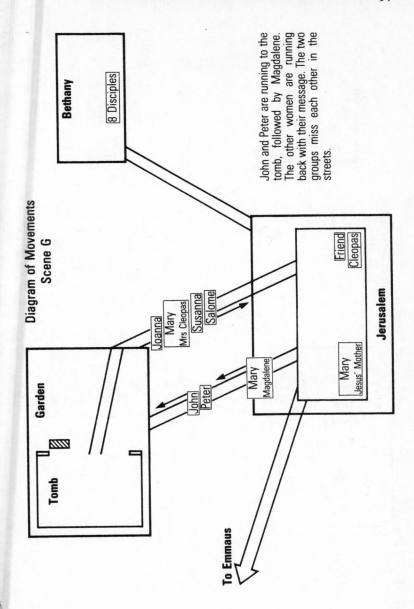

Diagram of Movements
Scene G

Bethany

8 Disciples

Garden

Tomb

Joanna
Mary
Mrs Cleopas
Susanna
Salome

John
Peter

Mary
Magdalene

Friend
Cleopas

Jerusalem

Mary
Jesus' Mother

To Emmaus

John and Peter are running to the tomb, followed by Magdalene. The other women are running back with their message. The two groups miss each other in the streets.

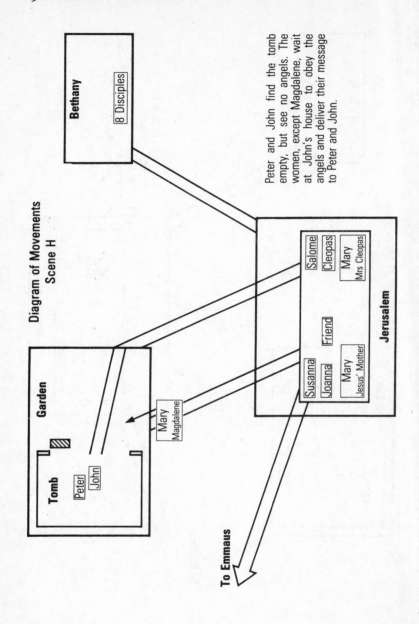

Diagram of Movements
Scene H

Bethany

8 Disciples

Garden

Tomb

Peter
John

Mary
Magdalene

Jerusalem

Susanna
Joanna
Mary
Jesus' Mother

Friend

Salome
Cleopas
Mary
Mrs Cleopas

To Emmaus

Peter and John find the tomb empty, but see no angels. The women, except Magdalene, wait at John's house to obey the angels and deliver their message to Peter and John.

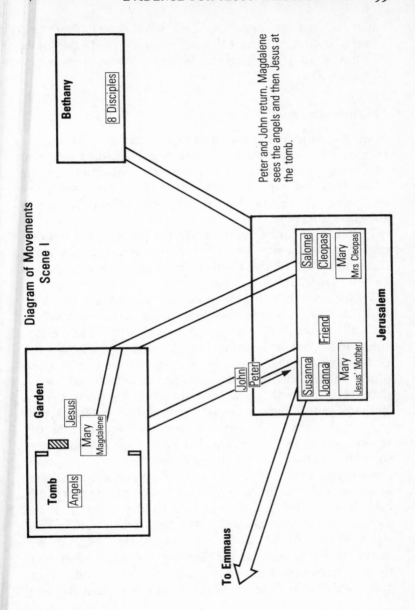

Diagram of Movements
Scene I

Bethany

8 Disciples

Peter and John return. Magdalene sees the angels and then Jesus at the tomb.

Tomb

Angels

Garden

Jesus

Mary
Magdalene

John
Peter

Jerusalem

Salome
Cleopas
Mary
Mrs Cleopas

Friend

Susanna
Joanna
Mary
Jesus' Mother

To Emmaus

and note that this specifically included Peter). Peter and John, of course, were not there, having run off to the tomb. The group of women must, therefore, await their return (*Diagram I*).

## Meetings with Jesus (J)

Immediately after the return of Peter and John, the women hurried off — not waiting for Mary — to go across the Mount of Olives to Bethany, to tell the other disciples (among whom both Salome and Mary, Mrs Cleopas, had sons) and thus complete the task given them by the angels. This is shown in *Diagram J*.

Fortified, presumably, by the first-century equivalent of a cup of tea whilst waiting for Peter and John, they *ran* along the rough path. At this point occurred the meeting reported by Matthew (28:8–10).

Why does only Matthew report this encounter? For John and Peter in Jerusalem only Mary Magdalene would come and tell of meeting Jesus, and this is exactly what we find John and Mark (reporting Peter) record (Jn 20:18; Mk 16:10). Peter, unlike John, did not yet believe (Jn 20:8), so Mark, unlike John, naturally reflects unbelief in Mary's news (Mk 16:10). Matthew, getting the news as he waited in Bethany, naturally telescoped the women's meetings with the angels and with Jesus — for as they breathlessly recounted events to him, this is exactly how it would have sounded. The only slight puzzle is Luke, who mentions *neither* encounter with Jesus. Two points need making, however. Firstly, in his main chronological account Luke describes neither the men's visit to the tomb nor the appearance to Peter himself — but he refers to both in later reported speech (Lk 24:24, 34), so clearly Luke did not intend to imply that his account was complete. Secondly, there is no obvious place in his narrative that he could insert either incident without spoiling the drama of that dawning

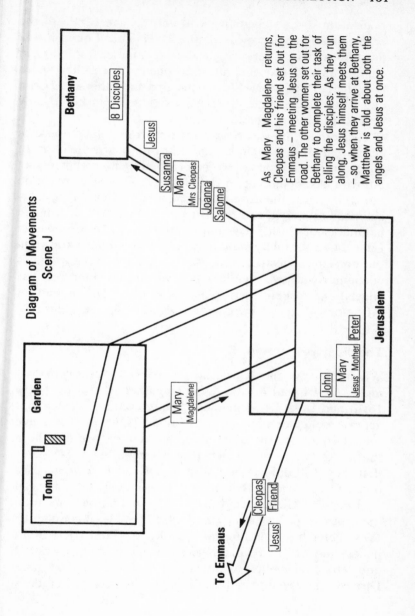

Diagram of Movements
Scene J

As Mary Magdalene returns, Cleopas and his friend set out for Emmaus – meeting Jesus on the road. The other women set out for Bethany to complete their task of telling the disciples. As they run along, Jesus himself meets them – so when they arrive at Bethany, Matthew is told about both the angels and Jesus at once.

Bethany

8 Disciples

Jesus

Susanna
Mary
Mrs Cleopas
Joanna
Salome

Jerusalem

John
Mary
Jesus' Mother
Peter

Garden

Tomb

Mary
Magdalene

To Emmaus

Cleopas
Friend

Jesus

realisation on the Emmaus road and the crescendo of the unmistakable appearance in Luke 24:36. Thus Luke 24:9–12 must be seen as a very vague summary, indicating the main characters and the general atmosphere of unbelief which prevailed. Both Mary Magdalene and the others *had* seen angels and *were* generally disbelieved, so what he actually says is true if incomplete.

Two others, however, also set out from John's house in Jerusalem. Jesus' uncle Cleopas, having heard the story of angels from the group of women (including his own wife) set out with a companion to go to Emmaus. Why he went we do not know, but the Emmaus road account has been characterised as a vivid and realistic piece of writing, bearing all hallmarks of truth.[9] The information given by Cleopas in Luke 24:22–4 exactly matches what he would have known in our present reconstructed account. He knew of the women's encounter with two men in white (which they interpreted as angels) and of Peter and John's experience. But he had set off before Mary got back with news of having seen Jesus.

### The disciples gathered (K)

When Cleopas and his friend got back to Jerusalem that night, they found all the disciples gathered. But do Mark 16:13 and Luke 24:34 give conflicting accounts of whether general belief or scepticism prevailed? Only a very naïve reader could see these as in conflict. Firstly, we may note that Luke (who implies belief) says only a few verses later that they 'still did not believe it because of joy' when Jesus himself was standing there! (24:41). More basically, one can well imagine Cleopas and his friend bursting back in upon the group to be greeted by a confused babble of comments. 'Yes, Peter has seen him too!' said one. 'Well I just don't believe any of it,' said another. The situation simply was not one where a spokesperson voices a unanimous opinion. Discussion swayed to and fro — and both Mark's and Luke's

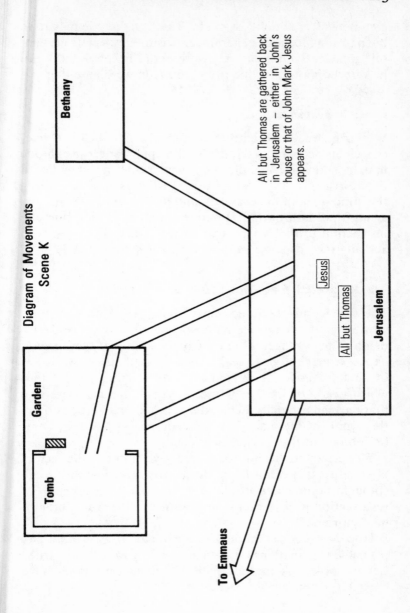

Diagram of Movements
Scene K

Bethany

Garden

Tomb

To Emmaus

Jerusalem

Jesus

All but Thomas

All but Thomas are gathered back in Jerusalem — either in John's house or that of John Mark. Jesus appears.

comments were doubtless made. Then, as the tide may have been turning towards general scepticism, they saw Jesus himself appear. Even then, they were not fully convinced, until he offered more tangible proof. But can we blame them?

## Other appearances

We have already noted that whilst Luke in his Gospel telescopes his account as though all the appearances are in one day, he shows in Acts that he is well aware that they lasted over forty days (1:3). All the other instances occurred during this time — both in Jerusalem and in Galilee. Interestingly, again it is Matthew (28:7) and Mark (16:7) who report the instruction to the disciples to go to Galilee, but John who actually records some of the appearances there (21:1).

## The Resurrection accounts: alternative theories?

The five Resurrection accounts, then, are all first-century, written at dates between fifteen and fifty years of Jesus' death. They fit together in exactly the kind of way we would expect from good historical accounts based on eye-witnesses of actual events. They contain corroborating cross-details which would be hard to fabricate. Again and again we find that particular details included match the precise position in the events of the main first-hand source — Matthew, Peter or John — of that particular account.

The accounts claim to record two things: the actual physical disappearance of Jesus' body from the tomb (though none claim to have witnessed the moment of resurrection itself) and the appearances of a risen Christ to his followers.

How are these accounts to be explained? Are there any plausible explanations other than that they were simply true? Let us look at some alternative explanations which have been suggested by various sceptics.[10]

Firstly, could the accounts simply be 'legend'? This really will not do. As we have seen, the five accounts bear all the hallmarks of independent accounts of actual events, they were written close to the events themselves, and bear none of the usual indications of 'myth'.[11]

Secondly, could it all have simply been a mistake? Could Jesus' followers simply have gone to the wrong tomb? This seems highly unlikely. Not only had the women watched the burial, but surely Joseph of Arimathea would have known where his own family tomb was. It is inconceivable that such an upright, socially important man would remain silent while so important a mistake was being propagated. It is hard to see that the Jewish authorities would set a guard on the wrong tomb, or fail to produce the body afterwards to scotch the rumours of the Resurrection. It would fail to explain the Resurrection appearances. It may be added that the suggestion that it was all a 'big joke' which got out of hand is even more ludicrous — for very similar reasons.

Thirdly, could Jesus himself have perpetrated some kind of plot? Perhaps he had arranged to be cut down early from the cross, and to be resuscitated. If Jesus really had such a plan, it seems highly impractical. Any Roman soldier caught involved in such a thing would have been executed, and soldiers experienced in crucifixions would have been unlikely to have been fooled. Crucifixion is too public a thing. In any case, having been flogged (as standard for a crucifixion) and nailed up to a cross for hours, could he really have expected to pass himself off as a risen glorious Lord? An even more basic question concerns his motive. Could the founder of so high a moral code really have agreed to a massive lie to propagate his views? The whole thing is absurd.

Fourthly, could the body have been stolen? The question then would be, by whom? Ordinary grave-robbers would not steal a body and leave the grave-clothes and spices, they would not easily have got past the guards, and such a thing would not explain the Resurrection appearances. The Jewish authorities would have had no motive to steal the body, and would surely have produced it again to destroy any accounts of a resurrection. The only group with any possible motive, then, would have been the disciples.

Now the idea that the disciples stole the body is one of a group of 'conspiracy' theories, all implying that they actually knew that the whole Resurrection story was a fabrication. Other alternatives are that Jesus only fainted and they resuscitated him later, or that they bribed the soldiers to crucify someone else. The fundamental flaw in all of them is that they would mean the whole moral foundation of Christianity would be based on a gigantic lie. Would men who knew this really preach a religion demanding the highest standards of truth and morality — even to the point of being prepared to be martyred for it? This seems highly unlikely. Could it, then, have been just one or two people (perhaps unknown to the disciples) who arranged the fraud? But how would this explain the Resurrection appearances? How could it explain the astounding fact that from being a pathetic, frightened little group of insignificant people whose leader had been killed, the early disciples emerged a few weeks later, bold, certain, and ready to spread a new world faith? It would surely have taken more than a missing body to create this kind of change. Moreover, how could the disciples have then fabricated four Gospel accounts which bear all the marks we have seen of independent accounts of actual events?

Finally, could the whole thing have been based on mass hallucination? This is perhaps the most plausible alternative explanation, but there are reasons against it. The accounts make it clear that they were not expecting anything to happen. They were not buoyed up by faith, expectancy and religious fervour. They were frightened, defeated, and thought it was all over. One does not go to a tomb with burial spices if one expects the occupant to be resurrected. The women's first thought on seeing the tomb open was not, indeed, that Jesus had risen but that the authorities had moved the body. What can have happened to transform these people? Did they all have the *same* hallucination together — men and women of such vastly different backgrounds and temperaments? Did the 'hallucination' really eat a piece of fish to show that it was 'real' (Lk 24:42)? And what happened to the body?

In all this we have mentioned the immediate effect on the disciples several times. But we have also to account for the place the Resurrection held in the early church. The Jewish Christians would have required something very remarkable to have changed their practice of meeting from the Jewish Sabbath (Saturday) to the first day of the week (Sunday).[12] If it was not, as early tradition has it, the Resurrection being on the 'first day of the week', then what was it? How did the Resurrection come to have so central a part in the early church's preaching?[13]

## Summary and conclusion

None of the sceptical alternatives really make any sense. The most obvious conclusion — assuming that one does not rule out beforehand the supernatural — is that the accounts do actually describe events as the witnesses to them saw them. Christ is risen, not just in some mystical 'his-ideas-will-live-for-ever' sense, but in some sense in which the actual person of Jesus of Nazareth lives on and interacts with people. It is not that he had the same *kind* of physical body (1 Cor 15:35–8). But the resurrection and transformation of his physical body was to emphasise that his new 'self' was the continuation of the old. The same person was involved in both.

## Notes

1. We consider objections to the possibility of the miraculous in Chapter 8.

2. E H Carr's classic *What is History?* (1961, second edition 1987) reinforced this point for modern historians and it has been accepted even by conservative historians such as G R Elton, in *The Practice of History* (1969). Colin Brown's excellent short book *History and Faith* (1987) summarises some of these points about the current thinking on the nature of historical work, and also gives a Christian viewpoint.

3. The degree to which interpretation is involved is controversial, and few today might take the extreme relativism of such as C A Beard and C L Becker. We find, however, that in philosophies of history as diverse as, for example, those of R G Collingwood, E H Carr, William Dray, W H Walsh, John Passmore, Patrick Gardiner, etc, the role of interpretation is recognised. For some of these views see, for example, P Gardiner (ed), *The Philosophy of History* (1974).

4. Some expansion on these is given in Appendix 1. For more detailed analysis the reader is strongly recommended the excellent book by John Wenham, *Easter Enigma* (1984). It was interesting to find that his reconstruction agreed in all basic essentials with an unpublished 'harmonisation' worked out more than twenty years ago by one of the present authors. The wealth of detail Wenham gives, however, makes his book invaluable.

5. The identification of Mary Magdalene and Mary of Bethany is not certain, but a strong case is outlined for it in Appendix 1 (see also Wenham, *op cit*).

6. Wenham's expansion on these in *Easter Enigma* is interesting, though not all essential to our present themes.

7. For details of Gospel authorship, see any standard work, eg Donald Guthrie, *New Testament Introduction* (1974), chaps 1–8.

8. Justin Martyr (c100–c165) refers to this as current in his published 'Dialogue with the Jew Trypho', *Ant Nice Fath*, i, 253.

9. Thus Malcolm Muggeridge, speaking from the perspective of a writer, in *Jesus Rediscovered* (1969), p 98.

10. We could list names for each of the options looked at, but it seemed tedious and unnecessary so we forebore.

11. See also E M Blaiklock, *op cit*.

12. See, for example, the references in the *Illustrated Bible Dictionary* under the 'Lord's Day'.

13. Various books consider in detail 'the alternative theories' to resurrection from the classic, F Morison, *Who Moved the Stone?* (1930), through to the more recent popular treatments in Val Grieve, *Your Verdict on the Empty Tomb of Jesus* (1988) and Josh McDowell, *The Resurrection Proven Beyond Doubt!* (1988).

# 7

# WHY IS ALL THIS HISTORICAL EVIDENCE NOT BETTER KNOWN?

## Introduction and examples

WE HAVE SEEN THAT THE evidence both for Jesus as a historical figure, and for the Resurrection is very strong. Yet through the media, especially on television, we all too often see theologians presenting Jesus as a semi-mythical figure. In the UK some school religious pro-grammes can give a similar impression. How can this be?

Before attempting to answer this, let us look at one prime example, focusing on the Resurrection evidences. It came in a series on British television called *Jesus, the Evidence* shown in 1984. The programme introduction was a dramatic picture of a china statue of Jesus being shattered. The message implied was that now, at last, in the light of hard evidence, our traditional pictures of Jesus must all change. Jesus was presented as 'one in a long line of Jewish holy men from Galilee, more revered than the rest, but in the same tradition'. The presenter did not tell us much about these supposed holy men, or how many of them went about claiming to be sinless and the only way to God. With this approach, however, he passed on to ask, 'What is the evidence for Jesus' Resurrection itself?' A pertinent question.

The presenter distinguished two kinds of Resurrection story. The first concerned 'apparent stories in which divine beings appear in glory, surrounded by blinding light to give commands', while the second kind 'tell of Jesus' followers finding his tomb empty'. The first kind, which the presenter interpreted to be the kind experienced and spoken of by Paul, were claimed to be common; the second, unique to Christianity. The presenter continued:

> For most Christians, the empty tomb is proof that Jesus did physically rise from the dead. But are the Gospels' blunt assertions that the tomb was empty reliable? The Gospels, after all, were not eye-witness accounts, they were written forty to sixty years later. All four Gospels contain remarkable discrepancies. In Mark's Gospel; the earliest, the women see a young man in a white robe. In Luke's Gospel they see two men in brilliant clothes. In Matthew's Gospel they see one angel. In John's Gospel, the latest, Mary Magdalene sees two angels. It is as if each successive Gospel writer has embellished the earlier story. Paul's letters were written twenty to thirty years before the Gospels, yet nowhere does he mention the empty tomb — a striking omission.

This 'analysis', then, began with a bland and unsupported statement about 'remarkable discrepancies' contained in the Gospels. Since it was so vague, it cannot be seriously considered. Next, came the part about the angels — during which the viewer was presented with images of what everyone knows angels look like (provided their main source of research is Christmas cards), ie bright creatures with wings and halos! Naturally, if one insists on this kind of picture, then the Gospels contradict each other. But, as we know, the biblical picture of angels is simply of men in shining white clothes. 'Each successive Gospel writer,' said the presenter, 'has embellished the earlier story.' Now Luke, who is supposed to be second, actually reports the women's experience in Luke 24:23 as a 'vision of angels', ie the 'men' of Luke 24:4 were taken (quite naturally) to be angels. Moreover, Luke mentions two, whilst Matthew in his later account only one, which does not sound like 'embellishment' (28:2). John's account, written last, is actually the least dramatic (even though the most vivid) of the four. When Mary Magdalene saw the angels, she obviously did not recognise them as such at the time. Had she thought them angels, she would hardly have replied as she did, that she was crying because 'they have taken my Lord away and I don't know where they have put him' (Jn 20:13). At the time, clearly, she thought they were ordinary men — and only later concluded that they were angels. To suggest that John's account is an 'embellishment' of the much more dramatic Matthew or Luke makes no sense.

The reference to Paul's 'omission' is equally strange, and one wonders just how carefully the advisers to the programme had read the New Testament. Acts 17, for example, records Paul's sermon to the Greek intellectuals:

'God . . . commands all people everywhere to repent. For he has set a day when he will judge the world with justice by the man he has appointed. He has given proof of this to all men by raising him from the dead.' When they heard about the resurrection of the dead, some of them sneered (Acts 17:24–32).

Why did they sneer? If, as the programme suggested, Paul was really talking about a kind of resurrection known through the Greek stories of Adonis and Aphrodite, why on earth should anyone sneer?[1] Surely a vision of a glorified god would have been quite acceptable? What they sneered at was the suggestion that Jesus rose physically, leaving an empty tomb. The pattern was repeated later in what was supposed to be a defence but was really a sermon that Paul preached to Agrippa and Festus in Acts 26! His recounting of his heavenly vision of Jesus on the Damascus road passed unremarked. Then, however:

'I am saying nothing beyond what the prophets and Moses said would happen — that the Christ would suffer and, as the first to rise from the dead, would proclaim light to his own people and to the Gentiles.' At this point Festus interrupted Paul's defence. 'You are out of your mind, Paul!' he shouted. 'Your great learning is driving you insane' (Acts 26:22–4).

This gives background to Paul's words in his letter: 'Christ died for our sins according to the Scriptures, that he was buried, that he was raised on the third day according to the Scriptures, and that he appeared to Peter, and then to the Twelve' (1 Cor 15:3–5). Now Paul was not writing, as were the Gospel writers, a historical account as such, in which the reactions of the various observers are mentioned. He was interested in the fact that Jesus *was* raised — and all that this implied. He was not very interested in the rather obvious fact that if Jesus were buried and then raised, this meant that *where* he had been buried was now empty. His sceptical hearers at the time naturally deduced this, but he was apparently not used to meeting the tortuous logic of those modern theologians who make some other assumption.

So what kind of explanation did the programme go on to offer us for the Resurrection stories? It told us:

Helmut Koester and colleagues at Harvard University have developed a new theory which may explain how the story arose. It was common practice among the Jews to worship at the tombs of prophets and martyrs ... 'So we can safely assume that from an early date there was worship at the tomb of Jesus. But then, just before the Jewish revolt in AD 66, the Christians were forced to leave Jerusalem, so they no longer had access to Jesus' tomb. We also know that somewhat later the practice of worshipping at the tombs of martyrs had begun. So the Christians had to explain why there was no longer any worship at Jesus' tomb. To avoid embarrassment the Christians may have excused the lack of worship at Jesus' tomb by saying that it no longer contained his mortal remains ... it seems likely that the Christians decided to explain the lack of worship at Jesus' tomb by saying that the tomb was empty.' But as the Gospels were written down years later, the story could have begun to serve a different purpose ... 'In time, then, the empty tomb story was put together with stories about Jesus' appearances to the apostles, to produce the story of the Resurrection in which we now know it, in which the empty tomb and the physical resurrection is emphasised.

So what theory are we being offered here? It might be summarised thus:

1.  For some thirty-three years after Jesus' death, whilst Paul was being sneered at by Greeks and Romans for preaching a resurrection which involved purely heavenly visions, the Christians were worshipping at their most important shrine containing Jesus' body.
2.  Around AD 66 the body disappeared.
3.  The Gospels were written 40–60 years after Jesus' death, ie AD 73–93 (actually this is rather a late date by today's estimates).
4.  Thus between AD 66 and AD 73, the Christians had time to make up a pack of lies about an empty tomb, put together these fabrications with the stories of heavenly visions of Jesus, and produce the accounts as we now have them. They then convinced the whole Christian world that this was really what had always been Christian teaching, and were prepared to be (in many cases) martyred for it.

This, then, is the kind of cock-and-bull story concocted as a supposed scholarly reconstruction based on 'the evidence'. It is so strange that it could hardly be taken seriously — were it not that millions of viewers in prime time (many of whom had no background of New Testament study) were subjected to it. A later programme showed a number of scholars (Christian and Jewish) — some not particularly traditionalist — who tore the whole programme to shreds. But, as we shall later discuss, there is a difference in impact between a 'documentary' and a 'discussion' format.

One of the present authors, Roger Forster, actually had a debate with the producer of the programme during the year it had been shown. As himself a professing (though obviously not evangelical) believer, the producer was prepared to credit real the evangelical *experience* of God. On the objective and historical issues, however, he had consulted 'expert' advice for his programme. What must then be asked is why was he guided towards advice which was bizarre and sensational rather than sober and mainstream?

There are explanations both for the existence of the bizarre, and the tendency of the media to present these rather than the results of more sober scholarship. To understand them we need briefly to look at some history of the way people have looked at the Bible, as well as the nature of the media today.

## The Bible and criticism

Christians believe that the Bible is an authoritative and divinely inspired book. But they accept that it is also about God's dealings with concrete human situations and individuals, compiled by human beings, and transmitted through human processes. There is nothing necessarily irreverent in recognising this and taking it into account. What might it actually imply?

Firstly, if we accept that men like the apostle Paul spoke God's message, the historical background helps us understand what was meant. When, for example, Paul speaks of 'works' (Eph 2:9), historical background can clarify what he meant by it, and so help Christians think through its message for them today.[2]

Secondly, it should be clear what Christians are claiming about how God used the Bible writers. Few take it that God used them like, say, a typewriter — without reference to their own thought processes and ways of expressing them-selves.[3] Luke, for example, tells us how he consciously set out to compile an account from eye-witnesses (Lk 1:2), and the writer of John says what principles he used in selecting stories (Jn 20:31). There is nothing impious in wondering what kinds of source materials each used — verbal or written. Christians have long, in fact, recognised that each of the Gospels presents a different aspect of Jesus.

It will, moreover, be useful to recognise the different literary conventions or genre adopted by writers in different parts of the Bible: poetry, parable, history, etc.

Finally, anyone who believes the Bible authoritative will want to ensure that the actual text used is as near the original as possible. This involves painstaking work by scholars to compile the best consensus where there are small differences between the available manuscript copies.

The technical name for all these processes is 'criticism'. This term may be unfortunate, as it need not imply that some-one is 'critical' of what the Bible says. Like any activity, it can be well or badly done, but it is not in itself anti-Christian.

## Origins of criticism

It is virtually impossible to say when criticism in the above sense began. Textual criticism (ie the close comparison of different manuscript copies of the Bible) was practised by early Christians like Jerome, and carried on by Erasmus, Wycliffe and other editor/translators of the text. Historical criticism in, for example, the sense of recognising the importance of Jewish studies for New Testament interpre-tation was recognised by such as John Lightfoot (1602–75).[4]

A maxim does, however, seem to have circulated in the nineteenth century: 'Study the Bible like any other book.' This had a good sense when Paley, for example, applied historical methods of analysis to conclude that both the Gospels and Paul's letters were genuine.[5] Others used the maxim to urge people to read what it actually said and understand what it meant to its hearers, stripping away the later centuries of 'reading into' it other ideas.

On the other hand, there was a quite different implication put on it by those who associated with it two basic pillars of assumption:

1. The New Testament was presumed a late compilation, mostly second century or later, set down after a long period of oral transmission and build-up of legend.
2. There was an anti-supernaturalist presumption that the physical world was a closed system, God had no existence independent of it and so miracles could not occur.

Varieties of this were carried by early works of F D Schleiermacher (in 1821), H E G Paulus (in 1828), D F Strauss (in 1835 Tr 1846) and F C Baur (in 1831). The term 'higher criticism' was coined to refer to those concerned with broader issues beyond textual comparisons.

We cannot here be concerned with a detailed analysis of all the different schools of ideas based on these foundations. Some had undoubted scholarship — but it is not the scholarship but the assumptions which need questioning.

The first assumption (the late date of the Gospels) was challenged by the Cambridge scholars Westcott (1825–1901), Hort (1828–92) and J B Lightfoot (1828–89), who showed a first-century dating. Since then, as we have already seen, archaeological evidence has totally demolished the 'late date' theory: we now have actual fragment copies of John which are earlier than the date Baur set for the original!

The second assumption of the higher critics was based on the circular reasoning on miracles adopted by the eighteenth-century sceptic David Hume.[6] In essence Hume argued:

1. Human experience indicates that the laws of nature are regular.

2. This means that overwhelming evidence would be needed to conclude that these laws had been violated.
3. On this basis we can discount any actual human testimony to the miraculous as insufficient.

This is blatantly circular, since it establishes the inviolability of natural laws by the use of human testimony, and then discounts the reliability of human testimony to the miraculous based on the laws. This is analysed in greater depth in our next chapter.

The point is, however, that not only were the twin-pillar assumptions of the higher critics the *basis* rather than the *conclusions* of their studies, but both turned out to be demonstrably false.

At the time, though, the assumptions led naturally to two further questions. Firstly, if all miracles (including the Resurrection) are to be presumed impossible, none actually happened, so what was the *real* Jesus like? This started a 'quest for the historical Jesus' — a Jesus free from the supernatural. The failure of this quest has been recognised in the twentieth century. For one thing, a Jesus stripped of the supernatural is hardly recognisable as Jesus, and carries no conviction. For another thing, each theologian (with a free hand to 'edit out' bits he didn't like) simply created a Jesus in his own image.

A second line of enquiry, stimulated by his assumption that Jesus could not actually have performed miracles, was: how did those who reported him come to ascribe them to him? Thus the focus moved away from the objective truth of, say, the Resurrection, and on to the supposed quality of the experience of the disciples which made them want to ascribe miracle stories. Everything becomes subjective or relativised, nothing is objective truth.

### The twentieth century

There have been various twentieth-century heirs of the higher-critic movement which carry similar problems. Insofar as they simply help us better to understand the biblical text, Christians may welcome them (though they are generally not new); but insofar as they adopt the old twin assumptions of higher criticism, they lead to confusion.

In the 1920s, for example, arose 'form criticism'. Recognising that the Gospel writers used previously circulating material (and Lk 1:2 virtually implies this), scholars looked at the different literary forms (eg parable, miracle story, etc) which these may have had. Christians need see nothing sinister in this, and it might help understanding of why some parts of the different Gospels are verbatim the same. Unfortunately, however, leading form critics like Rudolf Bultmann began with the old anti-supernaturalist assumptions. Beginning by assuming miracles were impossible, it could lead only back to scepticism.

Most of these movements (form criticism, source criticism, redaction criticism, etc) can be seen as extensions of activities Christian scholars have always been involved in, and in themselves they offer no threat.[7] They become suspect only when radical critics have combined the activities with adoption of the twin pillars of assumption we have considered — taken as presupposition rather than conclusion to their studies. Yet, during all of the last 150 years, there have always been first-rate scholars who did *not* begin with these presuppositions but were more open minded — and whose work often involved strong dissent from the radical critics on both philosophical and historical grounds.

### The media and the truth

So what kind of thing is the secular media likely to present to the general public? Let us say at once that we regard any kind of 'conspiracy' theory as naïve. Problems arise rather in the very nature of the media as a product of modern Western society, and in the traditions with which it is approached. Evangelicals need be neither paranoid nor isolationist, but should seek to try to understand the processes at work, and to present their own position intelligently. What are those processes?

Firstly, we must recognise the effects of image in the television domination of media, which is a feature of the late twentieth century. In the 1960s Marshall McLuhan wrote much about this, and has more modern disciples, eg Neil Postman.[8] We believe them to oversimplify, as well as to over-idealise earlier ages, but they make some valid points. The news, for example, Postman calls a 'format for entertainment, not for education, reflection or catharsis'.[9] Details of grisly murders or accidents, of little or no relevance to viewers, are brought before us presumably for entertainment. The 'lighter' items which follow, the advertisements, and the 'smooth' and pleasant demeanour of the newscasters, all serve to defuse the real gravity of any events. Postman makes some valid points about the way in which political and other discussion is forced into assessing 'performance' and 'image' rather than real issues. This is not because of any lack of integrity of broadcasters, but the natural effects of the medium itself in a democracy. Entertaining sensation, impact, and image are important. The unusual, the controversial, and the unexpected all focus on this.

A second vital point concerns the different modes, particularly of television presentation. The 'discussion' mode is one in which viewers expect to hear opinion, or, even more, projection of conflicting images. The protagonists in a political discussion are not involved in a search for 'truth', but a presentation of viewpoint and party image. The 'documentary' mode, in contrast, contains a series of 'ex-cathedra' statements by 'experts' (suitably framed in white coats and other trappings of 'impartial' knowledge), strung together with a voice-over by the commentator who explains it all for the viewer, harmonises it, and assures him or her that all this is carefully documented. The viewer is expected to believe that all this is 'fact'. Other modes, of course, exist. The 'worship service', for example, is not even primarily about objective fact at all, but about personal involvement of participants. Usually it demands no particular response from uncommitted viewers. The 'tele-evangelist' broadcasts, in contrast, do demand reaction. At present, of course, the UK has no such broadcasts, but they have been a feature of American television. Generally, however, what is projected is not any careful judgement made with reservations after a weighing of evidence, but rather a certainty based on personal spiritual experience. This is also coupled with the creation of a personal image for the 'tele-evangelist' not unlike that of political figures. The inevitable danger of this is that the image can be more important than the spiritual reality — for the image is what impacts the viewer. When, in 1988, one of the best known American 'tele-evangelists' joined a growing number of this group discovered to have some serious secret immorality, his public 'contrition' left one wondering whether he were really repentant or simply playing out a role. God (and possibly some close associates) may know — the ordinary viewer has no way of knowing.

In Britain, religious broadcasting is monitored by a group which is intended to represent all viewpoints, but in practice seems dominated by a liberal theological ethos. Many hours are allocated to religious broadcasting, but most of these are either worship or discussion modes — neither of which the viewer takes as presenting fact. Statements of personal religious experience *may* be taken as a challenge by viewers to respond similarly, but direct 'proselytising' is disallowed. This is not a liberal conspiracy. There are real reasons for wanting to avoid the 'tele-evangelist' type of television in Britain which could otherwise result, and no reason to suppose that if it were allowed, the pursuit of truth would then be paramount. Nevertheless, it is unfortunate from an evangelical viewpoint. Liberal Christianity may be reduced to warm feelings when hearing about Jesus and the encouragement of hearers to 'do good'. This kind of 'lowest common denominator' is one which all people of goodwill may share. But the evangelical view is, by its nature, committed to the objectivity of the risen Christ and the requirement to 'make disciples' of others, ie to evangelise. To disallow these on television, for whatever good reasons, comes near to excluding anything distinctively evangelical from access. Television religion, like school Religious Education in Britain, may exclude the specifically evangelical altogether in its efforts to be conciliatorily ecumenical.

Presentation, then, of facts (such as evidence for a risen Jesus), which may challenge the viewer to respond, is unlikely to be given air time. On the other hand, as already discussed, other media sectors look for the controversial, the entertainingly unexpected. If a bishop or Christian scholar proclaims Jesus is risen, it has no 'news value'. If one can be found to proclaim that Jesus was a myth, a homosexual, or a terrorist (or even better all three), then it is 'interesting'.

How can we illustrate this? The documentary mode of the British Channel 4's *Jesus, the Evidence*, in contrast to, say, the worship mode of long hours of religious broadcasts, told the viewer that what was to be presented was 'fact' as ascertained by the 'best experts'. Yet it had also to be entertaining and controversial, and preferably *not* actually demand any response from the viewer. The actual programme fitted the bill well, leaving Jesus securely dead but allowing anyone a warm feeling about him if they wanted and any amount of subjective experience.

In contrast to this, a series called *Jesus, Then and Now* was offered to Channel 4 in 1987. Made by an award-winning team, it looked at Jesus as a historical character, his life and teachings, including the 'controversial' issue of his Resurrection. Reflecting the traditional teachings of the church, it had the support of the British Council of Churches, the Roman Catholic Conference of England and Wales, as well as widespread evangelical support across all mainstream denominations. Robert Towler, Religious Programmes Chief, rejected the series saying: 'To broadcast a series of programmes made explicitly to promulgate one religion in particular would be to introduce a religious equivalent of party political broadcasts.'[10] This is sincere but muddled thinking. The bizarre and idiosyncratic views presented in *Jesus, the Evidence* were a party political broadcast on behalf of a small party bordering on the eccentric. The 1988 Channel 4 documentary archaeological series *Testament*, by John Romer, was nearer mainstream, but on some issues could well be described as 'party political' by more theologically conservative archaeologists. The more extreme 1987 Channel 4 series *Gnosticism* had a *TV Times* write-up: 'Some scholars believe these [gnostic] scriptures to be just as authentic, or more so, than the books we know as the New Testament'; the implausibility of such a 'party political' claim was referred to in Chapter 3. The documentary-mode television series by the various Cupitts, Sagans, Bronowskis, Millers and others may be even more individualistic. So why cannot evangelicals have an occasional documentary-mode programme in which to present their objective beliefs?

The group which commissioned *Jesus, Then and Now* suggested that their programme was rejected because Channel 4 did not find it 'scandalous enough'. There may be something in this (though we would wish to put it more euphemistically), but there is also the fact that ostensibly neither *Jesus, the Evidence*, Cupitt, Sagan or others call for much response in the viewer — even though they would (if taken seriously) undermine the faith of any evangelical.

Unfortunately, the phrase 'party political broadcast' applied to anything *distinctively* evangelical (ie which goes beyond the 'lowest common denominator' to assert the objective truth of Christianity and ask for personal commitment on that basis) has become something of a stock phrase in religious broadcasting. Not only Robert Towler, but the current head of Granada Religious Broadcasting, David Boulton, and the head of BBC Religious Broadcasting, John Whale, have expressed similar views in discussions with evangelicals. In a *Network* programme in 1988, John Whale asserted:

> It's not our business to evangelise. There are too many different kinds of Christianity ... It's not our business to choose between these alternatives for viewers. All that we can do is to present viewers with the rich diversity of religion and leave the choice to them.

Evangelicals (ably represented by Elaine Storkey of The London Institute for Contemporary Christianity and Peter Meadows of The Evangelical Alliance) were less than convinced. For one thing, an exaggeration of the supposed diversity of Christian belief is to ignore the fact that in Western Christianity there are (apart from cultists who cut themselves off from the Christian community) three main groupings: Catholic, evangelical and liberal. Catholics and evangelicals share a belief that their faiths are based on objective fact — and to write off programmes like *Jesus, Then and Now*, which had support from both, is to *neglect* to present the 'rich diversity of religion', as claimed. Diversity is presented by *allowing* such groups (and others, such as Muslims, if they wish) to put forward their objective claims, not by excluding all but the 'lowest common denominator' of liberal scholarship from anything claiming objectivity.

John Whale's claim that evangelicals were represented 'in proportion to what we judge to be their current strength in the community' did not convince his evangelical hearers. The views of those who do get documentary-style series often seem representative of few in the Christian community. Perhaps 'orthodoxy' is simply too unsensational. In 1986, the House of Bishops of the Anglican Church, with unusual unanimity, published a statement that the Resurrection of Jesus was an actual historical event, not merely a kind of subjective spiritual experience of the disciples:

> We believe that Jesus' Resurrection was something that happened, regardless of observers, narrators or believers. Jesus truly died and was buried, and as truly rose again to eternal life. Those who preface any reply by saying that it all depends on what you mean by 'happen' or 'fact' or 'historical' ... convey less of the truth.[11]

The clear rejection of subjectivism from which this extract is taken received a small media mention. Shortly earlier, one particular university don and Anglican priest, Don Cupitt, had his own television series *The Sea of Faith*. Stringing together a sequence of assorted figures (D F Strauss, Freud, Jung, Schweitzer, etc) as supposed epoch-making thinkers, he launched us out in his series on a sea of relativism, where there was no such thing as objective truth. One of the most obviously true statements in his book based on the series was: 'Critics will complain that I have prejudged the issue by choosing as my examples a group of deviant and marginal figures.'[12] The Revd Dr Cupitt is undoubtedly a sincere and clever man, but his system is surely idiosyncratic — a 'party political broadcast' on behalf of a very small party. How does he stand in relation to the Anglican Church in which he was ordained in 1959? In July 1986, following a rather critical reception of Dr Cupitt's relativism from a mixed-discipline group of academics, Paul Marston (who was also giving a paper) read out part of the then newly published bishops' statement, and asked what part Dr Cupitt saw for such statements in the Christianity of the future. His reply was that the bishops had 'got themselves in a twist' over that statement.

Yet Don Cupitt is only one of the sequence of very individualistic figures selected for documentary-style television series. Perhaps the criteria for choice — given the numbers of orthodox scholars who would be available — is controversy and individuality. Plain orthodoxy is not 'interesting', and might come too near to demanding a response.

In Britain, another Anglican guaranteed good media coverage is the Bishop of Durham, David Jenkins. In his speech to the Synod the bishop urged acceptance of the statement (including the part on the Resurrection) just mentioned. But in the same speech he added:

> What sort of God are we portraying and believing in if we insist on what I will nickname 'the divine laser beam' type of miracle as the heart and basis of the Incarnation and the Resurrection? ... we are implying, if not actually portraying, a God who is at the best a cultic idol, and at the worst the very Devil.[13]

Though the bishop accepted that God *could* do this kind of miracle (an advance over the higher critics!), he added that this 'would not seem to be a choice which he cared or would care to use'.

Now on what basis was such a pronouncement made? On a careful analysis of the actual record of the Gospels? On a careful sifting of the evidence for miracles today? Not at all — the bishop does not even begin to look at any of the actual data in the Bible, the creed of his own Church as reiterated by the bishops, or historic Christianity. He offers us his own argument based on an (unfounded) assumption that knockdown miracles, if done, must be to 'let a select number of people into the secret of his Incarnation, Resurrection and salvation'. The bishop then pronounced this incompatible with a God who does not miraculously stop Auschwitz, Hiroshima or apartheid. We therefore, says the bishop, all have to read the actual accounts of the Gospels presuming that 'there are no knock-down miracles which prove to everybody that God is around'.

Now most Christians would surely agree with the bishop that miracles are primarily 'gifts of love' rather than proofs to *make* the unwilling *accept* God. But when he speaks of the scientific revolution and the 'modern world view' of Marx, Freud and Durkheim (the last of whom, incidentally, died over half a century ago), does he mean that we cannot now believe in what he calls 'monophysitely divine manipulations of the physical' (ie what in our next chapter we call type-ii miracles)? Is his insistence that he is 'quite clear that miracles occur' just an assertion that in some conditions believers get warm feelings about things?

In spite of the trendy and provocative language David Jenkins chooses to use, it is hard to make much consistent sense of it. The general public certainly take it that he is denying the objective physical reality of the Resurrection. This is what the media, television and Press have shown interest in. It is far more sensational for one bishop to effectively deny his creed than for ninety-nine bishops to reaffirm it!

Not only the television but also the Press show the same interests. One famous example of this was in the late 1960s when Manchester University scholars included F F Bruce, who held the top post of Rylands Professor of Biblical Criticism and Exegesis. Professor Bruce's stream of scholarly works showing the objective evidence for Christianity are much appreciated by Christians, but have received little Press coverage. In 1969, however, a fairly junior Hebraist in the department, John Allegro, came out with an expensive book arguing that Jesus was really a mythical product of a 'sacred mushroom' cult. The Press serialised it, and many of the general public were questioning their faith. On 23rd May 1970 *The Times* carried a devastating letter of criticism by twelve professors, 'specialists in a number of relevant disciplines and men of several faiths and none'. They affirmed that they felt it to be 'their duty to let it be known that the book is not based on any philological or other evidence which they can regard as scholarly'. It was, in short, a work of fantasy. But how many read *The Times* letters page compared with headlined articles?

We must be careful in all this not to exaggerate. We found, for example, the Zeffirelli Channel 3 film *Jesus of Nazareth* profoundly moving (in spite of its strangely ambiguous and inaccurate Resurrection section), and it must surely have challenged some viewers. On more objective issues, Channel 3 recently broadcast an encouraging interview-mode programme (which is at least halfway to being a documentary!) between Jonathan Miller and Christian minister and ex-physicist John Polkinhorne. Brian Magee some years ago did a useful series on scientists who were Christians, including some evangelicals like MacKay and Berry. In just the last few years there has been an awakening among evangelicals to the media situation, and a desire to react positively to it. Some recent experiences of Roger Forster with ITV *News*, LWT, and Radio London have shown an encouraging trend towards greater opportunity to present what evangelicals really stand for in news, documentaries and some filming of training in Ichthus Christian Fellowship. As responsible evangelical leaders develop a dialogue with media controllers, it is to be hoped that clearer recognition will be given to the necessity, if the 'rich diversity of religion' is really going to be presented, to allow those who believe in the objective truth of Christianity to set out the evidence as they perceive it.

## Conclusion

We must never lose sight of the fact that the heart of Christian faith is the adventure of a relationship with the living God through Christ. We need also, however, to assert firmly that there *is* coherent evidence for the historical truth of Christian beliefs about Jesus' life, teaching, death and Resurrection. This assertion is not in any way lessened by the recognition that there are, as we have seen, various reasons why this evidence often remains less well known than it might be.

## Notes

1. Actually the transcript of the programme, for reasons best known to its writers, has the Greek 'Adonis' and Semitic 'Astarte'.
2. The whole Jewish theology of works is known from other sources, eg Alfred Edersheim, *The Life and Times of Jesus the Messiah*.
3. See, for example, H D McDonald, *Ideas of Revelation* (1959).
4. For introductions to textual criticism see, for example, J H Greenlee, *Introduction to New Testament Textual Criticism* or Bruce Metzger, *The Text of the New Testament*.
5. W Paley, *Horae Paulinae* (1790), *A View of the Evidences of Christianity* (1794).
6. D Hume, *An Enquiry Concerning Human Understanding* (1748).
7. An evangelical perspective on some of these was given in I H Marshall, *New Testament Interpretation* (1977). More recently, Craig Blomberg's *The Historical Reliability of the Gospels* (1987) contains a useful summary.
8. Marshall McLuhan (1911–80) published *The Medium is the Message* with Quentin Fiore in 1967.
9. Neil Postman, *Amusing Ourselves to Death* (1986), p 88.
10. The story was carried in *The Christian Herald*, 18th April 1987.
11. *The Nature of Christian Belief* (1986).
12. Don Cupitt, *The Sea of Faith* (the book was issued in 1984, following the series), p 245.
13. David E Jenkins, *God, Miracle and the Church of England* (1987), p 4.

# 8

# ARE MIRACLES REALLY CREDIBLE IN AN AGE OF SCIENCE?

## Introduction

WHAT DO WE MEAN BY miracles? From today's stand-point, we have a strong concept of 'natural law'. In our culture we believe the operations of nature follow regular sequences. The analysis and description of these regular sequences of cause-effect is the work of science.

Now from this point of view, one may distinguish two kinds of miracle:

* Type-i:   Those which involve no alteration in the regular physical cause-effect sequences, but involve 'coincidences' to such a degree that participants see them as divinely provident.
* Type-ii:  Those which appear to have no possible way to explain them without suggesting an alteration in the usual physical cause-effect sequences.

Several points about this distinction may be made.

Firstly, it is by no means a new distinction. In the early fifth century, Augustine distinguished between miracles which are the outcome of inherent causes (*semina occulta*) introduced by God at the first creation, and those which result from God's intrusion into the natural order when he alters something to a 'wholly different nature'.[1]

A similar distinction has been taken up in one way or another by many writers who have analysed the question of miracles.[2]

Secondly, we must note that, although the distinction is ancient, the Bible writers themselves did not make it, since they had no strong idea of scientific law. When something remarkable or unusual happened, the Hebrew writers might note that such an event was 'unusual' or even 'unique' and that God had done it for some purpose. What they lacked was the purely intellectual curiosity as to whether it involved movements of matter within or outside what we would now call normal scientific laws. They simply did not think in those terms.

Now this is not to say either that they were naïvely credulous or that they were unaware of the normal patterns of physical sequence. Mary, for example, knew very well that babies are not conceived without sexual intercourse — and her reaction reflected this (Lk 1:34).[3] The newly healed man born blind knew quite well that what had happened was unusual; in fact, he proclaimed that it had *never* happened in the history of the world (Jn 9:32). But what we are saying is that their prime interest was in the meaning and origin of a remarkable event — not its relationship with what we call laws of science.

A third point, which is connected to this, is that if in the light of our present knowledge a biblical miracle is seen to come into the type-i rather than the type-ii category, then this is in no way to doubt the biblical record. Most, for example, of the famous plagues in Egypt may be explained by 'natural' causes, but this in no way challenges the truth of the Bible that God sent them. God is as much the author of natural causal sequences as of the type-ii miracles. It is God, in fact, who (according to Jesus in Matthew 6:26) feeds the birds — but he does it through natural causal sequences.

What we are left with, however, is some basic questions:

1. Are type-ii miracles logically possible and if so, is there sufficient evidence to believe that they have occurred?
2. In what relationship do these type-ii miracles stand to faith?
3. In what way can type-i miracles be ascribed to a personal involvement of God?
4. Why, if type-ii miracles occur, do they occur only in some instances and not in others with apparently similar circumstances? (This will be considered in Chapter 9.)

## Christian belief and the possibility of miracles

Are type-ii miracles rationally possible? This depends on one's assumptions. Consider the following three belief systems:

* *Deterministic Naturalism (which implies atheism)*
    (a) Physical nature is all that there is, a closed system.
    (b) Physical phenomena follow invariant patterns of cause-effect.

* *Deism*
    (a) God has created physical nature to function independently of him and to have invariant patterns of cause-effect.
    (b) God has left this as a closed system and has no further involvement or interaction with it.

* *Christian Supernaturalism (or theism)*
    (a) God exists separately from physical nature, which is only a part of total reality.
    (b) Physical nature does not function independently of God, but depends for its continuing existence on his will and power.
    (c) The laws of science represent our generalisations about God's usual patterns of working in physical cause-effect sequences.

Each of these has a kind of self-consistency, but none of them is obviously and self-evidently true. *If* physical nature is a closed system following invariant laws (as either of the first two would imply), then clearly type-ii miracles are impossible. But *if* the Christian God exists, then there is clearly no reason why he should not periodically vary his pattern of working, ie produce a type-ii miracle. This would imply that type-ii miracles would be possible — the only question being if and when they had actually happened.

Let us first explore further the implications of Christian supernaturalism. We use the word 'cause' in two rather different contexts, which we can call 'cause$_1$' and 'cause$_2$'. Within the purely physical world, science explores the sequences of events and discerns the patterns in them. The ideas of cause$_1$ and effect are used in the reduction of these to regularity in scientific discovery. But what is the cause$_2$ of anything being there at all? Christians believe that God holds together 'the universe by his word of power' (Heb 1:3 RSV; see also Col 1:17), that is, anything exists only because of his continued will that it should. But he is consistent; generally speaking we may discern regularities in the physical world.

A useful analogy is that given by Professor MacKay of a television screen.[4] Within, say, a cartoon we may observe cause$_1$, effect, and so on, operating in certain patterns. The cause$_2$ of the picture being on the screen at all is, however, not of the same order as cause$_1$ within the picture. Perhaps an even closer analogy would be the sequence of images you can project within your own imagination. You, as a personal being and centre of consciousness are the cause$_2$ of this sequence appearing there. You might, of course, choose to make this sequence follow some discernible pattern of cause$_1$ and effect which could be generalised in the manner in which science generalises. But causes$_1$ and effects within the sequence would certainly be of an entirely different level and order from the cause$_2$ of the image sequence being there. In a similar way the Christian views God as *the* cause$_2$ of the universe continuing as it does, and not merely as *a* cause$_1$ which operates within it.

Now this is by no means a new concept for Christians; both theologians and leaders in the field of science have especially suggested it. Thus, for example, Jean Buridan (c1295–c1366) followed early church figures in writing:

> One could say, in fact, that God, when he created the universe, set each of the celestial spheres in motion as it pleased him, impressing on each of them an impetus which has moved it ever since. God has, therefore, no longer to move these spheres, except in exerting a general influence similar to that by which he gives his concurrence to all phenomena. Thus he could rest on the seventh day from the work he had achieved, confiding to created things their mutual causes and effects.[5]

This refers back to early church teaching such as that of Chrysostom on John 5:17, that Jesus 'reveals his unceasing care for us: he calls "work" the maintenance of created things, bestowal of permanence on them, and governance of them through all time'.[6] Later, in the Reformation, Calvin's Genesis commentary also speaks of God sustaining the world, and that 'if God should but withdraw his hand a little, all things would immediately perish and dissolve into nothing'.[7]

Among founders of modern scientific thinking, the chemist Robert Boyle, one of the great early luminaries of the Royal Society, wrote in 1685 that it must produce adoration of God to know that all the complex machinery of animal organisms,

> as well as the rest of the mundane matter, are every moment sustained, guided and governed, according to their respective natures and with an exact regard to the catholic laws of the universe; to know, I say, that there is a Being that does this everywhere and every moment, and that manages all things without aberration or intermission.[8]

Boyle's later *The Christian Virtuoso* (1690) expanded on this theme. Now Boyle was probably *the* leading figure in what is called the 'mechanical philosophy', which arose at this time. This is the belief that the physical cause-effect sequence is unbroken and totally predictable. Yet, because he believed that this whole chain was there only because God was continually sustaining it, Boyle had no trouble in accepting the biblical miracles.[9] Boyle even gives an analogy of a quill pen writing, which is a kind of seventeenth-century equivalent to our one of the television screen![10]

Many other scientists could be used to illustrate this view. The following is taken from the great early nineteenth-century geologist William Buckland, who says that many people maintain:

> that the system of the universe is carried on by the force of the laws originally impressed on matter, without the necessity of fresh interference or continued supervision on the part of the Creator. Such an opinion is indeed founded only on a verbal fallacy; for 'laws impressed on matter' is an expression which can only denote the continued exertion of the will of the Lawgiver.[11]

Two further points need to be made. The first is the role of science. Suppose that we take, for example, Boyle's Law in physics, which states that the volume of a given mass of gas is inversely proportional to the pressure upon it if the temperature remains constant. This Law describes what is normally observed, but it does not say why it happens nor why it always should. As science progresses, we may break down existing laws into more basic units: in this case we may explain Boyle's Law in terms of the movements of molecules of gas. Yet this does not explain why molecules act this way nor why they always should. As we progress further, we may talk in subatomic terms. Yet no matter how far we reduce the phenomena to more and more basic laws, we will never be able to say why they behave as they do nor why they always should. Moreover, to say something like 'because it is in their nature to do so' really adds little more. Scientific laws may be valid or invalid, useful or useless, but ultimately they are no more than detailed descriptions of how things normally behave — which enables us to predict future behaviour. They answer the 'how' not the 'why' of physical existence. The Christian believes that this ultimate 'why' is because of the will and volition of God.

The second point concerns terms like 'breaking' laws, or 'God's intervention' in 'natural law'. To the Christian theist, the laws of nature have no existence independent of God. If we talk at all of God breaking them, then we must be careful what exactly we mean. You may speak of breaking a habit of early rising on a particular occasion, but that habit does not somehow exist independently of you. To say 'I intervened this morning in my habit of early rising by lying longer in bed' would be rather strange. Yet, to the Christian, laws of nature are nothing more than habits of God. We may doubt, then, whether terms like 'God's intervention' are really appropriate — and scientists such as those cited above actually tend to avoid them in their writings.

An acceptance, then, of the possibility of miracles, is a rational part of any Christian theism, ie a belief in a personal God who both created and sustains the universe by his word of power.

## Attacks on miracles

If, then, miracles are so obviously a rational part of a Christian world view, how did there come to be thought to be any particular problem with them?

We have seen how the Christian view sees God both as separate from and yet continually maintaining the physical world. Augustine, as we have seen, distinguished type-i and type-ii miracles. Unfortunately, however, his analysis of the type-ii spoke in terms of God changing the nature of what he has created. This could very easily be seen as God intervening in something to which he had given some kind of independent existence. To those philosophers whose experience of God is not that of the living personal God of the New Testament, but a rationally derived God from pure intellectual discussion, this smacked of inconsistency.

Perhaps one of the first was the Jewish pantheist Spinoza. As a pantheist, he believed that God was in everything but had no separate existence from the physical world. In other words, the physical world (even if embodying God) was a closed system. On these assumptions, as Colin Brown put it in a recent study,

> To Spinoza, laws of nature were divine decrees. They were perfect and simply could not be broken. To suggest that God broke his own decrees from time to time was unthinkable. It would be like suggesting that God was acting against his own nature, or that his wisdom needed correction.[12]

Naturally, however, one could very much question the basis on which he assumed his pantheism to be true. Yet this was also a kind of basis for the later deist movement. From 1624, began a tradition which 'rationally deduced' from experience and nature (with no reference to Jesus or the Bible) the idea of a God who created, but then took little further interest in, the world.[13] With such a God miracles would, of course, be impossible.

We must note the origins of this. The pantheist or deist believed that God had simply created perfect laws — and it would be against his nature to violate them. But we note:

1. These were usually philosophers, not 'scientists' in our sense.
2. They did not begin either from observation as a base for inviolable law, nor from the God of the Bible, but from a God deduced from pure reason.

David Hume, in his highly influential *An Enquiry Concerning Human Understanding* in 1748, argued rather differently. Both the pantheist Spinoza and the deists had emphasised reason rather than experience. Rationally they believed that deity must be self-consistent, which (in their minds) ruled out miracles. But David Hume, as well as speaking from a sceptical/agnostic position, was also a total empiricist, ie he believed that all knowledge came from experience. Thus his belief in the inviolability of natural law could be based *only* on experience.

Hume's basic argument, then, was:

1. Assessing the truth of any reported event is a balance of probabilities.
2. The *a priori* improbability of anything 'violating the laws of nature' is so great that 'overwhelming human testimony' would be necessary in order to make us accept it.
3. The right kind of human testimony (reliable, sophisticated, first-hand witness of incontrovertable miracle) is lacking.
4. Also, there is a natural human tendency to exaggerate, and miracles are usually more reported among 'ignorant and barbarous nations'.

Hume concluded that miracles have not happened and do not happen.

This is riddled with contradiction. Firstly, it is hard to see how anything for a real empiricist can be so '*a priori* improbable'. If all knowledge comes from experience, we have to wait and see. Secondly, as Colin Brown points out, Hume refused to accept in his own day the testimony of doctors and men of repute in Paris who had examined and accepted miracles. He replied only that 'the absolute impossibility' of such events must be sufficient refutation 'in the eyes of all reasonable people'.[14] In other words, having begun solely by appeal to the evidence, he finished by refusing to look at it.

In brief, the problem with his argument is that:

1. He begins from the 'firm and unalterable experience' that laws are inviolable.
2. But this is true only if he assumes that this experience must exclude the many claims throughout history to have witnessed them.
3. On such a basis — having ruled them out — it is not surprising that he concludes them to be impossible!

It is all really a classic case of assuming what you want to prove.

### Hume's philosophical offspring

Who, in the main, carried on the Humean position? In Chapter 7 we looked at some of those in various schools of Radical Theology which began in the nineteenth century. One of the twin pillars of assumption made was, as we saw, the impossibility of miracles. Thus one of its great early figures, D F Strauss, wrote in his *Life of Jesus* (1835–6, translated in 1846) that any narration must be presumed to be myth if it is 'irreconcilable with the known and universal laws ... according to these laws, agreeing with all just philosophical conceptions and all credible experience, the absolute cause never disturbs the chain of secondary causes by single arbitrary acts of interposition'.[15] Which are these 'all just philosophical conceptions'? Are they those 'rationally deduced' from the character of God by the deists, or 'derived from experience' by Hume? In neither case are they much of an alternative to looking at actual human testimony. Yet these shaky foundations, as we saw in Chapter 7, led to all kinds of supposedly rational emasculations of real Christianity. One famous early follower was J E Renan whose *Life of Jesus* (1863) began by assuming: 'Miracles are things which never happen; only credulous people believe they have seen them.'[16] Many other theologians followed, and some even today have made little philosophical progress. One of the great 'heroes' taken up by 1980s television theologian Don Cupitt was that very same D F Strauss!

A second group of heirs of Hume and Strauss is a small body of anti-supernaturalist philosophers. Apart from a suspicion that the strength of feeling exhibited by such unbelievers goes deeper than mere intellectual difficulty, the actual arguments seem either to be linguistic tricks or a kind of deification of science, and Christians have made detailed criticisms of them.[17]

Others who might go along with the impossibility of miracles are some artists. In D H Lawrence's controversial book *The Rainbow* (shown in 1988 as a BBC television series) Brangwen thinks about the water being changed into wine:

So much rain-water — look at it — can it become grape juice, wine? For an instant he saw with the clear eyes of the mind and said No ... Water, natural water, could it suddenly and unnaturally turn into wine, depart from its being and at haphazard take on another being? Ah no, he knew it was wrong.[18]

Artists, presumably, rely on gut reaction rather than rational thought. The 'clear eyes of the mind' should have said 'yes'. Obviously, the miraculous MUST be the out of the ordinary, otherwise it would not be miraculous. But there seems to be no rational reason to rule out, before actual examination, the possibility of type-ii miracles occurring.

The one group which, on the whole, seem to have had little trouble about the possibility of miracles is that of mainstream British scientists. As we have seen, this includes even those (like Boyle) who supported most

strongly a mechanical philosophy of cause and effect. Even
T H Huxley, one of the most famous agnostic scientists of
the age of Darwin said that 'the so-called a-priori arguments
against theism and, given a deity, against the possibility of
creative acts' appeared to him 'to be devoid of reasonable
foundation'.[19] Neither special creation nor miracle were a
priori impossible.

### Faith and type-ii miracles

Are miracles for the Christian a proof of faith, or are they only
accepted because of faith? In fact the relationship is complex.

Three main words are used in the New Testament: *semeia*
(signs), *terata* (wonders) and *dynameis* (mighty works). All
three go back to Old Testament ideas and words.

A number of things must be remembered about this.
Firstly, in the biblical context believers were not arguing for
the *possibility* of the supernatural. Even when Paul was
arguing his case before the sophisticated Greeks (including
Epicurean sceptics), his sermon simply begins with the
assertion of who God is, appealing to their own deeper
consciousness and religious roots. He does not argue that
Jesus' Resurrection proves the supernatural. His argument is
rather that the Resurrection affirms God's approval of Jesus
as the man by whom the world will be judged (Acts 17:31).
Even this, in itself, is not absolute proof, for Paul is well
aware that there may be false 'signs and wonders' (2 Thess
2:9).

The pattern goes back right to Israel's beginning. God is to
be distinguished from other gods in that he acted in bringing
out their nation for himself by 'signs and wonders ... and a
mighty hand' in actions never seen before or since (Deut
4:34). Yet, on the other hand,

> If a prophet ... announces to you a ... sign or wonder, and if the
> sign or wonder of which he has spoken takes place, and he says,

'Let us follow other gods,' ... The Lord your God is testing you to find out whether you love him with all your heart ... That prophet ... must be put to death (Deut 13:1–5).

The basic point is that whilst signs and wonders may be expected to accompany the activity of a supernatural God, they are not in themselves a proof. The genuineness of the true God and faith in him is attested by a wider range of human experience.

This pattern is followed in the New Testament, where Jesus also recognises that false prophets may do signs and wonders, whether type-i or type-ii miracles (Mt 24:24; Mk 13:22). Matthew 12 is very interesting. Jesus performs a miraculous healing (v 22–3), but his opponents put it down to evil arts. Jesus indicates that they should discern his genuineness from the wider moral context. Asked (v 38) for a sign, his reply indicates that they should look to the example of those who repented (like the people of Nineveh and the Queen of Sheba) at the preaching of the word. It is the response of the will rather than the unwilling conviction of the intellect which is the key to faith (Jn 7:15–16). He even obliquely acknowledges that a resurrection will not convict a person who refuses to repent at the message of the Law and the Prophets (Lk 16:29–31). The miracles which he did were 'signs' of his messiahship — for they were also parables of his kingdom. The driving out of Satan and the miraculous provision recalling God's manna in the wilderness were both things which one might only expect from God's Messiah — yet some saw these miracles and missed their significance by immediately afterwards asking for a sign (Mt 12:38, 16:1)!

None of the words used have as a primary meaning any kind of suspension of laws of nature. A sign is something by which one recognises a particular person or thing, a confirmatory, corroborative, authenticating mark or token.[20] They are extraordinary, but not necessarily type-ii miracles.

Their significance is in that in their wider context they point to God and his activity. A 'wonder' (which in the New Testament is used only together with 'sign') means a kind of portent. It is something which brings a person up sharply and seems to demand an interpretation.[21] Finally, Jesus' miracles are called 'mighty works' because 'in them God's rule on earth begins to have a powerful effect' and 'the fight against evil is carried out on the level of human existence'.[22] The work is paramount, the power is because God is involved.

Type-ii miracles, then, do occur, and their very unexpectedness may pull people up sharply and raise questions in their minds. But such miracles are not intended as magic tricks to convince unwilling atheists. Rather they are the natural expectation when God is at work in the Messiah (Jesus) or his followers (Mt 16:17–20). As such, they are further confirmatory signs to those who discern the work of God going on.

Christians have, in the main, recognised that miracles are proofs only in this kind of context. Origen, for example, the great early Greek Christian, wrote: 'Without miracles and wonders [the apostles] would not have persuaded those who heard new doctrines and new teachings to leave their traditional religion.'[23] He asserts that miracles are still being done in his day. Yet he admits that in and by themselves, the miracles are no infallible proof of divinity. The real tests are the purity of life of the miracle-worker and the betterment of mankind by their results.[24]

Great early scientists such as Robert Boyle (whose views we already mentioned) and philosophers of science like Bacon were just as clear. Boyle cites with approval 'one of the first and greatest experimental philosophers of our age, Sir Francis Bacon, that God never wrought a miracle to convince atheists'.[25] Bacon and Boyle believed in miracles, but not as self-standing proofs of the truth of any system of Christian doctrine.

Even where miracles have been presented as proofs, they

are usually thought to be part of a wider picture of prophecy and moral content. Wesley, for example, who led the evangelical revival in Britain in the eighteenth century, appealed to the classic proofs of miracles, prophecies and the moral character of its writings as proof of biblical authority.[26] These points were later repeated by such as William Paley, and early nineteenth-century evangelical leaders like Simeon and Chalmers.[27] Colin Brown cites several more recent leaders who have claimed to see miracles as proofs, showing that in no instance are they actually thought to be self-sufficient as proofs.[28]

Sometimes, of course, Christian apologists may have objectives which differ from those of the early church, because they speak to people of different viewpoints. C S Lewis, in perhaps one of the most widely known books on miracles, followed earlier writers like Paley in arguing against antisupernaturalists that miraculous occurrences would be only to be expected if the Christian world view were correct. He was aiming at those who doubted the possibility of miracles rather than those who doubted their significance. Earlier parts of the present chapter have had the same objective.

In what relation, then, do miracles, particularly type-ii miracles, stand to faith? Firstly, Jesus taught that miracles come in response to faith. The actual occurrence, then, is largely dependent on faith. To onlookers, it is not in any way irrational to believe in the possibility of miracles — even though there may be scepticism in particular cases. Yet the miracle will never be an absolute proof of the truth of Christianity. The miracle should be seen in its real context as a natural part of what may be expected if the Christian world view is true, and to come in a context of 'making whole', which is central to the Christian religion. In such a context miracles do, then, point as 'signs' to the spiritually discerning, confirming the truth and authority of Jesus.

## Type-i miracles and God's involvement

It must, of course, be noted that it is impossible absolutely to prove that a particular miracle is in one or other category. With our modern views that all scientific discoveries may be superseded later by further discovery, we cannot rule out the possibility that later discoveries will enable a type-ii miracle to be reassigned as type-i. On the other hand, it is impossible to tell if, in an individual incident, what we thought was a natural causal sequence did involve some change. Thus, for example, when Jesus calmed the storm, it might turn out that there *was* some suspension of usual physical laws — we cannot have the data to determine this.

But what of the type-i miracles themselves? Can we say that prayer, for example, has been answered only if a type-ii miracle occurs? Surely not. The universe as a whole is a creation of God. We cannot possibly know exactly the relationship in which he stands to time within it. Clearly, there is a sense in which he enters into time as a participant. He is said to 'change his mind' (Jer 18:8). Yet, on the other hand, he can apparently prophesy far future events. Now in some of these 'prophecies' he is, presumably, simply telling us what he knows that he is going to do at a later date. But the prophecies such as those looked at in Isaiah 53 and Psalm 22 cannot entirely be thus explained. The words 'Before Abraham was I AM' seem to indicate some degree of mystery in God's relationship with time. This 'mystery', however, is not simply obscurantism. We find a quite parallel mystery in the current exploration of the nature of time from a physics point of view — with paradoxes equally as strange.

Now here we might fall into one of two traps. On the one hand, as we have said, God does enter into time with us as a participant, and we cannot believe that he is simply 'playing at it'. On the other hand, there are aspects of both his and our relationship to time which are mysterious. The Christian does not claim to be able to comprehend the nature of this —

any more than physicists really comprehend the nature of time in relativity. But the Christian is one who has made the decision to enter as a participant in the world, just as he or she believes God acts as a participant. Only the bystanders are incurably worried to find out whether miracles are type-i or type-ii. The participants take them as signs, and get on with the adventure of Christian living.

## Notes

1. Augustine, *City of God*, bk 21, section viii (*Nic & Pos Nic Fath*, 1, i,460). See also *Contra Faustum Manichaeum*, xxvi,3 (*Nic & Pos Nic Fath*, 1,iv,322).

2. See, for example, R F Holland, 'The Miraculous', *American Philosophical Quarterly*, vol ii (1965): pp 43–51; Colin Brown, *Miracles and the Critical Mind* (1984), p 174, etc and *That You May Believe* (1985), p 65, etc.

3. See also C S Lewis, *Miracles* (1947), chap 7.

4. D M MacKay, *Science and Christian Faith Today* (1963).

5. Jean Buridan, *Quaestiones Super Octo Physicorum*, bk 8.

6. *The Fathers of the Church*, vol 74, p 140 (translated by R C Hill).

7. John Calvin, *Commentary on Genesis* (this edition translated by J King, 1965).

8. Robert Boyle, *Of the High Veneration Man's Intellect Owes to God*, (1685) p 140–1.

9. R S Westfall, though he outlines well Boyle's whole views on this (in *Science and Religion in Seventeenth Century England*, 1973), seems not really to grasp the consistency of Boyle's position — and sees his acceptance of miracles as a 'contradiction' to his general views.

10. Boyle, *Works*, vol 2, p 48.

11. William Buckland, *Vindiciae Geologicae* (1820), p 18. Buckland too has been misunderstood. Hooykaas, for example, correctly ascribes the 'biblical' view to Newton, but mistakenly describes Buckland as a 'semi-deist' *Natural Law and Divine Miracle: The Principle of Uniformity in Geology, Biology and Theology*, 1959).

12. Colin Brown, *That You May Believe*, p 8; see also his *Miracles and the Critical Mind* chap 2, and N L Geisler, *Miracles and Modern Thought* (1979), p 15, etc, and *Christian Apologetics* (1976), chap 14.

13. 1624 is the date of Lord Herbert's *On Truth*, continued in a tradition by Toland's *Christianity Not Mysterious* (1696), Tindale's *Christianity as Old As Creation* (1730) and Woolston's 1720s works.

14. Colin Brown, *That You May Believe*, p 22.
15. D F Strauss, *Life of Jesus* (1835–6, translated in 1846), 2nd edition, 1st volume (1892), translated by George Eliot (Swan, London), p 88.
16. J E Renan, *Life of Jesus* (1863).
17. See Geisler, *Miracles and Modern Thought*, p 48, etc.
18. D H Lawrence, *The Rainbow* (Methuen: London, 1915). Edition used: Penguin (1968), p 171.
19. T H Huxley, *On the Reception of the Origin of Species*, p 167.
20. Colin Brown (ed), see *The New International Dictionary of New Testament Theology* (1975–85), vol ii, p 626. Colin Brown refers to all three words in *That You May Believe*, p 74, etc.
21. See *The New International Dictionary*, vol ii, p 632, etc.
22. See *The New International Dictionary*, vol ii, p 603.
23. See Colin Brown, *That You May Believe,* and *Miracles and the Critical Mind*. Also Origen in *Against Celsus* I:ii, II:lxviii (*Ant Nic Fath*, iv, 397, 491).
24. Origen in *Against Celsus* III:xlviii (*Ant Nic Fath*, iv, 450, etc).
25. Robert Boyle, *The Christian Virtuoso* (1690), p 41.
26. John Wesley, *A Clear and Concise Demonstration of the Divine Inspiration of Holy Scripture*.
27. W Paley, *Evidences* (1794), p 7, etc; Simeon, *Works*, vol 14, p 351; Chalmers, *The Evidence and Authority of the Christian Revelation* (1814), p 253.
28. Colin Brown, *Miracles and the Critical Mind*, chap 8.

# 9

# DO MIRACLES HAPPEN TODAY?

## Miracles today

SHOULD CHRISTIANS EXPECT TO SEE miracles today and, if so, do such miracles in fact happen? There have been theologians who have argued that miracles, ie type-ii miracles in the sense of Chapter 8, were only for the age of Jesus and the apostles.[1] Yet Jesus put no time limit on his promise that miraculous signs would accompany those who believe (Mt 16:17). These 'signs' are an authenticating witness to the true people of God, they are not linked exclusively to the authority of apostles or the establishing of Scripture. They certainly were not restricted to the apostles alone, for Stephen is attested as a man who 'did great wonders and miraculous signs among the people' (Acts 6:8). Without recourse to a very strained reading of verses dealing with quite other topics, it is impossible to find in the Bible any indication that miracles would cease with the apostolic age.

There is, therefore, every reason to expect that, if the miracles in the New Testament were genuine, Christians should sometimes expect to experience miracles today. To show, then, that Christianity makes sense of our world and experience, we need to present good evidence that such miracles *do* occur — where 'good evidence' means that we are able to offer reasonable assurance of the facts from personal contact.

A problem in this, however, may be illustrated from a British television programme screened at around the time when we first began this chapter. The programme was presented by Robert Kilroy Silk (a former Member of Parliament) and it asked exactly this question: 'Do miracles happen today?' Several invited guests testified to personal experiences of miracles. One, a physiotherapist, testified that, after prayer with Christian doctor Tony Dale (Chairman of Caring Professions Concern), who was also present, her leg which was previously 1.25 inches too short was healed by Jesus. Another case was so remarkable that we wrote to the person concerned, Mrs Valerie Moreman. She wrote back:

> I was blind in my left eye and almost in my right, I had been confined fully in a wheel-chair for thirteen years, yet even five years before this I was only able to get about by swinging on crutches ... I had a catheter for organs to function below the waist ... I was totally dependent on bags, supports on spine, neck, hands and arms. Due to drugs I was almost a zombie. All this is confirmed by all the specialists I was under for the different parts of my anatomy. I will now list my full illnesses for you: bronchiectasis, degenerative spondylitis, pernicious anaemia, paraplegia.

Pronounced incurable, in constant pain, Valerie was under six doctors and specialists, including a neurologist and ortho-paedist. On Christmas Eve 1986, she felt a surge of intense pain, and heard a voice saying, 'Walk! Walk!' A friend was present, but no kind of faith healer. When her husband came home later that day, he found her healed — totally. Now a member of the Salvation Army, Valerie proclaims, 'I know Jesus healed me.' She ascribes her healing to prayer — a miracle — and various doctors can only agree.

These kind of cases seem to meet even David Hume's requirements for good evidence. But Mr Kilroy Silk, the programme presenter, then turned for comment to an unbelieving psychiatrist, Dr Colin Brewer. The latter stated:

'There are lots of possible explanations without invoking the miraculous.' Challenged to give one, he replied that lots of illnesses are 'purely psychological' or else they 'have a large psychological element'.

This really illustrates that the basic point made in the previous chapter about belief in miracles still applies today. It is not that we lack reliable human testimony that such things occur. It is that our own prior belief systems determine whether or not we accept that testimony. If, like Colin Brewer, we determine that type-ii miracles simply cannot happen, then we will have to seek some alternative explanation, however improbable. We will have to assume trickery, psychosomatic hysteria, wrong diagnosis, etc. We will have to assume that the X-rays were mistaken, all the examining doctors got it wrong, it just went away on its own (which sounds better if we call it 'spontaneous remission'), etc. Undoubtedly, all these things do sometimes happen. If in some particular instances (and degenerative spondylitis and reliably measured shortened legs both seem pretty observable and physical ailments to dispose of in this way) these kinds of explanation seem, to say the least, implausible, well, what else can an atheist do?

It must, of course, be recognised also that even the acceptance of a type-ii miracle does not mean acceptance of God. Such an event can be put down as an unsolved mystery, as a product of not-yet-understood scientific regularities, or as a product of the powers of the human mind. But that is not the present point at issue. The question here is simply whether or not there is evidence that type-ii miracles happen today. Not only is the answer to this question 'Yes', but modern medical knowledge now means that we can be virtually certain that they do. Methods of diagnosis of people later healed can now be so much more reliable. Naturally, these kinds of events are comparatively rare, for the whole definition of such events is that they are departures from the norm of scientific law. But they do occur.

There have been miracles in our own personal experience. One Friday evening Paul Marston, then nearly six years old, developed a headache, and soon became obviously very ill. After a night during which he became delirious, he was admitted into isolation hospital at 8.30 am on Saturday. No visits were allowed, but at 11.00 am on Sunday a consultant telephoned and advised his parents to come immediately. On arrival, they were told that there was practically no hope, as their son was having fit after fit. Though doctors were sure it was meningitis, no treatment could be given (though they had done a lumbar puncture in readiness) as the laboratories were closed over the weekend. He was unconscious, but throwing himself around in an odd way, and with eyes which, when briefly opened, were unseeing. The consultant said he was unlikely ever to regain consciousness — and if he did, would be brain damaged. Not wanting to remember their son like this, Paul's parents went for a walk, intending to return at 6.00 pm and expect the worst. Several Christian organisations and churches were, meantime, informed and were praying for healing. His parents also prayed, offering him (their only child) back to God, but praying that he would not return brain damaged. At 6 pm they arrived back at the hospital to be met by an amazed consultant, who reported an unexpected change in Paul during that afternoon. Their son was allowed to speak with them, slowly but determinedly asking for an item from a nearby shop — with a detailed description of its place in the window. Paul never lost consciousness again, though was kept in isolation for nearly three weeks. At the end of that time his mother was recalled to see the consultant, and writes:

He told me that he was amazed that Paul had made a remarkable full recovery without any medication at all while in hospital from that first Sunday afternoon when, according to his experience and knowledge, Paul should not have survived, especially in view of the severe nature of the attack so soon as three weeks after a tonsil operation. When I suggested that the many prayers of believers may have been answered, he replied that this could be the only explanation. He could find no brain damage and Paul could come home the next day.

Whether one calls this a 'miracle' or a 'spontaneous remission' is a matter of choice, but without it this book would obviously not have been written, as one of its authors would have been either dead or brain damaged.

The other author, Roger Forster, has seen a number of miracles, both physical and psychological, during his ministry. One of his fellow Ichthus founder members was diagnosed some years ago as having a brain tumour. After being anointed with oil and prayed over, he returned to the hospital a few days later and no trace of the tumour could be found.

Another instance was that of Phil, whose right elbow was injured when a car knocked him off his motor-bike. The other driver was found guilty of reckless driving, and Phil decided to sue for damages. The full hospital medical report which was required for this was made some five months later. It stated that his arm would never be straight again and he would never be able to participate in some sporting activities. Whilst waiting for the legal settlement he went with others of his church to a tent mission run by Ichthus Fellowship in Peckham. Phil writes:

There was a time of ministry during which one of the leadership team went to the mike and said that someone with a damaged right elbow was present and God wanted to heal him or her (I took no notice). One of the youngsters from my church dug me in the ribs and said 'That's you.' I laughed and said, 'No, I'm a lot better now thanks,' but the youngster persisted, 'No faith then.' So, very reluctantly and with no faith, I went forward. To my further embarrassment Roger prayed for me. I felt very silly and I didn't have the courage to say to Roger that I had no faith for my healing (I knew my elbow would never be straight). The next thing I knew I was on my back, thinking that I hoped none of the church saw me fall. Yet, while I was laying on my back, I physically felt something happen to my elbow, as though something was being moved. I got up and went back to my seat (Roger was praying for someone else by this time) and realised my arm was now completely straight, even a slightly damaged finger on my right hand was better.

Phil believes the lesson he learned was that 'healing is about obedience to God's word, not necessarily the person with the sickness'. Two years later, he reports an elbow undamaged and whole.

A second case is the psychological one of Sue, who was suffering from a progressively worsening bulimia. At a Christian meeting Roger's preaching on 'Power for Living' spoke so much to Sue that she nervously went forward for prayer. Sue was amazed to find that what had been said over weeks of counselling to her was covered in a few minutes by Roger and his co-worker (who had never met her) at the front of the meeting. Timidly, she said, 'I don't want to fall down when you pray for me like the others.' Roger at this point had a 'word of knowledge' (1 Cor 12:8) and replied, 'I can't do anything about that, but have you got a sister?' Sue was amazed because, she now writes, 'I could think of absolutely nothing at all that I held against her.' Going away from the meeting, she felt 'much better' but 'not feeling that anything particular had happened, other than I had acknowledged that I knew God was aware of my problem, and I had put my trust in him to deal with it in his way'. God had, however, given Roger the key to her particular problem, and later that evening in talking with her sister, Sue felt an overwhelming sense of God's love. God brought to mind some things she had, without being aware, held against her sister, and 'as soon as these things came to me, I just knew that I had been set free from my problem that night'. A twenty-year-long affliction ceased from that time onwards.

A Freudian psychologist would, of course, have no trouble explaining this as a combination of a lucky guess from Roger and accelerated release of subconscious repression through a religious equivalent of psychoanalysis. Indeed, as Christians, we could not say whether this was a type-i or type-ii miracle. But this is not important. What is important is that the kingdom work of God in healing and making whole is going on.

In preaching on a church weekend Roger pointed to a man in the congregation and said, 'What would you do if I cut off your ear?' The surprising reply was: 'Say thank you very much!' This led to much laughter, and at the end of the meeting Roger discovered that Nigel, who was unknown to him, had suffered ear trouble for twenty-three years, and heard nothing in his right ear for nine years. Roger and his wife prayed and layed hands on the man for healing. Nigel writes: 'I must admit I didn't have much faith because so many people . . . had anointed, prayed, layed hands on me . . . Faith doesn't always come into healing, although perhaps the faith of other people does.' A week later Nigel went into hospital for an operation on the ear. He writes:

I told them I felt better and could hear much better. They were rather sceptical and said, 'We will keep you in the night and do tests in the morning.' They did a pressure test on my ear drum and for the first time in nine years it responded nearly as well as the left ear. So when I showed the doctor on the ward the reports, he said, 'You're the one that got away! You can go home, you're all right.'

The doctors were not saying that it was completely healed, for it would always, they said, be prone to infection. Two years later, Nigel had an infection recommence in the ear, and came down from Norwich to London for prayer. The following week his doctor confirmed that his ear was now in perfect health, and he has kept correct and disease-free hearing since. Nigel believes that he learned much of God through his illness, though he rejoices now in his healing.

Between August 1986 and May 1987, Mark, aged three years, had failed three hearing tests and was referred to the audiologist in Winchester. On the last morning of the Christian Literature Crusade conference at Herne Bay Court in May 1987, Roger was leading the morning devotions, and held a time of healing. Mark's parents write:

> As the time was coming to an end, we felt it right to take Mark forward for healing of his ears (it was possible that repeated ear infections as a baby had caused ear damage). Mark was touched by the power of the Holy Spirit and we knew that he had been healed. This was confirmed by the audiologist in early August.

Alistair was (long ago!) at university with Paul and later became one of Roger's co-workers in Ichthus. A sporting accident resulted in a twisted left knee, which some years later a Christian osteopath identified as the underlying cause of a recurring back problem. He also stated that one of Alistair's legs was actually shorter than the other. On the second day of a leaders' conference, Ian Andrews had a word of knowledge from God, that there should be healing for someone present who had a knee injured in a sporting accident. When Alistair went forward, Ian said that he needed a new cartilage, and asked for someone to pray for this. One of the leaders in the group (which included Roger) did so, and in October 1987 Alistair was able to write about the healing: 'I felt the part of my left leg below the knee move downwards. My legs were now both the same length . . . From that time, I have not had back trouble in the same way at all.'

God is also concerned with what we consider small things. A boy and his father came to Roger after a Sunday morning meeting in North London. The father said that for over a year the boy had been having treatment for warts, and now they had given up because none of the treatments had worked. Roger prayed for him, and within two weeks all the warts had gone.

A much more major incident came with Roger's own son Chris. He was diagnosed in 1982 as suffering from a malignant lymphoma cancer. There were greatly enlarged glands in his chest, neck, arm, spleen and stomach, as well as cancer cells in his spinal fluid, indicating a possible spread to the brain. He was given a very slim chance of survival. Many Christians were fasting and praying for Chris, while Roger and his wife, Faith, went to the hospital with a friend and a visiting Canadian preacher who had seen miracles of healing in his own ministry. There was a dramatic breakthrough when they prayed and by the next day, all Chris' symptoms had disappeared. From that moment there has been, in fact, no medical evidence of any cancer cells in Chris' body. The hospital doctors, however, like Dr Brewer who was cited above, were very cautious about admitting the miraculous — it didn't fit their established procedures. Although the doctors later stated that, from the time he had been prayed for, no cancerous cells had been found, they did not immediately tell the family this. A lumbar puncture done a few days after the prayer for Chris was plainly marked 'clear' on the notes, though the hospital at this time withheld this information from the family and said that cancer cells were still present in the spinal fluid, insisting that cancerous cells 'don't just go away like that'. They pressed on with debilitating chemotherapy. The family declined some even more drastic forms of treatment they were recommended, but the regular course of chemotherapy was given and Chris had to suffer the bodily weakening and loss of hair that went with it. It is understandable that the hospital felt it must do all it could and all it knew how to do in order to save Chris' life. The scientific analysis of cause and effect was the only instrument at the doctors' disposal, and the regularly ob-served behaviour of cancerous cells excludes their sudden disappearance by natural causes. The family was sympathetic to the doctors' position and grateful for their care over Chris, but it does indicate clearly the problem of evidence for type-ii miracles — how you read it depends on your prior assumptions about the world.

Actually, there have been recorded instances of miracles throughout church history. The well-educated and philosophical Justin Martyr (c100–c165) wrote in his open letter to the Emperor of the 'many Christian men' in the city who had performed healings — a claim he would hardly have made without foundation.[2] Irenaeus (c130–c200) also states that in his times Christians have spiritual gifts and 'heal the sick by laying hands upon them ... the dead even have been raised up'.[3] Origen (c185–254) refers to 'signs and wonders' and adds 'traces of them are still preserved among those who regulate their lives by the principles of the gospel'.[4] Augustine (354–430) lists a number of specific miracles — attested by the secular physicians of his day — performed by Christians.[5] Rex Gardner, in his book *Healing Miracles: A Doctor Investigates*, refers to the incidence of healings in the church through the centuries.[6] He also, as a doctor, has carefully compiled quite a number of modern case histories in which verified medical conditions were healed in ways for which natural explanations simply cannot be conceived. This is the difference with miracles today: we can be *much more certain* of the medical condition of the sufferer, using modern diagnostic techniques, and therefore *much more certain* that a type-ii miracle *has* actually occurred. In this way, science, far from destroying a faith in the miraculous, strengthens our confidence that it does occur. The few examples, moreover, which we have cited from our own modern experience can be multiplied from the work of many servants of God today.[7]

## Why only these?

Perhaps the biggest question in most people's minds is why does God only heal *some* of those who pray for healing? Some indeed, like the sceptical Bishop Jenkins of Durham, as we saw, may doubt the existence of what he calls 'knockdown laser-beam miracles' — even including the bodily Resurrection of Jesus, which is an Article of Faith — because he cannot see why God doesn't step in and miraculously remove all the evil in the world.

But is there an answer? In asking this we need first to address the intellectual problem which looks for a pattern in God's working and secondly, the more practical problem of how to go about praying for or expecting healing miracles.

Briefly stated, the intellectual problem is this. If God is all-good and all-loving, why does he not heal more people miraculously? Why, indeed, is there any illness at all, since he could apparently stop it?

One possible approach would be to say that sickness is a judgement, and God shows his justice as well as mercy by selecting on a purely Sovereign basis who to heal and who to leave to suffer. The idea harks back to days when a total despot was deemed merciful even if only some of the people captured in a war — selected according to the despot's whim — were spared from torture and death. God does, of course, distribute spiritual gifts as he sees is best for his church. But surely the God of the Bible cannot be pictured as arbitrarily distributing such basic individual benefits as healing or new birth? Could anyone really try to explain in such a way the painful illness of many saintly people of God?

More plausibly perhaps, there are those who say that really 'all things work together for good', and, in spite of all appearances, all sickness is for the best welfare of Christians. The view is often based on the King James translation of Romans 8:28. In fact, however, the modern renderings of the RSV, NEB or NIV seem much more likely, and in several important ancient manuscripts an extra clarifying phrase (*ho theos*) puts the issue beyond doubt: God works 'in all things' for good, together with those who love him. This fits better the whole context of God working with the Christians in prayer (Rom 8:27). It does not make God sole author of all situations, but affirms that whatever the situation, God is there, working in it, and wanting to co-operate in the work with those who love him and are called according to his purpose. Often, of course, things which seem to be tragic do turn out later to have been for the best. One cannot, in fact, prove that things are not always for the absolute best in spite of all appearances — but in many situations this seems highly implausible.

Some Christians claim that in reality miracles are part of natural law. If the individual faith conditions are right, the healing will always occur. This is, of course, impossible to prove or disprove, because faith cannot be scientifically measured. It also has something to recommend it — because we all want to think that God is consistent in his actions. But there are problems with it. Many of us know instances (like those mentioned earlier) where the healed person appears to have had little or no faith that they would be healed. Some of Jesus' healings seem in the same category, and in the case of Jairus' daughter and Lazarus both were dead and in no position to exercise faith at all (Mk 5:41, though note 5:36; Jn 11). Jesus does speak of the necessity for faith both in the one using a gift of healing (Mt 17:20) and in the healed one (Mt 9:29), but there seems no simple pattern here. We would wish to assert that Jesus bore both our sin and our 'infirmities and . . . sorrows' (Is 53:4). Salvation and healing are there for the church to appropriate in faith. In experi-ence, however, whatever the faith of the individual, we do find occasions when the healing does not occur. Even the apostle Paul found this (Phil 2:25–7; 2 Tim 4:20) though at other times remarkable miracles happened through him (Acts 19:11–12).[8] It is no use in such instances pretending that the healing has really happened when the symptoms are there as plain as ever. Nor is it any use blaming the sick individual for a lack of faith, when experience often tells us that he or she is a faithful person in a close walk with God. Healing is, according to the Bible, there to be appropriated, but seeing sickness as an intellectual problem of blame to unravel rather than an opportunity to press on is a temptation Jesus taught us to avoid (Jn 9:2–3).[9]

In trying to make sense of it all we must, of course, be aware that a spiritual warfare is in progress.[10] This is why as we take hold of what God has given us in Christ, we need to 'fight the good fight of faith' (1 Tim 6:12); faith is an important factor in the forces involved in healing. Yet we also find in the Bible hints that God wants mankind to love righteousness, goodness, and love for their own sakes, not merely for avoidance of unpleasant personal consequences. Thus the miraculous may be a mark of the genuine work of God — but, as we have seen, false signs and wonders may be a test of steadfast commitment to it. On a personal level the drama of the Book of Job shows us that the righteous may suffer at times, because it has to be shown that love of righteousness is not simply for reward. Job's sickness did, in fact, lead him in the end to a fresh personal experience of God — but this is not given as God's motive in allowing it to happen.

The intellectual problem of suffering is one we hope to consider in a later volume, but there is no completely sewn-up answer. However many hints we have, there does remain a central mystery in it. We can only be true to our own experience and that of other Christians, and assert that there *is* healing, it *does* depend in some way on faith — though not in any simple way we can discern — and it *does not* seem to happen in an inevitable cause-effect way.

Where, then, does this leave us at the personal level? It leaves us with a great paradox. A proverb which might well have been (but isn't) in the Book of Proverbs would be:

'Those who expect nothing shall in no wise be disappointed'! Usually, healing involves some kind of faith, or laying open to the power and possibility of God. Paradoxically, whilst recognising with the mind that healing miracles do not always and inevitably take place, we have to lay hold of God in faith that one will in a particular case (Mk 11:24). Even when, sometimes, it doesn't, we have to lay hold again both for the same sick person later and for others who come. Jesus told a parable to show that we ought always to keep praying and not give up (Lk 18:1). This involves an inevitable tension — and those who like everything neatly and consistenly spelt out may find it very hard to operate on this level. Perhaps this is a part of the deep meaning and significance in a God who chooses the foolish things of the world to confound the wise (1 Cor 1:18–21). Though we do believe in a God who is rational and consistent, it does not follow that all ultimate reality may be reducible to apparently consistent propositions. If we find this in the spiritual realm, it is comforting to know that, at present at least, physicists studying the physical world, which God has also made, find similar paradoxes involving time and indeterminacy. This is not a charter for cultists to manufacture what blatantly inconsistent doctrines they wish from Scripture, but simply a plea for us to remain faithful to all evidence and experience — even when we cannot always build a complete system from it.

Christian living in faith is an adventure. Christians have to go out committed to working, praying, and fighting for the kingdom of God. Jesus declared that the advance of the kingdom of God was a 'forceful' or 'violent' affair, and 'forceful men laid hold of it' (Mt 11:12). Jesus declared this in the context of John the Baptist being in prison and losing out in his faith, and being encouraged by this message:

Go back and report to John what you hear and see: The blind receive sight, the lame walk, those who have leprosy are cured, the deaf hear, the dead are raised, and the good news is preached to the poor. Blessed is the man who does not fall away [literal translation: 'is not scandalised'] on account of me (Mt 11:4–6).

Perhaps John was tempted to be scandalised because Jesus had not mentioned in his list of evidences for the kingdom the 'freedom for the captives' mentioned in Isaiah 61:1. Though later Peter (Acts 12:7–10) and Paul (Acts 16:26) were to experience that particular hint of the kingdom, John was instead going to continue his captivity into martyrdom — as later too were Peter and Paul. Jesus does not reveal the factors causing such differences, but does challenge us to an aggressive faith as we bring in what of the kingdom we may before his return — perhaps reflecting the aggressive faith which Adam would have needed to 'subdue the earth' (Gen 1:28).

We have to lay hold of God in faith, expecting to see miracles happen. We rightly seek to understand God, his workings, and his world, but God does not require us to have a perfect understanding before we participate in the work. There are, after all, many things in his world which we may use and in which we may participate without understanding fully. If the relationship of faith and miracles is one of these, it does not stop Christians from rejoicing when healing and wholeness (whether type-i or type-ii miracles) are brought into the world by the power of God operating through his servants.

## Notes

1. In particular B B Warfield, *Counterfeit Miracles* (1918).
2. Justin Martyr, *Second Apology*, vol ii, *(Ant Nic Fath*, i, 190).
3. Irenaeus, *Against Heresies*, xxxii, iv, *(Ant Nic Fath*, i, 409).
4. Origen, *Against Celsus*, vol i, p 2 *(Ant Nic Fath*, iv, 398).
5. Augustine, *City of God*, vol xxii, p 8 *(Nic & Pos Nic Fath*, 1, i, 484–91).

6.   Rex Gardner, *Healing Miracles: A Doctor Investigates* (1986), chaps 4 & 7.

7.   Many are unwritten, but there are accounts in Kathryn Kuhlman's classic books, such as *I Believe in Miracles* (1968), or in works of Colin Urquart, Francis McNutt, or John Wimber.

8.   1 Timothy 5:23 indicates how Paul regarded faith as complementary to rather than any substitute for the use of available medicinal remedies for ailments.

9.   It should be noted that good commentators such as Leon Morris (*The Gospel According to John* (1972) p 478) admit as a 'possible' translation of this verse something like: 'Answered Jesus, "Neither this man sinned nor his parents. But that the works of God might be manifested in him it behoves us to work the works of the one who sent me while it is day."' This being so, we are puzzled as to why so many commentators and translations punctuate it as they do and so see Jesus' words as a monstrous suggestion that God purposely and arbitrarily caused an innocent baby to be born blind and deprived of sight for many years, just to show off his own power. Actually, John's use of the phrase *all ina* (but that) seems to offer little support to the usual translation. The structure of his use in John 9:2–3 does not resemble the 'not only . . . but that' of 11:52 and 12:9. It might seem more to resemble the structure 'not that . . . but that' of 3:17, 12:47, 17:15. But we should note that the latter structure is actually:

'Not X so that Y

but [X] so that Z' (*parenthesis implied*).

This differs radically from the usual translation of 9:2–3, which takes it to be:

'X so that Y?' (*question*)

'No, not X, but [Y] so that Z' (*answer — parenthesis implied*).

John uses the phrase rather more nebulously in 1:8 and 13:18, and neither offer any support to the usual translation of 9:2–3. When we look at the other three instances in 1:31, 14:31 and 15:25, they all appear to support the translation we suggest above. The way the RSV, for example, has reordered the words in 14:30–1 makes us puzzled as to why it did not do the same for the very similar structure in 9:2–3 and adopt the translation of it we suggest. It makes at least as much sense linguistically, and a great deal more sense theologically.

10.   See our book *God's Strategy in Human History* (1973).

# 10

# DOES MODERN SCIENCE LEAVE ROOM FOR A SPIRITUAL VIEW OF MAN?

## Introduction

IN OUR PREVIOUS TWO CHAPTERS we considered the evidence for a supernatural realm. A further question, however, is whether or not it is still sensible to hold a Christian belief that, in addition to the occasional supernatural miracles, we daily experience a spiritual as well as a natural realm. Does not physical science today offer expectation of a total explanation in terms of physical cause-effect which leaves no room for belief in a spiritual dimension — or indeed for mind itself? The question of mind is, of course, one which has concerned many philosophers outside the Christian faith, and it is this we will first address. Should we believe only mental phenomena are real (idealism), only physical things are real (materialism) or that both are real (dualism)? Whichever we decide, what is the relationship between mental experience (whether real or illusory) and physical objects and causation? Are, say, 'feelings' and 'brain states' just equivalent ways of describing the same things? Or is there a causal connection between the mental and the physical? If there is a causal connection, does it just work one way (eg apparent mental experience deterministically caused by the true realities of physical brain states), or is there a two-way interaction between the human *mind* and the physical *brain*?

163

These are the primary concerns of the present chapter, with some comment also on whether or not it is rational today to believe in personal spiritual forces such as a devil or demons.

## One realm or two?

As human beings, we *feel* as though we are aware of two realms: the physical realm of matter, incorporating length, weight, movement, etc, and the personal realm of mind, incorporating love, hate, morality, personality, etc.

Are both these apparent dimensions of existence real, or is one or the other some kind of illusion? The possibility of denying reality to one or the other or neither makes three basic philosophical views possible:

1.  *Idealism* In a philosophical sense this means not someone with high ideals, but someone who denies any ultimate reality to the physical. It holds that only perceptions are known to exist, and there is no reason to suppose that there is any kind of different mode of existence (matter) which causes them. Idealism is monistic: it believes only one kind of reality (ie consciousness/perceptions) exists.
2.  *Materialism* This is also monistic, but the sole kind of reality it accepts is the physical. The modern term 'physicalism' seems to be used by some to mean much the same thing. Statements about mind (and about justice, love, beauty, etc) are either meaningless or else are simply alternative ways of stating some particular fact about the physical position of atoms and molecules. The statement 'I love you', for example, would mean *nothing more than* that the physical arrangement of chemical components in the part of physical matter which I call my brain has a particular definable pattern.
3.  *Dualism* This accepts that what we might call the two realms of mind and matter both have a reality. Within

dualism, however, views may widely diverge about the relationship between them. Firstly, some may say that all physical objects have a mental dimension (panpsychism); others, that mind emerged when matter reached a particular stage of organic organisation. Secondly, there is the question of the causal relationship between mind and matter; several positions are possible:

(a)  *Independence* This holds mind and matter as causally independent. On this view the coincidence of my act of volition and, say, the physical raising of my hand was 'pre-programmed' by God into the order of events, but there is no causal connection between the two levels of reality. Though it is logically possible, most people find this far-fetched.

(b)  *Epiphenomenalism* This (which is not far removed from materialism) sees the fundamental reality as matter, and mental phenomena as a kind of by-product caused by events on the material level.

(c)  *Identity Theory/Perspectivism* Identity theorists see both mental and physical phenomena as real, but simply different ways of describing exactly the same events. In this case there cannot be *any* causal connection between the mental and physical, because they merely describe different dimensions of the same thing. This approach has, as might be expected, many variations — some verging on materialism. Perspectivism is a version of it, claiming that the same phenomena can be seen from a number of perspectives or at different levels of description, each equally valid.

(d)  *Dualistic Interactionism* This holds that mind and matter are both real, and in some way causally interact with each other.

From the Christian point of view, idealism is a possible position (indeed, one of the most famous idealists was

Bishop Berkeley). Though some scientists (eg Mach) have adopted it, however, it is not popular — and seems to have no particular advantages over dualist systems.

Some form of dualism is the most usual Christian position. Later we will consider problems about this, in particular the question of whether or not physical determinism (ie the view that on the physical level the cause-effect chain is complete without any reference to mental acts of will) is compatible with Christian faith.

The most obvious threat to faith, however, comes from the various forms of materialism (even where these may have idealist, panpsychic or epiphenomenal connotations). Central to many of these is the question of reductionism, which we will now consider.

## Reductionism

Clearly, we *do* have a language which relates to mind, as well as one which relates to matter. How, then, can the materialist deny that the former has any reality? The essence of this is part of a wider approach which we may term 'reductionism'. One system of ideas is reduced to another.

Though some of us may not like the long words, it is helpful to note the distinction elaborated by Arthur Peacocke between methodological, ontological and epistemological reductionism. Methodological reductionism is:

> The necessity the practical scientist finds of studying problems that are presented to him at a given level of complexity, and particularly with respect to the living world, by breaking down both the problem and the entities studied into pieces and proceeding by exploring the lower as well as the higher levels of organisation.[1]

This, he rightly argues, is an inevitable part of the process of scientific progress. But, he adds, the danger is that this process of methodological reductionism can slide into a belief that the essential nature or being involved in the higher order system is *nothing more than* the sum of the beings of its constituent parts. This view that the whole is nothing more than the parts is called 'ontological reductionism' (from *ontology*, the study of 'being'). Thus he says:

> The procedure of analysis which is required by their own discipline becomes almost unconsciously a philosophical belief about biological organisms being 'nothing but' the bits into which they have analysed them ... Biological systems, on this view, are 'nothing but' complex patterns of atoms and molecules.[2]

It is the 'nothing but' which is the key. None of us would, for example, deny that brains are composed of molecules, and that for certain purposes (eg to study brain chemistry) this is the best way to regard them. But this does not mean that brains are 'nothing but' collections of molecules.

Ontological reductionism has a further implication. If the higher order system is actually 'nothing but' the lower order one, then any language used to describe the higher order system means exactly the same as (and no more than) the language used to describe the lower order system. It simply says exactly the same thing in a more concise way. The lower order description is an exact translation of the higher order one. This Peacocke calls 'epistemological reductionism' (from *epistemology*, the study of 'knowledge of truth'). Ontological and epistemological reductionism are, therefore, bound up together, but both are a radical step from the methodological reductionism which is proper to science.

Ontological reductionism is not new, and there seems little to support either the view that it is a recent problem of 'bourgeois science'[3] or the view that it is a recent aberration of a godless Darwinism. In the ancient stoicism of Zeno (c 300 BC), everything in the universe (including time and thought) was supposedly reducible to some kind of bodily substance: a kind of ultimate materialism. The apostle Paul met stoic philosophers in Athens and actually quoted from a stoic source, though his own philosophy was very different (Acts 17:18).[4] Later, reductionism ran rife in the stoicism of the second-century Roman Emperor Marcus Aurelius (of whom it has been remarked with some justice that he loved humanity, but didn't much like people!):

> You can become indifferent to the seductions of song or dance or athletic displays if you resolve the melody into its several notes, and ask yourself of each one in turn, 'Is it this that I cannot resist?' ... In short, save in the case of virtue and its implications, always remember to go straight for the parts themselves, and by dissecting these achieve your disenchantment. And now, transfer this method to life as a whole.[5]

The fact that he persecuted the church sets his destructive philosophy in its true colours — even if stoic ideas did influence Ambrose of Milan and, through him, St Augustine's austere and deterministic system. The idea that the aesthetic enjoyment of music in human consciousness is 'nothing but' the sum of hearing a series of individual notes is, to most of us, patently absurd. Both the present authors can play all the notes in Beethoven's *Appassionata Sonata*. It is our inability to play them in the right order and relationship which makes us unlikely to win the Tchaikovsky Prize!

In the eighteenth century, the writings of atheist philosopher David Hume abound in the phrase 'nothing but'. Hume began by assuming that 'all our ideas are derived from impressions' and are 'nothing but copies and representations of them', and impressions 'may be divided into two kinds, those of sensation and those of reflection ... posterior to those of sensation and derived from them'.[6] Having assumed that the only kind of admissible realities were sensorially based 'perceptions', he was forced to explain consciousness (which, ironically, is implied in his continual use of the word

'I' throughout his treatise) as a kind of bundle of perceptions: 'What we call a mind is nothing but a heap or collection of different perceptions, united together by certain relations, and supposed, though falsely, to be endowed with a perfect simplicity and identity.'[7] With disarming candour Hume later admits:

> Of the section concerning personal identity ... I neither know how to correct my former opinions, nor how to render them consistent ... all my hopes vanish when I come to explain the principles that unite our successive perceptions in our thought or consciousness. I cannot discover any theory which gives me satisfaction on this head.[8]

Hume is a kind of patron saint of modern atheists, and the failure of his reductionist programme might well have served as a warning.

From the examples already cited, it may be obvious that ontological reductionism can occur at various levels. Within science, for example, the behaviour of gases in the general gas law ($PV=kT$) can be explained by reduction to the kinetic behaviour of their individual molecules. This is the reduction of one physical system to another. In similar vein, but greatly differing in scope, is the idea that the functioning of the brain is nothing more than the behaviour of its constituent atoms. This, however, is still reducing the physical to the physical. Of a rather different order altogether is a claim that consciousness is 'nothing but' patterns of brain cells, and that justice, beauty, and morality are in turn 'nothing but' manifestations of social consciousness.

Reductionism exists today in the sciences. Francis Crick, famous for the discovery of DNA, has said that the ultimate aim in modern biology is 'to explain all biology in terms of physics and chemistry'.[9] E O Wilson, in his 1975 book *Sociobiology*, looked for the social sciences to be 'biologicised'.[10] Wilson is an atheist anxious to win converts to his atheistic creed, seeking to replace Christian belief with an artificially created myth of science, though it remains rather obscure just what is the object of it all! Another atheist with proselytising zeal is the organic chemist Peter Atkins, an ultimate reductionist who wrote:

> The motivation of all change is the natural dispersal of energy, its spontaneous collapse into chaos. The richness of the world, the emergence into it of art and artefacts, of opinions and theories, can be traced down to the level where it can be merely the gearing together of the steps to dispersal.[11]

At a 1985 conference in Oxford, Peter Atkins presented a paper suggesting that all knowledge might one day be translated into mathematics. Atkins' self-image as a leader in a supposed march of scientific philosophy seemed belied by a naïve realist view of knowledge long since abandoned by philosophical thinkers as unworkable, and his programme of reductionism remained unconvincing.

Evangelical scientists, such as D M McKay, have made penetrating criticisms of reductionism.[12] We also value the detailed comments of those from non-evangelical Christian standpoints, such as Arthur Peacocke, Mary Hesse, and Geoffrey Price.[13] But, to most of us, the logical flaws in Atkins' kind of extreme 'nothing buttery' are too obvious to need much expansion.

## The question of mind

Whether or not we feel that biology, say, is 'nothing but' chemistry, many of us feel that phenomena like consciousness, justice and beauty are of an order altogether different from physical things. Statements, for example, like 'child molestation is wrong' or 'I love you' mean more than 'nothing but' the existence of certain patterns of molecular structure in particular individuals' brains.

How, then, may we regard consciousness? In the seventeenth century, Descartes, whom many regard as the father of modern philosophy, suggested that our own consciousness is the one thing of which we may be certain: 'I think, therefore I am'.[14] This has been criticised on some rather trite linguistic grounds by some later philosophers, such as atheist Bertrand Russell. We believe, however, that Descartes' basic starting-point is valid (although we cannot follow him in some of his later arguments). It implies that even if all my experiences and perceptions were mistaken or hallucinatory, I could not doubt that there is an 'I' experiencing them. This knowledge is more certain than all the knowledge of, say, science which concerns the physical — the very existence of which is a logical deduction made by that 'I' which is perceiving the world. It is this which causes problems for any system of pure materialism, for materialism tries to make physical matter the *only* kind of reality. It is hard to deny the reality of ourselves without self-contradiction or, at least, the kind of unsatisfactory philosophy of mind cobbled together by Hume.

This basic point was recognised by modern philosopher John Searle, who, though no follower of Descartes, wrote in his 1984 Reith Lectures:

I'm conscious, I AM conscious. We could discover all kinds of startling things about ourselves and our behaviour; but we cannot discover that we do not have minds, that they do not contain conscious, subjective, intentionalistic mental states; nor could we discover that we do not at least try to engage in voluntary, free, intentional actions.[15]

If, then, we take mind as real, what about matter? Philosophical idealism, as we have seen, believes the *only* kind of reality to be mental. This is self-consistent, for it is virtually a truism that we only ever experience our sensations and have no other more direct way to experience a material world. Logically, then, we only know for certain that our mental experiences are real; we have no way to be certain that there is anything beyond which causes them. There is, in fact, even a kind of logical consistency in solipsism: an extreme form of idealism in which the individual believes the existence of his own mind to be the *only* certainty. Solipsism, however, seems too far fetched to have gained much support (and each supporter thinks he or she is the only one!). A non-solipsist idealism has more appeal, though we ourselves do not find it acceptable.

Descartes' own solution was dualism. He knew mind existed from immediate experience, and concluded that matter existed by a process of observation and reasoning. He supposed that the two were quite different in kind. Descartes has been criticised, even ridiculed, for a suggestion that the mind controls the body through the pineal gland, but actually he was much less naïve about this than is often supposed:

> I am not only lodged in my body as a pilot in a vessel, but that I am besides so intimately conjoined, and as it were intermixed with it, that my mind and body compose a certain unity. For if this were not the case, I should not feel pain when my body is hurt, seeing I am merely a thinking thing, but should perceive the wound by the understanding alone, just as a pilot perceives by sight when any part of his vessel is damaged.[16]

Descartes schema was interactionist, assuming a constant interaction between body and mind in the unity of the human individual. This is, perhaps, the most obvious position for the Christian, though there have been other forms of Christian dualism.

The twentieth-century debate — which involves both philosophers and brain scientists — has inevitably followed the same basic lines as earlier debates, even if at a more sophisticated level. We intend briefly to mention some of the issues here, but not because we believe that any one system can be proved. Rather, we seek to demonstrate that, in the present state of late twentieth-century knowledge about the brain mechanisms and science, there is no reason not to be a fully biblical Christian.

Pure materialism has not been popular. The early Greek atomic version of it, which held mind itself to be material, has not appealed at all. The few twentieth-century figures sometimes seen as advocating it, such as Quine, prefer to 'repudiate' mental phenomena altogether, which sounds to most of us like just pretending they're not there.[17]

But if we admit some kind of dualism, ie that both the physical and the mental are real, what is their relationship? One prime question is, of course, whether or not there can be said to be any causal link between them. In everyday terms if a man says, 'I made my hand go up,' he implies that his mind caused his hand to be raised. Arguably, in fact, it is this that gives us our whole intuitive concept of cause. But is it strictly accurate to speak of a causal effect of mind on matter?

As we have earlier noted, two main systems would answer 'no', and we may consider each briefly:

1. *Epiphenomenalism* This sees mental states as real, but as a kind of by-product of the physical events. Darwin's friend T H Huxley wrote: 'Consciousness ... would appear to be related to the mechanism of body, simply as a ... [side] product of its working, and to be ... completely without any power of modifying that working.'[18] Epiphenomenalism seems to fail to do justice to our actual experience of acts of the will. In saying this we are, of course, aware that our natural tendency to interpret these experiences in a dualistic way *could* be mistaken. Such a mistake would, however, as John Searle also points out, be of a different order from a mistake such as believing the world to be flat.[19] It

would concern the whole basis on which we conceive of a reality at all.

The powerlessness of mind, as conceived by Huxley, to alter the train of pure physical causation would also bring into question the meaningfulness of morality. Not only the insane, but everyone else would be unable to help the way they acted or thought, which would raise big questions about what it would mean to say that they 'ought' to have done otherwise. Moral codes could still be studied as ideas correlating with brain states which affect behaviour, or as ideas associated with brain states which increase probabilities of genetic survival — but morality itself would appear to have no meaning. This does not, of course, disprove epiphenomenalism, but it does imply that the majority of epiphenomenalists (as people keeping a sense of right or wrong) are inconsistent.

2. *Identity theory, perspectivism, and minimal dualism*
Identity theory, as already seen, denies a causal relationship between mind and matter as both actually refer to the same events. Its most influential formulation was that of Feigl and it found a number of advocates in the 1970s and early 1980s.[20] Basically it holds that mental descriptions and physical brain-state descriptions are in reality saying identical things. It is, for example, quite correct in this view to say, 'I raised my hand.' But a description of the same event in terms of brain chemistry would say exactly the same thing, no more and no less.

The identity theory has been popular among modern neuroscientists. One of the main problems with it is to determine exactly what its proponents are saying. This is not helped by their own lack of consensus. Thus the editor of one useful compendium on the identity theory noted three main different versions of it — the collected papers well illustrating his point.[21] At times its proponents talk like pure physicalists (ie materialists), at times like panpsychists, etc. So what does it really mean? Clearly brain-state and mind descriptions are not in a literal sense logically equivalent. If, for example, we did not have the inside experience of mind, but were angelic observers, we would have no reason to think that brain-state statements could be translated into mind statements. So what is identity theory saying? The two kinds of statements must be describing different kinds of reality. So is identity theory really a kind of parallelism — in which the different levels of phenomena follow exactly parallel paths? Or are the mind phenomena a different dimension of the same reality as the physical? This dimensional view would not be dissimilar to the perspectivism of modern evangelicals, such as the brain scientist Professor D M MacKay. Clearly in this case, it might be accepted by a Christian.

The difficulties of determining exactly what identity theorists are saying has been emphasised by Sir Karl Popper, one of the best-known philosophers of science in the twentieth century.[22] This encourages us in the confession that we have not been able to encapsulate it in a form of words which seems satisfactory. Ironically, Popper's main criticism is that it fails to account for the emergence of consciousness in terms of Darwinian evolution, because consciousness has no causal effect and so cannot help the organism in the struggle for survival! This would indeed be a genuine point of difficulty in any atheistic version of identity theory which rules out the supernatural, though the point is also repeated by the Christian Eccles.[23]

In practice the more profound problem is that if identity theory is combined with a deterministic view of physical cause-effect, it leaves us with all the same problems as epiphenomenalism.

One of the most popular approaches among modern evangelicals is what may be called perspectivism. An undoubted leader in this is Professor D M MacKay. MacKay speaks in terms of an 'I-story' (an inside view of events) and an 'O-story' (an observer view of events). Seen thus man is: 'a unity with many complementary aspects, each needing to be reckoned with at a different logical level, and all interdependent'.[24] By 'interdependent' however, he does not mean that interaction takes place — a thing he specifically denies.[25] Professor D Gareth Jones is another leading evangelical advocate of similar views.[26]

## Dualistic interactionism

In contrast to all these systems, dualistic interactionism asserts that mind and matter (including the brain) are different in kind, but can interact with each other causally within the unity of the person.

How does this differ from other views? As we have seen, reductionism suggests that mind statements and brain-state statements are nothing but different linguistic ways to say the same thing — and ultimately the 'mind' way of speaking is redundant. Perspectivism sees mind statements and brain-state statements as dealing with different *kinds* of reality, but these are different dimensions of a single phenomenon and each can retain at its own level a complete description, ie successive brain states are perfectly explicable on a level purely of physical description without any reference to mind. In contrast, dualistic interactionism holds that mind (or the human psyche) is different in kind to the physical brain, but causally interacts with it. Thus some changes in brain states are causally inexplicable without reference to mind.

Among experts in the field of mind, a modern revival of this classic view of Descartes was heralded by the 1933 Rede Lecture and 1937-8 Gifford Lectures of Nobel prize-winning neuro-scientist C S Sherrington.[27] An interesting convert was neurosurgeon Wilder Penfield, whose startling conclusion after a distinguished career of brain studies as a monistic materialist was: 'It is easier to rationalise man's being on the basis of two elements than on the basis of one.'[28]

From a Christian view point, Catholic scientist and historian of science Stanley Jaki has argued for a form of dualism.[29] In 1977, a massive volume arguing for dualistic interactionism was issued by leading Christian neurophysiologist Sir John Eccles, FRS, and leading non-Christian philosopher of science Karl Popper: *The Self and Its Brain*. In it they have also given much useful criticism of the alternative views described earlier.

Popper and Eccles' form of interactionism asserts the unity of consciousness both on philosophical grounds and on the grounds of evidence from empirical studies by Sperry.[30] But within consciousness two 'worlds' may be distinguished, making three in all including the physical.

| WORLD 1 | WORLD 2 | WORLD 3 |
|---|---|---|
| PHYSICAL OBJECTS AND STATES | STATES OF CONSCIOUSNESS | KNOWLEDGE IN OBJECTIVE SENSE |
| 1. INORGANIC | Subjective knowledge | Cultural heritage coded on material substrates |
|    Matter and energy of cosmos | |    philosophical |
| | Experience of |    theological |
| 2. BIOLOGY |    perception |    scientific |
|    Structure and actions |    thinking |    historical |
|    of all living beings |    emotions |    literary |
|    — human brains |    dispositional intentions |    artistic |
| |    memories |    technological |
| |    dreams | |
| 3. ARTEFACTS |    creative imagination | |
|    Material substrates | | Theoretical systems |
|     of human creativity | |    scientific problems |
|     of tools | |    critical arguments |
|     of machines | | |
|     of books | | |
|     of works of art | | |
|     of music | | |

Animals exhibit conscious behaviour, but Eccles quotes Sperry with approval: 'Self-consciousness appears to be almost strictly a human attribute according to present evidence ... It seems not to be found in animals below the primates, and only to a limited extent in the great apes.'[31] The 'World 3' of Popper is exclusively human, for it consists of human-created mental products. John Polkinghorne seems to mean something rather similar by his 'noetic world', though he appears to lean more to perspectivism than dualistic interactionism.[32]

All this leaves the human mind or psyche, the self-conscious observer, in a somewhat privileged position — interacting with the physical realm (through the brain) in a unique way. Interestingly, though in a different context, such a privileged position for the observer is also given in various mainstream versions of the modern uncertainty principle in quantum mechanics. In them it is the act of observing which 'collapses' the various potential positions of a particle into one actual one; observer interaction is essential to determination of what becomes physical reality. It is, of course, *possible* that physics *may* one day abandon this idea, but at our present state of knowledge it offers powerful analogical support to the suggestion that human minds (and any other similar minds God may have created elsewhere in the universe) are special.

Some have thought that the possibility of surgical division of the brain is threatening to the Christian idea of mind. Both Eccles and MacKay, however, see the effects of such division (commissurotomy: the severing of nerve fibres joining the two brain halves) simply as dividing off a part of conscious mind, while leaving an intact self-conscious mind and its associated personhood.[33] The possibility of chemical manipulation of the brain, and hence the mind, is no more inherently mysterious than any of the daily experiences we all have of the physical world touching our consciousness through sensory experience. Yet this can continue to be presented as though a problem for strict dualists even by so thoughtful a book as that by Christian social psychologist Mary Stewart Van Leeuwen.[34] Cartesian dualists have never claimed that mind is independent of body — that is the whole point of dualistic interactionism. What they do assert is that the physical causal sequences cannot be established without the recognition of a non-physical causal agent: mind.

## Ryle and the problem of mind

Having defended a basically Cartesian view of mind, we need briefly to refer to Gilbert Ryle's famous 1949 attack on it (or rather on his own straw-man version of it). Ryle felt that with his book *The Concept of Mind*, the Gordian knot of the mind problem had now, at last, been cut! Ryle says the basic mistake of Descartes and his followers (made, we are solemnly assured, because Descartes' religious scruples were in revolt against the rising mechanical determinism in science!) was a 'category mistake'. Such a mistake is one such as when having noted on the cricket field the bowler, batsman, etc, a foreigner asks where on the field is the esprit de corps of which he has heard. Ryle argues that when we say that both mental and physical 'exist', it does not simply mean a different kind of existence; rather, the word is being used in an entirely different way — to suppose otherwise is a 'category mistake'.[35]

Now, obviously, we must concede that we, like anyone, *might* have made such category mistakes. But what Ryle actually does is to produce a series of special pleadings which supposedly show illogical implications of Cartesianism. We will look briefly at one example, which concerns our common experience that we may *plan* an action in our minds before we attempt to put it into practice. This experience is, in fact, the basis of our idea of design. Ryle asks, then, if we can take as a mark of rationality the planning of actions before they are taken. In analysing this, however, he seems to be taking this to mean that we assent to abstract principles of rational action before doing something. But, he says, 'It is perfectly possible to plan shrewdly and perform stupidly.' Actually, this statement itself seems a 'category mistake' on his own principles, as it mixes two levels of meaning, and he is confusing here various things. Firstly, no one seriously means by 'shrewd' merely an assent to some rational principles. A person can be rational without being shrewd, for the latter implies a perception of practicalities (which is still a mental capacity) as well as rationality. Ryle also confuses ontology (what *is*) with epistemology (how we *know* it). A mind *is* shrewd if it can plan practically. We *know* that it is shrewd because we see the evidence of this capacity in the resulting actions. Finally, Ryle argues that if rationality consists in prior planning of actions, then should there not also be prior planning of the planning and so on in infinite regress? This is a 'category mistake'. If the mark of a rational action is prior rational thought, it does not follow that the mark of a rational thought is more prior rational thought, for this would be to assume that action and thought are on similar levels of being, which they clearly are not. He also seems to focus on the priority in time of the thought, whereas any sensible Cartesian (ie a believer in Descartes' dualistic interactionism) would accept that the rational thought can go on interactively with the action it plans.

Although he does not accept its mechanistic views, Ryle sympathises with behaviourism, ie the view that psychology should be based on people's observable behaviour and should ignore 'consciousness and introspection'.[36] Actually, extreme behaviourism was quite mistaken in supposing that physical science concentrates only on what is observable. Throughout history, scientific advance has involved creation of unobservable concepts like atoms, charge, genes, microbes, etc. Physicists today hypothesise the existence of unobservable subatomic particles, in order to explain what they do observe. Of course, in a sense, as Eddington and others pointed out, electrons 'exist' in a different sense from elephants — just as mind exists in a different sense from body. There has also, in recent years, been a new realist movement in which the meaning of 'observable' has been questioned and extended. But the logical positivist attempt to suppose that atoms were really oblique ways of speaking about large-scale phenomena has now been recognised even by Ayer as absurd.[37] In a similar way, Cartesians hypothesise the existence of other minds to explain observed behaviour. Of course, both physicists and Cartesians might be wrong in their respective hypotheses. In specific instances a Cartesian might mistakenly believe that a mind was directly involved in a body, when in fact the body was a robot into which a mind had preprogrammed particular actions; but then physicists also sometimes make mistakes and this does not make their theories meaningless. We cannot, of course, even be certain that there are other minds at all — any more than that electrons, for example, actually exist. The only difference is that we are sure that our own mind exists, whatever arguments philosophers like Ryle may construct which effectively deny their own reality. In the final analysis, we believe that the philosophy of Ryle will join that of the logical positivists — both magnificnt attempts to discount as pseudo-questions some basic issues concerning reality, and to disprove, mainly by sounding confident, the patently obvious.

## Perspectivism and determinism

Perhaps the most significant query on the mind-brain question concerns determinism. Two questions may be asked:

1. Are human brains deterministic on the physical level?
2. Would an acceptance that they were deterministic be compatible with Christian belief?

First, then, what is the present state of empirical evidence for determinism? Since 1928, it has been generally accepted that at the very lowest subatomic level phenomena are predictable only in probabilistic terms. This is not merely a feature of our lack of knowledge, but is considered by most interpreters to be inherent in the phenomena themselves. But is the brain chemistry associated with mental decisions similarly indeterministic? At its own level the present state of neurophysiology does not, according to its experts, allow us to decide on this. The brain is far, far too complex.

Only two real arguments for brain determinism may be raised at the present time. The first is that over history more and more phenomena have been shown to conform to scientific predictability, and so we might expect a similar pattern for the brain. Up until the twentieth century this was broadly true — but it is no longer. Since 1928, the uncertainty principle of physics portrays an unpredictability in principle (not merely for practical reasons) at the heart of subatomic phenomena. From its inception, the theory was applied by leading scientist Eddington to the determination of atomic behaviour by 'mental decision'.[38]

The second argument is that, whilst it may be true that at subatomic level there is unpredictability, the brain is composed of so many atoms that prediction of its movements as a whole becomes virtually certain. So is this true? Since the 1960s, there has been increasing scientific interest in the physics of chaotic systems. These are systems in which very small changes in initial conditions can result in very large changes in long-term results. Recent scientific work has only enhanced what I G Barbour in 1966 called 'one established view', that:

> There are some cases in which a small variation is 'amplified' or a minute change 'triggers' a large one. According to some biologists it is not implausible that a few atoms (for which Heisenberg indeterminacy would be pronounced) at critical

neural junctions could start a switch-over from one pulse-conduction pattern to another.[39]

We will return to look at various important issues about human freedom, chance and determinism in our last chapter, but wish at this point simply to insist that there is at the present time no scientific imperative to believe the human brain is either totally deterministic or totally predictable.

What about the second point? Is brain determinism compatible with moral responsibility and Christian doctrine? As a Christian dualistic-interactionist, neurophysiologist Sir John Eccles states strongly:

> If physical determinism is true, then that is the end of all discussion or argument; everything is finished. There is no philosophy. All human persons are caught up in this inexorable web of circumstances and cannot break out of it. Everything we think we are doing is an illusion.[40]

In contrast, as a Christian perspectivist, Professor of Communications and Neuroscience Donald MacKay argued that it would not be problematic for the Christian if it turned out that 'knowledge of our brain mechanisms and the forces acting on and in them were sufficient to allow our actions to be predicted (secretly) by a detached observer'.[41]

The present writers are dualistic-interactionists, and do not believe that the succession of human-brain states can be totally deterministically described. It is, we suppose, possible for a perspectivist to share our view of the brain as a chaotic system (in the technical sense described earlier) and, like us, to believe it to have *some* elements of inherent unpredictability. Such a one would, then, differ from us only in wanting to leave the elements of unpredictability unexplained rather than introduce the concept of mind to explain them. Such a difference would not seem to us serious.

The perspectivism of Donald MacKay, however, is specifically claimed by him to be compatible with a strict determinism of brain states. We have, therefore, to assert that although he undoubtedly made great contributions to thinking on issues of science and Christianity, we believe this view of determinism is mistaken. It is, then, precisely because of his great influence on evangelical thinking that this needs to be looked at.

MacKay states that he 'finds something to agree with' in both dualism and monism. He states that mental and physical phenomena are both 'real', but that they do not 'interact':

> It seems to me sufficient rather to describe mental events and their correlated brain events as the 'inside' and 'outside' aspects of one and the same sequence of events, which in their full nature are richer — have more to them — than can be expressed in either mental or physical categories alone.[42]

His references to the inside view ('I-story') and observer view ('O-story') as perspectives on the same events sound like a version of identity theory, though MacKay himself (when one of us asked him at a conference in 1985) appeared not to associate his own ideas either with identity theorists or with Eccles. Is he, however, right in arguing that determinism (in the sense of the quotation given above) presents no problems to Christianity? Actually, we can ask several distinct questions about it:

1.  Would it not mean that our feeling of making decisions was in fact illusory?
2.  Would it mean that we were right to be fatalistic in the sense that if someone predicted our actions with certainty and told us, then we would have no choice but to follow the predictions?
3.  Would it make moral responsibility void?

4. Would it not imply a strange behaviour on God's part to create a world with humankind deterministically programmed to sin?

Question 1 is really little problem, for in MacKay's terms it confuses the 'I-story' with the 'O-story'. What is referred to as 'I' is still making the decision — even if on the level of the 'O-story', that decision is entirely predictable and inevitable.

To answer 2, MacKay took two lines of approach. The first was a development of an argument first put forward by the outstanding twentieth-century physicist Max Planck (who was deeply religious). Planck took as starting-point: 'An event which can be foretold with certainty is in some way causally determined.'[43] Suppose, then, that it turns out that the human will is also causally determined, in the sense that if a man makes a decision, 'an observer, if sufficiently intelligent, and if he remained perfectly passive, would be in a position to foretell the behaviour of the man in question'.[44] The point here is that if the observer communicates his prediction to the man who is in the process of deliberating, then he has ceased to be passive, the man actually faces a *new* situation (he now knows more of his motives, he knows what he *would have* decided if the observer had not spoken to him, etc). This new situation, then, may change his decision. But if the new situation is similarly analysed by the observer, and similarly communicated, then the situation is changed yet again, and so on ad infinitum. Put another way Planck asks: 'Can we, at least in theory, understand our own motives so exactly and so completely that we are able to foretell accurately the decisions necessarily arising from their interplay?' His answer is that our conclusions as observers, as it were, of our own brains, if communicated to the decision-making 'participant' side of us, change the situation — again leading to an infinite regression. In a sense, then, says Planck, 'A man's own will ... can be causally understood only as far as his past actions are concerned.'[45]

This whole idea was later termed by MacKay 'logical indeterminacy' and worked out in great detail in several books.[46]

We accept that logical indeterminacy does succeed in answering the objection: 'Surely if a super-intelligence predicts for me what I will decide, then I have no choice but to believe him or her?' In other words it answers the classic problem of fatalism.

Rather more questionable is whether it answers objection 3: the question of sin and moral responsibility. MacKay argues:

> There is no logical way in which I could pass from the data of the O-story to a valid conclusion, from *my* standpoint, that 'I didn't do it: it was inevitable-for-me'. The logical answer would be 'You did, and it was not inevitable-for-*you*, even though your brain went through physically determinate motions.'[47]

The view that sin is 'reduced to the category of mechanical malfunctioning' is therefore wrong, because it 'disastrously confuses the categories and standpoints of the I-story and the O-story. "Mechanical malfunctioning" is an O-story concept. "Sin" is something *I* commit. The one does not necessarily exclude the other: they might even be complementary correlates.'[48] Morality is an 'I-story' concept, and cannot be negated by an 'O-story' concept like physical determinism, for they are complementary perspectives. To negate it would require a concept on its own 'I-story' level. A *fatalism* would be such a concept, for it convinces the *I* at its own level of 'I-story' that no decision is to be made. Since, in MacKay's view, logical indeterminacy makes fatalism impossible, morality is in no danger.

MacKay is, however, inconsistent, for on the same page he states: 'Obviously there will be special cases of brain malfunction in which responsibility is diminished or abolished because the normal link between rational decision and action is weakened or overridden.' Unfortunately, 'brain malfunction' is an 'O-story' concept, whilst 'rational decision' is an 'I-story one', and by MacKay's own rules they cannot be mixed like this. If the mind were (as dualistic-interactionists suppose) interacting with the brain, then one could see how it might be possible to argue that the mind was not wholly responsible for actions resulting from faulty brain mechanism. But according to MacKay, the mind is simply a different dimension or perspective on the same events described in brain mechanism terms — there can be no interaction. Both a normal deterministic brain and an abnormal deterministic brain have an 'I-story' dimension, and neither can — according to logical indeterminacy — be subject to fatalism. Both types of person, therefore, must logically remain equally culpable for their actions.

MacKay goes on to argue that it would be as fallacious to reduce sin to a mechanical malfunction as to imagine that a programming fault in computer software must imply a mechanical failure. But this analogy is even more confusing, for in his system the *mind* does not *use* the brain (as software uses a computer), but describes from a different perspective exactly the same thing.

When we turn to point 4, the problems get worse. Perhaps logical indeterminacy might, as MacKay claims, help us understand divine foreknowledge.[49] But it does not explain why a good God would want to create and sustain a world in which human wills were causally determined to sin. A suitable adjustment of the physical starting conditions would have meant a sinless world. This argument has nothing to do with the individual human's 'I-story', it concerns God as Creator and observer.

MacKay himself responded to this question (actually asked him by one of the present authors, both as a student in the late 60s and for the last time in 1985) in terms of his own Calvinist tradition. In this, in the final analysis man cannot question God, who is viewed as literally incomprehensible.

The present authors, however, do not share that tradition, nor believe that this is a proper use of Romans 9:20.[50]

On the analogy of the writer to his or her novel (sometimes used by MacKay), we can only sympathise with John Polkinghorne's recent words:

> That is the exercise of a naked power of disposal which seems to bear little analogy to the subtle relationships of God to the world to which he has given a large measure of creaturely freedom.[51]

We believe Polkinghorne right to insist on a radical freedom for God:

> If God makes no specific response to particular individuals 'it would seem misleading to characterise what is taking place as a personal relationship at all'.[52]

We also believe him right to insist that God 'allows radical freedom to his human creation'. This position (as we will reconsider in Chapter 16) seems most consistent with biblical theology and the universal teaching of the early church. It is our present belief, therefore, that physical determinism is not logically reconcilable with biblical belief in God — though we recognise that many fine Christian people would not agree with us.

## Some conclusions

Even in the secular world monistic materialism is in decline. In a thoughtful book, Christian social psychologist Mary Stewart Van Leeuwen states: 'It is safe to say that almost all Anglo-American psychologists are becoming "token" perspectivists, inasmuch as they are beginning to acknowledge that science cannot give a complete account of personhood.'[53] We would wish to go further and join those who have developed the dualistic interactionism of Descartes, Eccles, and Popper — shared by other neuroscientists including S S Kety,[54] W H Thorpe[55] and W Penfield.[56] At the present time this seems best to synthesise Christian theology, philosophical argument, our subjective experience of self-consciousness, and what is known about the physical brain. At some future time, of course, some better synthesis may emerge, but each generation can only seek to snythesise (however tentatively) the knowledge presently available. What certainly has to be said is that the present state of scientific knowledge in the area of brain mechanism does not contradict this synthesis.

Certain aspects of brain mechanism and the natural powers of the mind are not yet fully understood, and in this regard we must now consider the existence of the demonic.

## Demon possession

'Surely,' we sometimes get asked, 'you can't take seriously all that stuff in the Bible about demon possession? Surely that was just a primitive view of psychology?'

Now, firstly, it must be said that there are Christians who explain the Bible reference to demons as a figure of speech, pointing out that even the great psychologist Jung talked in 1945 about 'reviving the doctrine of demons'.[57] We may later reconsider this approach to see whether it can do justice to the biblical language.

Some people might go further than this and admit the reality of the paranormal or psychic, ie such things as extra-sensory perception, telepathy, telekinesis, and psychometry. There are great inherent difficulties in assessing the evidence for this. For one thing, much of it involves statistics, which can never be totally conclusive. For another, there certainly are many frauds who make money from their supposed psychic powers (although this does not prove all psychics are frauds). A third point is that — just as for the evidence for miracles — a person's assessment of the evidence will be affected by basic presuppositions. Thus, a generation ago, two intelligent people — neither of them arguing from a viewpoint of Christian commitment — each considered the same evidence. One, Martin Gardner, concluded that apparent evidence for psychic phenomena was misleading, because only the chance occasions which were positive were published (negative results being thought uninteresting).[58] The other, Arthur Koestler, was so convinced that he not only wrote a book but left money to support psychical research.[59] The debate remains inconclusive.

Our own assessment — both from the published evidence and from personal contact with those who have experienced it — is that psychic phenomena do exist. The human mind possesses some natural powers which are not yet understood. Such natural powers might account for some of the biblical manifestations, but we do not believe that either the biblical language or all aspects of contemporary Christian experience can best be explained by them.

The real question is this. Is it rational to believe in the possibility that there exists a realm of spirits, ie centres of consciousness which are in a dimension outside the physical, but which in certain ways can affect the physical? Obviously, we may find absurd both the comical Devil of medieval plays and the crude animism of some primitive societies in which almost every object is seen as having a spirit. We may find both absurd and morally repugnant the witch mania which led to cruel deaths for many innocent people in Reformation Europe — on a basis of ideas of witchcraft neither biblical nor empirical. This is, however, no reason to treat as absurd the essential concept of a world of spirits. To say that science has not demonstrated such a world is naïve, for the scientist is concerned with recurring physical causation, and if spirits exist that are personal and non-physical, then they must by definition be excluded from the whole range of scientific study.

Occasionally, we meet someone who feels that we must be unbalanced or prejudiced to suggest that there is a spirit world. Even in the second century there were those who doubted its reality, in spite of its apparent manifestations.[60] But we should remember that throughout history many major scientific advances have been opposed by well-meaning hard-headed realists as too bizarre to be credible. Illustrious early seventeenth-century mathematician and astronomer Johannes Kepler suggested that the moon's gravitational pull affected tides on the earth. His contemporary, the famous Galileo, rejected this as absurd, lamenting that Kepler had 'lent his ear and his assent to the moon's dominion over the waters, to occult properties and such puerilities'.[61]

Other unobservable or intangible concepts have similarly been opposed. J J Waterston's kinetic theory of gases (ie that gases could be seen as made of constantly moving molecules) was rejected as absurd by the Royal Society, to which it was submitted in 1845. Lister's nineteenth-century theory that disease was caused by microscopic (and so unobservable) organisms aroused much opposition until his results finally convinced the medical world. Often it has been only those (frequently people of sincere religious conviction) whose minds have been open to the seemingly intangible or bizarre, who have made the breakthroughs in scientific thinking. The twentieth century has, if anything, only served to underline the need for open-mindedness towards ideas which are intangible or outside the directly observable. Who would have thought a century ago that we would today be seeing pictures on a small screen in our houses of events thousands of miles away, brought to us by invisible waves bounced off a satellite? Scientists now accept the mysterious features of the Einsteinian system. They accept the strange world of the uncertainty principle in particle physics, and take seriously physicists' theories of multiple universes etc. The atmosphere in science today, then, is more conducive to the admission that, in the words of Shakespeare's Hamlet, there may well be 'more things in heaven and earth, Horatio, than are dreamt of in our philosophy!'[62]

What is unfortunate is that the more modern open-mindedness to such questions has contributed not merely to acknowledgement of the possible existence of spirits, but to a continuing resurgence in dabbling in spiritism and things of the occult. A string of films (going back to the most famous *The Exorcist*, which claimed to be based on a real case) demonstrates the fascination, even among the sceptical, for the most horrific aspects of the subject.

Our own belief is that a sober study can lead to the conclusion that demonic manifestations are real. This is based both on the testimony of others, and on our own personal experiences. But what exactly does the Bible say about these? Let us look at the words 'Satan', 'devil', 'demon' and 'spirit' and consider their biblical use:

1. *Satan/devil* The word 'Satan' (*satanas*) simply means opponent, and the word 'devil' (*diabolos*) means a slanderer or accuser. Sometimes the words mean no more than this, as when Jesus called Peter 'opponent' (Mt 16:23) or Paul spoke of human slanderers (1 Tim 3:11). Sometimes, however, the words are used to describe '*the* Satan' (Mk 1:13) or '*the* Devil' (Mt 4:1–11).[63] This might, just conceivably, be argued to be a personification of evil, but we ourselves find no problem in taking the more straightforward approach to the biblical language and believing him to be an actual conscious spirit being.

   The Bible never describes anyone as possessed by Satan or the Devil.[64] Rather, Satan is pictured as the ultimate orchestrator of opposition to God's plan.[65] Thus Paul pictures both God and Satan as 'energising' in the world, and urges his readers to plug in to the right energy! (Eph 1:11, 2:2) As we have elsewhere written, on a spiritual level there is continuous warfare between God and the forces of evil.[66] Paul speaks of conflict in the dimension of the 'heavenlies' between the church in Christ and a hierarchical group of evil spiritual powers — a concept real in the experience of many Christians in prayer today (Eph 6:12; Col 2:15). But this does not refer to the 'demonic' in the usual sense. Thus, whilst in one sense we may say that Satan tempts us (1 Cor 7:5), we are still responsible for our actions because it is our own desires which lead us on (Jas 1:14, but see 4:7).

Thus there is, on the question of illness, a sense in which it all is ultimately a product of opposition to God and thus a work of Satan (though the sick individual is often in no way to blame). Thus for Jesus to heal a woman of infirmity is to free her from 'Satan's bondage' (Lk 13:16). But this need not imply anything which might be called 'demonic' in the sense meant in modern terms like 'demon possession' and 'exorcism'.

Satan is, however, also pictured as the orchestrator of this more direct kind of demonic activity. Thus Jesus pictures Satan as a 'strong man', and his own healing of the demonised as binding Satan and limiting his power (Mt 12:29; Mk 3:27; Lk 11:21). Jesus went about healing those 'oppressed by the Devil' (Acts 10:38), whether in physical illness or in demonisation. This, however, implies neither that demonisation and illness are the same thing, nor that the Devil was personally and directly involved in such cases. The picture is one of an overview.

2.  *Demon/unclean spirit* The word 'demon' (*daimon* or *daimonion*) seems to be used in the New Testament to mean a personal and conscious spiritual force. Paul, following the Old Testament, identified pagan gods as demons — adding force to rejection of idolatry (1 Cor 10:20–1; Deut 32:17; Ps 106:37; Is 65:3, 11). The more common use, however, is for the Greek New Testament

text to refer either to someone as 'demonised' or as 'having a demon', which terms are shown by the contexts to mean the same thing.[67] The Greek New Testament, however, never refers to anyone as 'possessed *by* a demon' or as 'oppressed *by* a demon', though both terms are used by some Christians today. In New Testament language the person possesses the demon, not the other way around.

Wherever details are given, it appears that the demon can at times take over the personality of the person, and in most cases can speak through them. Any which cannot so speak are exceptional enough to be noted, and result in a dumbness in the person which is cured when the demon is expelled (Mt 9:33; Mk 9:17, 20; Lk 11:14). Jesus (or Paul) dealt with demons by 'expelling' them by word of authoritative command — speaking to the demon and not the person concerned (Mt 17:18; Mk 1:34, 3:15, 6:13, 7:26–30).[68]

To 'have a demon' is the same thing as to 'have an unclean spirit'.[69] Slightly more care is needed with such wording, however, for the word 'spirit' can also be used in a non-personal sense. Thus, in the phrases 'spirit of wisdom' (Ex 28:3; Eph 1:17) and 'spirit of meekness' (1 Cor 4:21; Gal 6:1), although meekness and wisdom are fruits of the Holy Spirit, it seems to be using the word in some sense other than as a centre of consciousness.[70] We might see similarly a 'spirit of slumber' (Rom 11:8) or a 'spirit of whoredom' (Hos 4:12) or a 'spirit of jealousy' (Num 5:14, 30).[71] Thus, when Jesus cured a woman with a 'spirit of infirmity' (Lk 13:11–13), there is no necessity to assume that a demon was involved — and Jesus spoke to the woman not to a demon.

Some general points may be made. Both physical healing and casting out of spirits are activities which 'make whole' and can loosely be referred to as 'healing' (Mt 4:23;

Lk 6:18, 7:21). Yet the two are clearly distinguished. In his own ministry and in giving his followers authority Jesus distinguished between 'performing cures' and 'casting out demons' (Lk 6:18, 7:21, 8:2; Acts 14:16, 19:11). Thus, whilst sometimes a physical illness (like blindness) can be a result of demonisation, physical illness and demonisation are by no means the same thing. This also applies to mental illness, and Matthew actually uses a different word for mental illness from that for demonisation (4:24). In one instance only, Jesus discerned a demon where the symptoms resembled those of epilepsy (Mt 17:14–18; Mk 9:17–29; Lk 9:37–42): an illness we know now is associated with an electrical discharge which could arise in a brain damaged by virus or accident. There is, however, no reason from this to conclude either that Jesus would have believed all cases of epilepsy to be demonic or that Jesus was mistaken in this particular instance. The fact that a demon could cause epilepsy no more implies that all epilepsy is demonic than the fact that a demon could cause blindness (Mt 12:22) implies that all blindness is demonic. There is, moreover, no basis in the Bible to assume that all instances in which people hear voices are demonic and none are, say, a result of damaged brain chemistry or drugs forcibly administered to a Christian prisoner of conscience.

Are demons, then, definitely pictured as centres of consciousness? On this, one further aspect of Jesus' approach should be noted: his use of direct commands. In physical healing (even of the dead) he generally commanded them to be well (Mk 5:41; Jn 11:43). In dealing with demons he 'rebuked' them (Mt 17:18; Mk 9:25); but he also directly 'rebuked' a fever (Lk 4:39, and let us remember Luke was a doctor!), and directly 'rebuked' the winds and waves (Mt 8:26; Mk 4:39; Lk 8:24), where the absence of any reference to 'spirits' makes it quite natural to take it as a personification. He commanded demons to leave, but his illustration of a prayer of faith to his followers was to command a mountain to be moved (Mt 17:20, 21:21; Mk 11:23). Could it be, therefore, that his direct speech to 'demons' is simply a personification (like of the fever, the winds, the waves, or the mountain) and does not imply the presence of an actual centre of consciousness? In strict logic this might be, though some of Jesus' sayings would need to be taken in a strained way to be interpreted thus (Mt 12:43–5; Lk 11:24–6).

On a purely philosophical level, of course, logicians have long realised that we cannot strictly prove the existence of any minds (human or demonic) other than our own. Most people, though, assume other human minds exist because of apparent signs of conscious thought. Demonic manifestations may be seen similarly.

Interestingly, the question of the reality of demons is also analogous to the scientific question of the reality of electrons, neutrinos, quarks or gluons in physics. Whether or not such entities are real little affects recognising the phenomena concerned, or dealing with them, but it is generally much simpler to assume their reality. The evidence is that demonisations as phenomena (however explained) existed both in New Testament times and today — and some of our own personal experiences have involved the casting out of demons. It would not be rational for anyone to deny that such phenomena exist, simply because he or she has not personally experienced them. In some cases the cure has been instantaneous, and the problem has not recurred. It is, we suppose, possible to assume that those concerned were really experiencing nothing more than faulty brain mechanisms, instantaneously righted through the effects of a brief external stimulus applied by the Christian counsellor. But such an assumption would seem to promise neither to offer a convincing explanation nor to enable anyone to deal effectively pastorally and psychologically with these kinds of cases. Various other modern writers relate experiences of demonic phenomena which, even if we are not always able to accept all the details of their interpretation of these experiences, broadly parallel our own.[72] In a useful summary, Anglican minister Dr G H Twelftree has outlined some of the manifestations, noting the recognition given both by churches and some psychologists to the ministry of deliverance.[73]

We cannot, therefore, support either extreme found among Christians: the extreme of denying any reality at all to demonisation or the extreme of discerning or casting out spirits in all manner of mental and physical illnesses for which there is no evidence that demons are involved. We stand by the three basic Christian missions of preaching, healing and casting out spirits to which Jesus called his chosen apostles in Mark 16:15–18 (see also Mt 10:1, 8; 28:18–20; Lk 9:1).[74] We preach. We pray for healing, rebuking both physical and mental illness. We emphasise the role of the person's own spirit (in a way now being increasingly recognised in holistic medicine). We see all of this as part of the Christian activity of plugging in to the energy of God and fighting that of Satan. But much of this need not be seen as involving the demonic, except in those instances where some specific signs may be present or a proven gift of discernment is used.

There remain, however, instances where the third ministry is called for because the specific signs are present, and we fear these instances will increase with the increase in occultism.

No professing Christian could, of course, dabble in things of the occult. Jesus himself obviously accepted the moral authority of the Jewish Law (Mt 5:19, 15:3, 19:17; Mk 10:19; Lk 18:20), which clearly and emphatically forbids any form of mediumship, communication with the dead or activities of witches or warlocks (Lev 19:31).[75] He affirmed, moreover, that anyone who loved him would keep his commandments (Jn 14:15). It seems, therefore, that anyone who is truly pious in the sense of following Jesus Christ would wish to be involved in none of these things, and we should not be misled by claims of those who are. Whether such phenomena be explained scientifically, spiritistically, or in any other way, they are clearly not pursuits approved by the Christian God, and our experience shows that anyone becoming a Christian needs to specifically repent of and renounce them. It should, perhaps, be emphasised that the Transfiguration (Mt 17–8; Mk 9:2–8; Lk 9:28–36) was neither a spiritistic materialisation nor necromancy; it took place in conditions alien to any such thing, and was intended as a one-off testimony of the Hebrew Law and Prophets to Jesus rather than as a pattern to follow. The Magi (Mt 2) have sometimes been compared to modern astrologers but again this is misleading, for they nowhere stated or assumed that the stars could influence human affairs, or foretell the future. The star was 'his star': it belonged to him, not he to it (Mt 2:2). It is noteworthy that when God wanted to communicate something more specific to the Magi, he did it through a dream — not through astrology (Mt 2:12).

Finally, it should be emphasised that the occult should be avoided not only because forbidden in the Bible, but because experience shows it to be psychologically destructive. However anyone chooses to interpret the phenomena (as spiritual forces, psychic forces, psychological forces or mere hocus-pocus), there is good evidence (some known to us through personal contacts) that dabblers in it do run a risk of becoming trapped in powers beyond their control. Such powers, however explained, may dehumanise them, or lead to mental disorder.[76] Even non-Christian sources may recognise this. Shortly after Halloween in 1988, the secular BBC national *News* carried an item by a secular charity for child concern emphasising the possible psychological damage to children becoming involved in occultism. No one should dabble lightly in such matters. Even the use of extra-sensory gifts (not forbidden in the Bible nor, necessarily, associated with demonic forces) carries a risk of mental disturbance or being drawn deeper into other more dangerous practices.

In short, it is perfectly possible for those in a scientific age to believe in the existence of the demonic. This should, however, be kept in proportion. Christians who become obsessed with it are no less unbiblical than those who dabble in it, and either extreme carries dangers.

## Notes

1. A Peacocke, *Reductionism in Academic Disciplines* (1985), p 9.
2. *Ibid*, pp 7, 11.
3. S Rose in *ibid*, p 29.
4. Probably Zeno's disciple Cleanthes.
5. Marcus Aurelius, *Meditations*, bk 11.
6. D Hume, *A Treatise of Human Nature* (1739), bk 1.
7. *Ibid*, bk 1, chap iv, p 2.
8. *Ibid*, Appendix.
9. F Crick, *Of Molecules and Man* (1966), p 10.
10. E O Wilson, *Sociobiology* (1975), eg p 4 etc.
11. P Atkins, *The Creation* (1981), p 41.
12. D M MacKay, *The Clockwork Image* (1974), chap 4; see also Tim Hawthorne, *Windows of Science and Faith* (1987), p 38, etc.
13. Eg in A Peacocke, *Reductionism*. See also Keith Ward, *The Battle for the Soul* (1985).
14. René Descartes, *Le Discours de la méthode* (1637) part iv.
15. John Searle, *Minds, Brains and Science* (1984).
16. René Descartes, *Meditations* (1641) bk iv.
17. W V Quine, *Word and Object* (1960).
18. T H Huxley, *Collected Essays* (1898), vol 1, p 240.
19. Searle, *op cit*, p 97.
20. H Feigl, *The Mental and the Physical* (1967).
21. J O'Connor (ed), *Modern Materialism: Readings on the Mind-Body Identity* (1969).
22. See K Popper and J Eccles, *The Self and Its Brain* (1977), p 81, etc.
23. J Eccles, *The Human Psyche* (1980), p 20.
24. D M MacKay, *Brains, Machines and Persons* (1980), p 80. See also *The Open Mind* (1988), p 56, etc.
25. *Ibid*, p 14, etc.
26. D Gareth Jones *Our Fragile Brains* (1981).
27. See C S Sherrington, *The Brain and Its Mechanism* (1933), and *Man*

on His Nature (1940). Also Sherrington and others in P Laslett (ed) in The Physical Basis of Mind (1950).

28. Wilder Penfield, The Mystery of the Mind (1975), pp 113–14.

29. Stanley Jaki, Brain, Mind and Computers (1970), and The Road of Science and the Ways to God (1978).

30. Eccles, The Human Psyche, p 6, citing R W Sperry, 'Forebrain Commissurotomy and Conscious Awareness', Journal of Medical Philosophy, vol 2 (1977): pp 101–26.

31. Eccles, The Human Psyche, p 11, citing Sperry et al, 'Self-recognition and Social Awareness ...', Neuropsychologia, vol 17 (1979): pp 156–66.

32. John Polkinghorne, Science and Creation (1988), chap 5.

33. Eccles, The Human Psyche, p 14; MacKay, 'Selves and Brains', Neurosciences, vol 3 (1978): pp 599–606 and Brains, Machines and Persons (1980).

34. Mary Stewart Van Leeuwen, The Person in Psychology (1985), pp 89–90.

35. G Ryle, The Concept of Mind (1949), Penguin edition, p 17.

36. Ibid, pp 308–9.

37. Ayer admitted this in an interview with Brian Magee in The Listener, 2nd March 1978, see also p 249 below.

38. Arthur Stanley Eddington, The Nature of the Physical World (1928), p 332.

39. Ian G Barbour, Issues in Science and Religion (1966), p 309, see also p 352. For one more recent reference see P Crutchfield et al, 'Chaos', Scientific American, vol 255, no 6 (Dec 1986): pp 38–49.

40. Popper and Eccles, The Self and Its Brain, p 546.

41. MacKay, The Clockwork Image, p 78.

42. MacKay, Brains, Machines and Persons, p 14.

43. Max Planck, The Universe in the Light of Modern Physics (1937), p 88.

44. Ibid, p 89.

45. Ibid, p 105.

46. Eg The Clockwork Image, p 78, etc or in Christianity in a Mechanistic Universe (1965).

47. MacKay, Brains, Machines and Persons p 96.

48. Ibid, p 97.

49. MacKay, The Clockwork Image, p 81.

50. See R T Forster and V P Marston, God's Strategy in Human History (1973).

51. John Polkinghorne, Science and Providence (1989), p 12.

52. Ibid, p 7, quoting David Brown, The Divine Trinity (1985), p 16.

53. Mary Stewart Van Leeuwen, op cit, p 68.

54. See S S Kety's article in Marczmar and Eccles (eds) *Brain and Behaviour* (1972).
55. W H Thorpe, *Animal Nature and Human Nature* (1974).
56. W Penfield, *The Mystery of the Mind* (1975).
57. Interview in *Weltwoche*, 11th May 1945.
58. M Gardner, *Fads and Fallacies in the Name of Science* (1952, 1957).
59. A Koestler, *The Roots of Coincidence* (1972).
60. Thus the satirist Lucian of Samosata (c AD 120–180) in *The Lover of Lies*, introduced a sceptic into a discussion of demonisation.
61. Galileo, *Dialogue on the Two World Systems* (First published, 1632; this edition translated by S Drake), p 462.
62. William Shakespeare, *Hamlet* (First published 1603; this edition: Routledge, Warne and Routledge: London, 1864), Act I, Scene V, line 166 (p 345).
63. Eg *satanas* Luke 10:18; 2 Corinthians 11:14; *diabolos* Acts 10:38; Ephesians 6:11; James 4:7.
64. We take the words 'Satan entered into Judas' (Lk 22:3; Jn 13:27) in the same kind of sense as Acts 5:3, not necessarily meaning any kind of demon-type possession, but even if it were the same, there would be obvious reasons for this exception.
65. Implicit in many references to Satan or the Devil.
66. R T Forster and V P Marston, *God's Strategy in Human History*.
67. 'Demonised': Matthew 4:24, 8:16, 28, 33, 9:32, 12:22; Mark 1:32, 5:15–18; Luke 8:36; John 10:21. 'Having a demon': Matthew 11:18; Luke 8:27; John 7:20, 8:48–9, 10:20.
68. See also: Mark 1:25, 3:11–12, 5:8, 9:25; Luke 4:36, 8:29; Acts 16:18.
69. Compare Matthew 10:1 and Mark 3:11. See Matthew 8:16; Luke 4:33–6.
70. See also 'spirit of faith' (2 Cor 4:13).
71. See also 'spirit of bondage' (Rom 8:15).
72. See, for example: K E Koch, *Christian Counselling and Occultism* (1972); R Gasson, *The Challenging Counterfeit* (1958); J Stafford Wright, *What is Man?* (1976); V Ernest, *I Talked With Spirits*; W Sabritsky *Demons Defeated* (1985), D Burnett, *Unearthly Powers* (1988); Graham and Shirley Powell, *Christian, Set Yourself Free* (1983). Walter Wink, *Naming the Powers* (1984) and *Unmasking the Powers* (1986) are also useful (though not written from an entirely conservative evangelical position), taking a more open view on the explanation, but asserting the reality of the phenomena.
73. G Twelftree, 'The Place of Exorcism in Contemporary Ministry', *Anvil*, vol 5, no 2 (1988): pp 133–50.
74. Early church fathers refer to this threefold mission, including Christians expelling evil spirits, as though common knowledge,

eg *The Constitution of the Holy Apostles*, VIII, 1 (*Ant Nic Fath*, vii 479); Justin Martyr in *Second Apology*, II (*Ant Nic Fath*, i, 190); Irenaeus in *Against Heresies*, XXXII, 4 (*Ant Nic Fath*, i, 409); Lactantius in *The Divine Institutes*, bk 5, XXII (*Ant Nic Fath*, vii, 159); and Origen in *Against Celsus*, bk 1, chap 2 (*Ant Nic Fath*, iv, 398).

75. See also Leviticus 20:6, 27; Deuteronomy 18:10–11; 2 Kings 21:6; 1 Chronicles 10:13; 2 Chronicles 33:6; Isaiah 19:3.

76. See some of the cases described in books in note 72 — irrespective of whether or not the Christian interpretation of these is taken.

# II

# SHOULD GENESIS BE TAKEN LITERALLY?

## Introduction

THERE ARE TWO OPPOSITE CATEGORIES of people who feel that Christians really ought to 'take the Bible literally' on issues like the Genesis account of creation. Firstly, there are unbelievers who are impatient with what they regard as modern attempts to reinterpret a Christianity which they believe, in the words of C S Lewis, 'implies a local "Heaven", a flat earth, and a God who can have children'.[1] 'If,' they say, 'Christians were really honest, then they would take the Bible literally and admit that it is based on primitive superstition.'

Taking a similar view, but with quite different motives, are the dedicated and sincere Christians who believe that it is 'honouring God's word' and 'giving God the glory' to take the Bible literally in all its apparent statements. As two leading moderns revered by such people, we shall take theologian E J Young and key young-earth creationist H M Morris. Thus Young, in rightly criticising the use of the term 'myth' for the Genesis accounts, then swings to the other extreme by arguing that it is 'straightforward trustworthy history'.[2] Likewise, Morris begins with the bold assertion:

The Scriptures, in fact, do not need to be 'interpreted' at all, for God is well able to say exactly what he means. Jesus

203

Christ himself, accepted the Genesis record as literal history. There are no allegories in Genesis unless the dreams of Joseph are so described.[3] The biblical record of origins was written to be understood, and therefore is to be taken literally rather than mystically or parabolically.[4]

They believe that if accounts of creation are taken as myth or allegory, then:

What is to prevent our interpreting any other part of Scripture in the same way? Thus the Virgin Birth may, after all, be only an allegory, the Resurrection could be only a myth or suprahistory, the Ten Commandments only a liturgy, the crucifixion only a dream.[5]

There is, of course, some truth in both these viewpoints. The unbeliever is right to be sceptical of those who find Einstein's General Theory of Relativity implied in obscure poetic verses of the Psalms, and the ardent literalist is right to object to those who abandon the historical basis of biblical Christianity. Yet both are also mistaken, for they encourage an approach to the Bible with preconceived human ideas of what kind of literature it 'must be', rather than seeking to understand the internal evidence of how God intended it to be interpreted.

The present chapter will show how the text itself, New Testament interpretation, the oldest Christian teachings, and the attitudes of modern literalists themselves all point to elements of metaphorical language in Genesis 1-4.

## Early Christian teaching

The earliest Christian leaders after the apostles — sometimes called the 'church fathers' — did not write with any apostolic authority. Nevertheless, anyone claiming to follow historic, biblical, Christianity needs to look carefully at the approach and teachings of those who stood closest in time (and in some cases language) to the New Testament.

These early Christians are commonly divided, according to the language in which they wrote, into Greek Fathers and Latin Fathers – though there was, of course, interchange of ideas between them. In both groups there was, compared with today, a very much greater emphasis on allegorical meaning of Scripture. Thus, for example, Psalm 90:4 and 2 Peter 3:8 led many of them to take an allegorical interpretation of the 'days' in Genesis 1 to mean millennia. This view is expressed, for example, by: Barnabas,[6] Irenaeus,[7] Hippolytus,[8] Methodius,[9] Lactantius,[10] Theophilus,[11] and John of Damascus.[12] They applied this allegorical meaning, however, to a supposed seven ages of world history. Whether or not the 'days' of creation were themselves literal is seldom discussed, and is usually incidental to their themes. There were those who seemingly took the 'days' literally as well as allegorically. Basil, for example, who claims to take it all literally, specifically refers to twenty-four-hour periods. Yet later he adds, 'Whether you call it "day" or whether you call it "eternity", you express the same idea,' and he actually adopts a complex interpretation.[13] Likewise, Chrysostom, who appears to take the 'days' literally in his homilies, also repeatedly emphasises that ideas are being given 'concreteness of expression' in Genesis 1-3 to help our 'limited human understanding'. Thus on the 'rib' used to form Eve he writes:

> Don't take the words in human fashion; rather, interpret the concreteness of the expressions from the viewpoint of human limitations. You see, if he had not used these words, how would we have been able to gain knowledge of these mysteries which defy description?[14]

Naïve literalism was never Christian orthodoxy.

When we turn, moreover, to the figures who are undoubtedly the leading intellectual figures of both the Greek and Latin Fathers, we find a much clearer commitment to a non-literal interpretation of the 'days'. The saintly and scholarly Origen (a man who suffered torture for his faith) is described in *Britannica* as the 'most important theologian and biblical scholar of the early Greek church'.[15] Origen was, of course, fluent in Greek, and was also a student of the Hebrew in which Genesis was written. He wrote around AD 231:

> What man of intelligence, I ask, will consider a reasonable statement that the first and second and the third day, in which there are said to be both morning and evening, existed without sun and moon and stars, while the first day was even without a heaven? And who could be found so silly as to believe that God, after the manner of a farmer, 'planted trees in a paradise eastward in Eden', ... And ... when God is said to 'walk in the paradise in the evening' ... I do not think anyone will doubt that these are figurative expressions which indicate certain mysteries through a semblance of history.[16]

Among Latin Fathers, *Britannica* calls Augustine of Hippo the 'greatest thinker of Christian antiquity'. [17] We believe this goes too far, and that some of his novel doctrines (for example, on predestination) owe more to his former Manichaeism than to Christianity — in spite of their later adoption by Reformation figures such as Calvin and Luther.[18] Nevertheless, it is undeniable that he was a dominant figure in much of both Catholic and Reformation theology. On the 'days' of creation he wrote:

> Of what fashion those days were, it is either very hard or altogether impossible to think, much more to speak. As for ordinary days, we see that they have neither morning nor evening but as the sun rises and sets. But the first three days of all had no sun, for that was made the fourth day.[19]

Elsewhere he suggested that everything was created at once, and the 'days' have a time-based or temporal character, not physical but ideal.[20] Today this would probably be called the 'framework theory'. Augustine thought the Genesis language reflected the angelic perspective, which could know something either directly in God ('morning knowledge') or in its later actual being ('evening knowledge').[21] The 'paradise' of Genesis 2 he interpreted by taking 'some things materially and others spiritually'.[22]

Naïve literalism was never a part of Christian orthodoxy in the earliest centuries of Christianity.

## Modern literalists

What about modern literalists? Is it actually possible to take the Bible literally throughout? We intend, in the next few paragraphs to demonstrate that it is not, by showing that several of the prominent modern writers most often cited by supposed literalists are forced to take numerous points figuratively. Some readers may think that this is obvious, and wish to skip these paragraphs, but to others it may be a question of some importance.

Leading young-earth creationist Henry Morris, as we have seen, makes the bold claim that he takes nothing allegorically in Genesis. When, however, he actually comes to consider the text, we find the following:

1. *Waters above the skies* God's creation of these is noted in 1:7, and most of us take them as a poetic reference to clouds. In Psalm 148 the psalmist calls upon various created things to praise the Lord in his day, including in verses 4–6: 'Praise him, you highest heavens, and you waters above the skies. Let them praise the name of the LORD, for he commanded and they were created. He set them in place for ever and ever.' The plain Hebrew text (testified by all translations from LXX onwards)

indicates a past creative act (as in Gen 1:7), and a present calling for the waters to join in the praise of God. Morris, however, wishes to interpret 1:7 as a 'water-vapour canopy' which disappeared in the Noachic Flood.[23] Without the slightest linguistic basis, he then interprets Psalm 148:4–6 as a future event describing waters which 'will be established for ever and ever'.[24] This is not only non-literal, but seems a distortion of the obvious meaning.

2.  *Dominion* God's instructions to subdue and have dominion are, says Morris, 'military terms – first conquer, and then rule. In context, however, there is no actual conflict suggested.'[25] In what context? Morris has painted a picture of a pre-Fall world without physical death and where the fundamental laws of physics are radically different from today — all of which is highly speculative and not accepted by all his sympathisers. It is on this basis that he effectively denies the meaning of the word 'dominion', though he does not explain why God used it if it was not what he meant.

3.  *Rib* Morris emphasises that the 'rib' is really a 'side', but presumably Adam was not literally one-side-missing after Eve's creation, and Morris stresses its immediate and ultimate spiritual interpretations.[26]

4.  *Death* God warned Adam concerning the forbidden fruit that 'in the day you eat of it, dying you shall die' (2:17). The latter phrase is a common Hebrew construction, emphasising the certainty of the event, thus the NIV's 'you will surely die'. Clearly Adam did NOT die physically in the day he took the fruit, but lived to a great old age. Those of us who take Genesis 2:17 straightforwardly (bearing in mind the interpretive passage of Rom 5–7 and the clear inference of Rom 7:9) take it to mean spiritual death, and that Adam did spiritually die in the moment he sinned. Morris,

however, has as a mainspring of his system the idea that human and animal physical death began with the Fall. He, therefore, takes Genesis 2:17 to mean that Adam 'died both spiritually and (in principle) physically the very day he ... disobeyed'.[27] This 'in principle' is not a literal interpretation.

5. *Snake* The curse of the snake Morris takes as 'more than a reference to the physical enmity between men and snakes'.[28] The 'real thrust' of the curse was not on the literal snake, but on 'that old serpent called the Devil'. Indeed, Morris imports into Genesis an elaborate picture of Satan or Lucifer as a 'fallen angel' based on verses from Isaiah, Ezekiel and the New Testament, which were written from six to thirteen centuries after Genesis. Genesis itself mentions neither Satan nor the Devil by name, and a literal reading would take it that there was only one character involved and that was a physical snake. Morris introduces two – the physical snake and the spiritual fallen angel — in a complex reinterpretation of the text.

6. *Dust* It 'would not "eat dust" in a literal sense, of course ... the expression is mainly a graphic figure of speech'.[29]

7. *Seed* In reference to the 'seed of the serpent' and 'seed of the woman' Morris says, 'The term "seed" of course has a biological connotation, but this is not strictly possible here. Neither Satan, who is a spirit, nor the woman would be able to produce actual seed.'[30] We note first that male snakes do, of course, have 'seed' — and that it is only Morris' interpretation of the 'snake' as 'Satan' which raises any problem for literalism. Likewise, Genesis 4:25 seems to refer to Eve's literal seed. A literal reading of 3:15 would therefore see a prediction of enmity between snakes and humans. Morris, however, takes the seed of the woman as: 'those in the human family who are brought into right

relationship with God through faith.' The 'seed of the serpent' is those who 'knowingly and willingly set themselves at enmity' with these faithful people. This is a highly allegorical interpretation.

8. *Blood* Morris appears not to interpret literally Genesis 4:10 (AV): 'the voice of thy brother's blood crieth unto me from the ground'.[31] Elsewhere he adds: 'The blood of animals could only figuratively cover sins, of course.'[32]

9. *Places* Morris does not interpret literally the biblical use of the place names before the Flood, but thinks them 'carried over' and reapplied to entirely different post-flood locations.[33]

10. *Days* We will need later to look at Morris' interpretation of 'days' in more detail, but here note that he allows the word 'day' in Genesis 2:4 (AV) to mean 'the whole period of creation', ie six days,[34] even though elsewhere he says that the word 'never' means a 'definite period of time with a specific beginning and ending'.[35]

We may now turn to theologian E J Young, who is also highly regarded by many who claim to take the Bible literally, and who himself claims that Genesis is 'straightforward, trustworthy history'.[36] When we look, however, at his two books *Studies in Genesis One* and *Genesis 3*, and at the book *In the Beginning*, which transcribes his lectures, we find the following:

1. 'We say: "God said". That does not mean that he spoke in Hebrew. It does not mean that he even uttered sounds. I cannot positively say what it does mean.'[37] 'God did not speak with physical organs of speech, nor did he utter words.'[38]

2. 'The Hebrew word *yom* is much like our English word "day" and it is capable of a great number of connotations

... The first three days are not solar days such as we now know ... the work of the third day seems to suggest that there was some process, and that what took place occurred in a period much longer than twenty-four hours.'[39] 'The length of the days is not stated ... The first three days were not solar days such as we now have.'[40]

3. 'It is almost universally taught nowadays that man is millions of years old ... if it could be proved that some of the figures that are being used are correct, it would not affect what is stated in the first chapter of Genesis.'[41]

4. 'We do not know how God breathed. That is certainly an anthropomorphic expression.'[42]

5. 'Genesis 2 ... a chronological order is not intended here.'[43]

6. 'I do not think we have to maintain that Adam died physically on that particular day.'[44] 'He did die, although not in a physical sense, the moment he disobeyed God.'[45]

7. 'What is meant by the "seed of Satan"? I am inclined to think that it refers to evil men.'[46] 'The serpent's seed is found in evil spirits.'[47]

8. 'The eating of dust is not necessarily to be understood as referring to the serpent's food. To declare ... that serpents do not eat dust ... is to miss the point of the language.'[48]

Interestingly, E J Young's son Davis A Young is also an evangelical, but is a professional geologist. His own commitment to a non-literal account of the 'days', etc, is even clearer, in spite of his evident respect for his father's theology.[49]

The leading British scientific sympathiser with Morris' ideas is probably Professor E H Andrews. Actually, in his more recent works, Andrews seems to be moving away from Morris on some points. Although he still seems to retain a

number of what we would see as philosophical incon-
sistencies, largely carried over from ideas of Morris or
Whitcomb, we can find much to agree with in what he says.
Though he sometimes forgets it (referring to the 'plain
meaning' where it is far from plain), he does recognise the
importance of metaphor in human speech, and his commitment to non-literality is explicit: 'If we try to interpret the
Bible literally at all points, we find ourselves in all kinds of
trouble.'[50]

When, for example, it says, 'God spoke,' Andrews takes
this as an 'anthropomorphism', and in fact: 'the word
"spoke" implies something far more significant in its metaphorical than in its literal meaning, and this is clearly the
import of God's speaking in Genesis 1.'[51] Another important
example concerns the apparent differences in sequence
between Genesis 1 and 2:

> If we turn to the second chapter, we find that man was
> apparently created before animals, for that is the order in which
> their respective creations are presented. If we interpret these
> chapters wholly literally, we have a difficult contradiction on our
> hands ... Once again, however, we recognise that a literary,
> rather than a literal, interpretation is in order. That is, a
> dramatic device is being employed in Genesis 2.[52]

In one place Andrews writes that 'to deny that the "days" of
Genesis 1 were normal days' would be to deny the context.[53]
Elsewhere, however, he finds acceptable the suggestion that
the first day was millions of years long (even though Ex 20:11
plainly says that everything including the heavens and earth
was made in six days), and that the other days may not have
been solar days either.[54] On the 'fourth day' the sun and
moon were not 'made' as a plain reading of Genesis 1–16
would imply, but simply 'became visible'. Referring to the
words in 2:17, Andrews takes the death as physical, but that
Adam 'died in the sense that he became mortal', which is a
very oblique interpretation.[55]

Finally, we might mention Francis Schaeffer, whose *Genesis in Space and Time* strongly defends the objectivity and historicity of the creation accounts. Yet he retains a deliberate openness, for example, on whether 'day' in Genesis 1 means an 'era' or some other non-literal interpretation.[56]

In spite of Morris' words about nothing in Genesis being allegorical, it is plain that he and those like him interpret many points metaphorically. Also, in spite of his claim that the meaning is very clear and does not need 'interpreting', those who take this view themselves disagree over the interpretation on some important points. To Morris the six 'days' are all literal, to Andrews only five of them are, whilst to Young just three have to be literal. To both Morris and A E Wilder-Smith, it is vital to believe that before the Fall of Adam neither death nor the second law of thermodynamics (which implies decay) existed.[57] Andrews, in contrast, believes that there were no carnivores, but there was death and the second law of thermodynamics did operate.[58]

The point, then, is that no intelligent Christian can possibly take it literally in all respects. It then becomes a question not of 'Should we take it literally?' but 'How literally should we take it?' On the one hand, there are Bible-believing Christians today who follow the most ancient Christian interpretations and take the 'days', for example, as a literary framework not intended literally in either Genesis 1 or 2. On the other hand, there are the moderns like Morris who, on a basis of what they term 'scientific creationism' take the 'day' in Genesis 2 as non-sequential and non-literal (along with various other non-literal interpretations), but the 'days' in Genesis 1 as sequential and partially or wholly literal twenty-four-hour periods. In our view, however, no one group of Christians should despise another or call doubt upon their commitment to Scripture because of such variations in the degree of literality, for no one takes it all literally. Nor can sceptics write off biblical Christianity as naïve literalism, for this it never has been and indeed cannot be.

## God's use of language

In this section we shall look a little more closely at the way the Bible itself uses language. Could the sceptic argue that Christians who take so many points as allegorical are departing from the intention of the original writer, who actually intended a primitive total literality?

The Christian believes that right from the beginning God chose to communicate with mankind through language: 'And the Lord God commanded the man' (Gen 2:16). Later he chose to use language again in communicating through the Bible. But the Hebrew and Greek languages, like our own, are used in a whole spectrum of ways. Metaphor comes constantly into language all the time. We just used, for example, the expression 'spectrum of ways'. But it would not be very honouring for someone to proclaim: 'We believe Forster and Marston are trustworthy witnesses. If they do not mean by this that language contains a whole lot of literal colours, then how can we trust what they say elsewhere?' Scientists, incidentally, use words just as metaphorically as anyone else. When physicists speak of 'waves' or 'electron spin', they are introducing terms used in other contexts but if pressed, will soon affirm that, say, light waves have properties quite different from the waves from which the term was taken, and electrons do not spin literally like tops. They may, of course, be misunderstood. People may even say, 'If we can't take Professor Andrews literally when he speaks of metal being "fatigued", then how can we believe him when he says that the number 7 bus leaves at 6.45?' Foolish though this would be, some of the supposed literalist arguments about parts of Genesis are not greatly different.

We need to be clear on some basic points on how words are used — both in religious and in other contexts, such as everyday or scientific ones. Firstly, it is difficult if not impossible simply to remove metaphor altogether and speak plainly. In scientific thinking there was one school of thought which saw 'models' as optional extras, but a more profound analysis realises that part of the whole dynamic of science involves metaphorical images of thinking.[59] In theology, C S Lewis, who was, of course, a professor in a field of languages, referred to those who ask:

> 'Would it not be better to get rid of the mental pictures, and of the language which suggests them, altogether?' But this is impossible. The people who recommend it have not noticed that when they try to get rid of man-like, or as they are called, anthropomorphic, images they merely succeed in substituting images of some other kind.[60]

Our images of God and of many spiritual things are inevitably in pictures or words which derive their richness from quite other contexts. This is true both of such biblical images as of 'fatherhood', 'spiritual power', 'ascending to heaven', etc, and of ones of human making, like 'ground of our being' or 'universal-substance'. Jesus' teaching is full not only of specific parables but a whole range of metaphorical language.

A second point is that, by definition, metaphorical language involves the use of terms used literally elsewhere. Suppose that someone were to make the following argument:

> The Greek word 'body' is used in the Gospels forty times. In thirty-seven cases it is clearly literal. The other three are all in Jesus' phrase 'Take and eat; this is my body' (Mt 26:26; Mk 14:22; Lk 22:19). Therefore it must be literal here too. To deny this would lead to the danger that the Resurrection accounts where they 'found not the body' (Lk 24:3) might also be taken figuratively, casting doubt on the central doctrine of the Resurrection!

No one actually argues like this; even the most ardent literalist takes it somewhat mystically and most of us take it as metaphorically as Jesus' words 'I am the ... vine' (Jn 15:1). What would we think, then, of such an argument?

This, however, is precisely the kind of argument used by supposed Christian literalists over the use of the word 'day' in Genesis 1:

> The Hebrew word for 'days' . . . which is used over 700 times in the Old Testament, never in any other place necessarily means anything but literal 'days'. Even when used in the singular, as it is several times in Genesis 1, it normally means literal day.[61]

What may be most surprising about this argument is that, as we shall see, both the plural and the singular are used many times in contexts where there is no emphasis on twenty-four-hour periods, and in some instances clearly refer to longer time spans. But the more basic point is that even if it were correct on this, as a form of argument it would make no more sense than the one about bodies. It is the context (or literary genre) which is important, as Morris himself elsewhere admits.

We will later return to consider this, but need also to note here that Jesus did not preface his words with the warning: 'What I am about to say is metaphorical'; he simply assumed that those who were spiritually discerning would realise this. In actual fact, the mistake most commonly made about the teaching of Jesus by both opponent and would-be-disciple was to take it literally when Jesus, without any explicit warning, meant it metaphorically and spiritually. It is not a sign of spirituality or desire to honour God to take as much literally as possible. Nor is it acceptable to argue that the 'days' of Genesis 1 must be literal twenty-four-hour periods because: 'This is the word of God, and God is surely well able to say what he means.'[62] Jesus was presumably well able to say what he meant when he told Nicodemus to be 'born again' (Jn 3:3), promised someone 'living water' (Jn 4:10), spoke of 'food to eat that you know nothing about' (Jn 4:32), told people that they had to eat him (Jn 6:53), and said, 'This is my body.' If Jesus, as Christians believe, shows us the

Father, then we will expect God to speak to us in metaphor, without any explicit warning, and God will expect us to be spiritually discerning in interpreting his words. It is not honouring to Jesus' chosen means of communication for someone to speak, as does E J Young, about 'mere symbols' as though there was something inferior about this kind of language.[63]

The kind of factual statements God makes about creation are reliable where they touch on history and on the nature of the physical world. But God's concern is neither that of the secular historian nor that of the physicist. On a historical level, a statement may have genuine historical content but be allegorical in form. This is quite different from a 'myth' in any usual sense of the word (which is taken by Andrews, for example, simply to mean a 'fairy story').[64]

This may be illustrated from the words of Jesus himself. Once he said, 'I sent you to reap what you have not worked for. Others have done the hard work, and you have reaped the benefits of their labour' (Jn 4:38). Now this is a historical statement; it is not myth or legend, which would be a fictional form of apparent history. It is not a fable or parable like, for example, that of the 'Prodigal Son', the point of which is unaffected if it has no connection with particular historical events. It is metaphorical history. Young, notably, ignores this category of language altogether, writing as though our choice were between, on the one hand, myth, fable, allegory and legend, and, on the other, pure 'Hansard-reported' history. But here, although Jesus refers to an actual historical commission which he had given them, his language is metaphorical: his commission concerned souls not agriculture. He could, presumably, have explained himself more clearly, but he chose not to do so. If Jesus showed us the Father, then it would be no surprise if we found that God had used language similarly. The story of the 'snake' may be meant no more to teach us about reptiles than Jesus was interested in agriculture. It is not myth, it is history, but its form is metaphorical. A similar point to this has been made by Douglas Spanner in his 1987 work.[65]

Likewise God often focuses on questions of why, rather than the scientific preoccupations with physical processes and questions of how. Jesus says that God feeds the birds (Mt 6:26), but does not imply any special creation of worms. God is the one who 'forms the mountains' and 'creates the winds' (Amos 4:13), but he does both through natural processes. Such statements are not unscientific, for they do not purport to tell us anything about the processes as studied by science; they concern meaning not method. If, therefore, the Genesis account says that God 'created', we must not prejudge whether some natural process was involved.

## Language forms and structure

What kind of literature is Genesis 1–3? As a document, it falls into two distinct parts, 1:1–2:3 and 2:4–3:24, which in turn form part of a wider pattern of sections of Genesis, each beginning with the words: 'These are the generations of . . .' (Gen 2:4, 5:1, 6:9, 10:1).[66] At one time critics tried to argue that these were two rival accounts from different sources, but we see no reason to doubt the traditional view accepted by many modern scholars, that the two passages were from the beginning seen as complementary.[67] Genesis 1:1–2:3 serves as a kind of prologue, while Genesis 2:4–3:24 speaks of what was engendered in a human sense from the creation of earth and heavens. Some scholars have emphasised a supposed role of the passages as a prologue to a covenant document made by God with Israel.[68] There may be some truth in this, though it seems clear that both accounts are intended to deal with far more fundamental issues of God's relationship with the physical world and with mankind.

A second point about both accounts concerns their mode of inspiration. However strong one's belief in biblical inspiration, clearly there are historical books, like Luke's Gospel, which 'were very definitely written by the human authors, using their own observations and researches and expressing their own feelings and convictions'.[69] Genesis 1:1–2:3 and 2:4–3:24 are not like this. They are divinely given accounts intended by God to explain his relationship with his world and mankind. As such, we find a problem in that they are (with the possible exception of some poetic passages, for example, in Job) unique kinds of document. This should make us wary of too hasty or dogmatic a classification of them with other kinds of literature in the Bible — whether historical, poetical, philosophical or prophetic.

Both creation accounts are in carefully constructed patterns. The medieval distinction of the word of 'separation' (days 1–3) and 'adornment' (days 4–6) led to recognition at least two centuries ago of the symmetry of the two triads of days. Sometimes these are called 'form' and 'fulness', reflecting the changes in the creation of a world 'without form' and 'void' in Genesis 1:2 (AV).

SEPARATION (FORM)    ADORNMENT (FULNESS)

DAY 1: Light and Dark    DAY 4: Lights (Sun, Moon and Stars) of Day/Night

DAY 2: Sea and Sky    DAY 5: Creatures of Water and Air

DAY 3: Fertile Earth    DAY 6: Creatures of the Land

Modern commentators identify a complex pattern of tens, threes and sevens in Genesis 1[70] and some discern a literary pattern in Genesis 2 as well.[71] Both, and especially Genesis 2, contain Hebrew plays on words. Henry Blocher asks: 'Is it prose or poetry? The choice is a gross oversimplification.

Even Young, who wishes to see in Genesis 1 only "straight-forward history", recognises without any sense of inconsistency that this chapter "is written in exalted semi-poetical language".[72] Blocher admits that we do not find 'the rhythms of Hebrew poetry' nor its 'parallelism', but concurs with the common view of scholars that it can be seen as a kind of 'hymn' which is a unique blend of prose and poetry. This does not mean, of course, that it is fictional. Many hymns contain a great deal of factual and historical reference, but they often couch this in metaphorical forms.

## Literality and the relationship of Genesis 1 and 2

Whether we call them two 'accounts', or 'chapters' (Young and Morris), or 'tablets' (Blocher), it is obvious that Genesis 1:1–2:3 and 2:4–2:25 overlap in what they describe. Two immediate points arise. The first is that the order of events in the two chapters appears different, and the second is that Genesis 1 speaks of six 'days', whilst in 2:4–7 (AV) we read: 'These are the generations of the heavens and of the earth when they were created, in THE DAY that the Lord God made the earth and the heavens and every plant of the field before it was in the earth ... And the Lord God formed man.' The obvious implication of non-literality in the contrast of six 'days' and one was seen by those in the second century who defended Christian orthodoxy against critics.[73] A plain literal reading of Genesis 2:4 would imply that all the succeeding events (described with no break) took place on the 'day' mentioned, and in the order described. There are, then, three possibilities:

1. The two are contradictory.
2. One account is intended as literal in chronology and time span and the other one not.
3. Neither are intended to give strict chronology and literal time spans.

Unbelieving critics have sometimes suggested the first, but it is frankly incredible. Even atheists must accept that whoever compiled Genesis was intelligent, and it would have been careless to leave together two obviously contradictory accounts. Clearly, the Hebrews did not understand their own language in any sense which would imply this.

So was just one, or were both intended non-literally? Let us first consider the meaning of 'day'. As already argued, it is primarily context which indicates that a word is being used metaphorically. Nevertheless, it will give added force to the view if we find that it is commonly used elsewhere in a metaphorical sense as well as a literal one. The plural is used elsewhere very commonly in phrases like 'full of days' (Gen 35:29; 1 Chron 23:1, 29:28; 2 Chron 24:15 AV), meaning 'old', and 'in those days' (Ex 2:11; Judg 17:6, 18:1; 1 Sam 28:1 AV), variants of which are the most common use of the word. In none of these are twenty-four-hour periods being emphasised. Even more marked is the use of the singular 'day'. Throughout Isaiah, for example, it is used countless times, in hardly any instance meaning a period of literally twenty-four hours, after which it stops. In Jeremiah 11:4 (AV) God says that he gave Israel a command 'in the day that I brought them forth out of the land of Egypt' — reference to Deuteronomy 11 shows that the event described actually happened well after their exit. Jeremiah 34:13 similarly refers to a covenant made in that 'day', whereas Exodus 19:1 shows it was made 'in the third month after' they went forth. Both these are very similar to Genesis 2:4.

All the modern writers such as Young, Schaeffer and Andrews accept that the 'day' in 2:4 is non-literal. With some apparent reluctance, Morris also concedes that the 'Hebrew word *yom* can, if the context justifies, be translated "time" in the general sense' and that the context of 2:4 'perhaps does justify such a meaning'.[74]

What of the 'days' in Genesis 1? Earliest Christian teaching, most evangelicals and early fundamentalists and modern writers like Schaeffer and to some extent Young have taken these as non-literal. Morris is sure they are all wrong and all six are twenty-four-hour periods. But what reasons for this does he advance?

Firstly, he emphasises the use of the terms 'evening and morning'. Yet not only do these have metaphorical meanings in some other contexts (Ps 65:8), but their use here would only heighten the drama of the metaphor. E J Young rightly remarks: 'If the word "day" is employed figuratively ie to denote a period of time longer than twenty-four hours, so also may the terms "evening" and "morning", inasmuch as they are component elements of the day, be employed figuratively.'[75] Actually, as Augustine long ago noticed, night is not mentioned at all, only twilight and morning.[76] Augustine (noting the difficulty anyway of having night and day before the sun was made) suggests either a physical meaning beyond our senses, or else a highly figurative one which emphasises the dependence of creation. Others might, however, from the same starting-point, almost paraphrase: 'There was a twilight and a dawning of a new creative unfolding in God's work.'

Morris' other key point in favour of literality, which is also emphasised by Andrews, is God's reference to the Sabbath: 'For in six days the Lord made the heavens and the earth, the sea, and all that is in them, but he rested on the seventh day' (Ex 20:11).

That this was never intended literally is implied by Jesus' reference to it, for Jesus takes it in a sense very different from Morris. Morris says that Genesis 'certainly does not mean that the seventh day is still continuing as some age-day advocates have suggested'.[77] Jesus, in contrast, in response to a charge of 'Sabbath breaking', pleads that he is 'working' on the Sabbath just as his Father is still 'working' on his Sabbath — 'to this very day' (Jn 5:17). The argument is valid only on the assumption that God's Sabbath is still in operation. Here, as so often, far from implying literality, the implications of the teachings of Jesus and the New Testament urge us to take it in some sense metaphorically. We can, of course, take literally neither the idea that God needed a rest, nor that his 'rest' was the reason for the Sabbath (as a strict understanding of Ex 20:11 would imply) as Jesus taught us that the Sabbath was made for man, not vice versa.

Finally, it may be added that the reasoning in Genesis 2:5 seems to indicate non-literality. It would hardly be logical to argue that the lack of crops or vegetation at the time of man's creation was due to a lack of rain or cultivation if they had only existed since their creation for less than two and a bit literal days.[78]

Now what of the chronology or order of events? The two chapters seem very similar in structure. Both describe a set of events, all couched in the simple past tense, and linked by the word 'and' (Hebrew 'waw', Greek 'kai' in the Septuagint version). Now Young, Morris and Andrews are all insistent that Genesis 1 is chronological and Genesis 2 is not. But what justification can they give?

Young argues:

I have been very insistent that the first chapter is to be understood chronologically. This is seen by the order of development, the progression of thought. It is also seen by the chronological emphasis — day 1, day 2, and so on. You do not find that in the second chapter of Genesis.[79]

This is a piece of special pleading. Many others have not seen the 'days' as especially implying a time sequence, and the language used in the two chapters is otherwise very similar. To back up the claim that Genesis 2 is non-sequential, Young sarcastically asks what God would have done with the man if he really made him before the Garden.[80] Actually, this would be quite a minor problem compared with creating night and day two days before the sun and moon! To get around the latter problem for Genesis 1,

Young has to suggest: 'On the third day God reconstituted the universe as we now know it.' This is unwarranted from the text, and it is simpler to assume that Genesis 1, like Genesis 2, was not intended to be chronological.

Morris has no problem with God keeping Adam somewhere west of Eden whilst he planted 'directly' the Garden. He has, however, to suggest interpreting 'and' (*waw*) as 'also' and 'formed' (*yatsar*) as the pluperfect 'had formed' in 2:19. This is, of course, possible, though hardly a straightforward reading, and the Septuagint rendering ('God further formed') speaks against it. Having thus artificially rearranged the time sequence in Genesis 2, Morris preserves the sequence in Genesis 1 by suggesting that God created the light from the sun and moon three days before he created the actual objects. Though this last interpretation was taken by some early Christian writers, for someone who (unlike them) has claimed that there is no need to 'interpret' Genesis at all, it seems extraordinary lengths to maintain a preconceived interpretation.

Andrews explicitly accepts (as mentioned earlier) that the apparent order in Genesis 2 indicates a literary rather than literal interpretation, for it is a dramatic device. Yet when some of us, trying to interpret Scripture consistently and following the approach of leading early Christian teachers, suggest the same about Genesis 1, he sees that as 'attacking the Bible'. Andrews, as we saw, accepts a first day millions of years long, and reinterprets the creation of the sun and moon in day three as 'making them appear'. There is no linguistic basis at all for this in either the Hebrew or Greek versions, and it is not what the text says. Andrews gives no clear reason for rejecting the view that Genesis 1 is to be taken (as he takes Genesis 2) as a dramatic device not intended chronologically. The only reason he seems to give is that his interpretation does not 'diminish in any way the miraculous act'. This does not seem to us to be a proper motive for Christian theism which — as Andrews himself clearly elsewhere says — sees God active in *all* natural processes.

All this confusion and divergence among supposed literalists only underlines for us that those early Christian teachers, following up indications in the actual text and the non-literal interpretations of Jesus himself, were right in taking both Genesis 1 and 2 as dramatic devices rather than literal in chronology. Andrews himself says:

> Their contents are presented plainly as historical fact. Those facts may be expressed using a variety of dramatic and literary devices, but the author nevertheless claims to be relating events which actually took place. The narratives are accounts, not of myth but of reality.[81]

We would agree that the contents are historical fact in the sense that God really did create the heavens and earth *ex nihilo*, and the subsequent appearance on the planet of vegetable, animal and human life was according to the unfolding of a divine plan. But both chapters do contain dramatic and literary devices, neither were intended to give scientific detail or strict time sequence, and neither should be pressed to do so.

## Details of the accounts: mainly Genesis 1

Genesis 1 begins with the simplest and most majestic statement of the creationist doctrine, which is central to all Christian theism: 'In the beginning God created the heavens and the earth.' The physical universe as we now see it is not eternal, it had a beginning. This is by no means self-evident. Chaos is not a divinity but itself a stage in purposeful design.

The world is not, moreover, some kind of by-product of warring gods, but the result of planned creation by the only true God. The sun and stars are not divinities, but created products, and the dramatic effect of not even introducing them until the fourth day must have been shattering to the star-worshipping neighbours of the Hebrews! There are many ways in which the chapter can be seen not as having affinities with other accounts (like the Babylonian), but as a devastating attack on their presuppositions.[82]

What is the essence of the creation? The Bible clearly presents it as the activity of a personal God: 'And God said, "Let there be light," and there was light' (Gen 1:3). God first formed the idea of light in imagination, then decided to make that thought actual, and then it appeared in physical reality. We, like God, are personal beings and, though our own experiences of volition are unlike his in being tied to the physical bodies and brains he has given us, we may experience from the inside something of the concept of choice in creative activity. Our mental picture precedes the thing which we later make.

But this leaves some basic questions about God's creative activity. The actual word 'created' (*bara*) is used only three times: to refer to the heavens and earth (1:1), the animal life (1:21) and mankind (1:27). Does the word itself always imply 'created out of nothing'? Are, as E H Andrews, for example, takes it, all the creative acts of Genesis 1 type-ii miracles as defined in our Chapter 8? To make such assumptions, however well meaning, if the Bible language itself implies otherwise, is neither intellectually acceptable nor honouring to God. We have already noted Jesus' clear teaching that God is at work in natural processes like feeding the birds. Thus when Scripture says that God 'creates the winds' (Amos 4:13), we can take it that he does this through the natural processes in which he operates.

If the language itself, then, does not tell us, are there other indications of whether type-ii miracles are involved? In the case of the very first event, elsewhere the Bible states: 'By faith we understand that the universe was formed at God's command, so that what is seen was not made out of what was visible' (Heb 11:3). Possibly this creation out of what is not visible could be stretched to mean what physicists call a 'singularity', which is not visible in any usual sense, or to mean 'quantum space', which is not quite the same thing as literally nothing. Personally, however, we favour the traditional interpretation of *ex nihilo* as literally created out of nothing (or not out of anything), implying that quantum space itself is a creation.

The nature of the creation of animal life (1:21) is not as easy to determine. Obviously, if we took the 'days' literally, then the creation would have to be a type-ii miracle, but we have already seen that consistent interpretation of Scripture would be against this. This being so, there is no obvious necessary reason to take creation of animal life as a type-ii miracle, though of course it may well have been. Some of the earlier language, such as 'Let the earth bring forth . . .' (Gen 1:24 AV), fits at least as well any idea of vegetation emerging through natural processes of spontaneous generation. Some early support may be found for spontaneous generation in teachings like Augustine's: 'As mothers are pregnant with young, so the world itself is pregnant with the causes of things that are born.'[83] The church never ruled it out.

If we consider human creation, there is a clear biblical sense in which *all* mankind is created and, unless we take such biblical statements in a highly oblique and allegorical sense, they are 'created' through the natural processes of human procreation (Ps 89:47). God, indeed, is specifically said to have formed man out of pre-existing material (Gen 2:7), just as he 'formed' Jeremiah in the womb (Jer 1:5). If there is no reason to suppose that Jeremiah's prenatal growth involved any type-ii miracle, we have to accept that the Scripture language concerning the forming of Adam's body may have needed none either.

What of the breathing into man's nostrils of the 'breath of life' (Gen 2:7)? We have seen that even Young takes this as an 'anthropomorphic expression', and it is hard to determine how far the metaphor goes. Mankind shares with animals the breath of life (Gen 1:30), and other poetic references to the 'breath of God' (Job 37:10) seem to indicate that it may also imply working through natural processes.

Where does all this leave us? What it emphasises is that it is not good enough — whether we are devout Christians or sceptical enquirers — simply to read into Genesis a weight of presupposition as to what it must mean. To be faithful to the text we should look to the Bible language itself to set the limits of interpretation. What we then find is that, whilst God could, of course, have used type-ii miracles in all his creating and forming, the language used carries no such implication. If anything, in fact, phrases like 'Let the earth bring forth ...' and the deliberate reference to the pre-existent materials of man's body could give a hint of the use of natural processes. Certainly if this is what is meant, then it gives an even greater contrast to some of the pagan early accounts where there is a nature independent of the gods who create in acts of magic. On balance, however, we would conclude that the Genesis accounts are neutral as far as deciding whether God used natural processes or type-ii miracles after the first initiating act. If we do feel that it is important to decide this question, then we will have to look to other sources of information rather than force the Genesis accounts to give information they were evidently not intended to give.

## Details in Genesis 2–3

As we turn to Genesis 2, we must again, as Christians, look to the New Testament for guidance as to how to interpret it. God planted a garden in Eden, where the trees included the 'tree of life' (2:9). The other four Old Testament occurrences of this phrase are all allegorical (Prov 3:18, 11:30, 13:12, 15:4). It is also mentioned in Revelation 2:7 as being (present tense) 'in the paradise of God'. The whole Book of Revelation is full of picture imagery, and to take it literally would be absurd. Thus when the tasting of the 'tree of life' is linked with blessings for those who 'wash their robes' (22:14), it is not really about laundering, and the exclusion of 'dogs' (22:15) need not concern literalist members of the Canine Defence League! The 'tree of life and the tree of knowledge of good and evil' could, of course, have been literal in Genesis, but as we look to the New Testament to guide our interpretation, we tend to take the account of them as metaphorical history. Man faced a real, historical choice between *life* and the *knowledge of good and evil*, but the language used to describe this choice (like so much of Jesus' language) is metaphorical.

The account of the creation of Adam and Eve is, for Christians, one of the most important in the Bible. Our own clear commitment to interpreting it as the basis for marriage and family life is shown elsewhere.[84] The order of events, though, cannot here be intended to be literal, as it would then contradict Genesis 1. Thus 2:19–20 should not be taken to imply that God literally trooped all the world's land and air creatures before a bachelor Adam. Rather it tells us two basic truths:

1. Mankind alone was created with an in-built urge to create conceptual language in naming animals.
2. No animal can have a truly personal relationship with a human person in the way epitomised by marriage.

God could, of course, have literally put Adam to sleep and used one of his ribs to make Eve, but we do not believe the story was meant literally. For one thing the order of events would then contradict Genesis 1, and for another the actual word means 'side' not 'rib'. The Genesis writer surely did not mean us to imagine that Adam was lop-sided after Eve appeared. It does not intend here to teach human anatomy, but a deeper truth. Blocher describes some of the richness of Hebrew word play involved, and also the spiritual meaning taken throughout Christian history by Augustine, Aquinas, Matthew Henry, etc.[85] Woman was not created from man's head to rule, nor his feet to serve, but from his side as a companion and equal, reflecting the phrase 'a helper suitable for him' in 2:18. Were we actually to take it literally, two questions might be asked. Firstly, why should God put Adam into a deep sleep to do it? Since it was, presumably, miraculous anyway, he could surely have done it painlessly with Adam awake? Secondly, if Adam had been asleep, how did he know that Eve was 'bone of my bones' (2:23) as soon as he saw her? God might, of course, have told him — though one then wonders why the text does not mention it. For these reasons, we like Douglas Spanner's suggestion that the 'deep sleep' was so that God could speak to Adam in a dream about the building of Eve from his 'side'.[86] The dream was a particularly vivid way to teach, sensitise and prepare Adam for the truth about his relationship with Eve in the Creator's sight.

Paul, again, confirms the non-literal interpretation. In 1 Corinthians 11 he is arguing on a point of symbolism between men and women, and states: 'For man did not come from woman, but woman from man' (11:8). His argument carries weight only if Genesis is about a deeper meaning than anatomy. Paul's words also might leave some doubt about the literality of Adam as an individual. The word 'Adam', of course, simply means 'man', and the word is not used as a name (ie without the definite article) until Genesis 3:21. In 1 Corinthians 11 Paul refers simply to 'man' and 'woman', ie seeing the Genesis story as personifying the species and gender as a whole.

In 1 Timothy 2:11–15 Paul again seems to be playing on the idea of Adam and Eve as representing 'man' and 'woman', the 'she' of verse 15 referring to Eve, but then changing to 'they' in the same sentence.

Romans 5:12–19 parallels the 'one man' Adam and the 'one man' Christ, and so offers more indication that Adam was a single individual. But what Paul does not say here (or anywhere else) is that Adam was the physical forebear of all present humans.

The early church seems to have generally taken the story of the creation of Eve allegorically. The second-century anti-Christian Celsus ridiculed the passage on a literal basis, but even he had to admit that 'the more modest among Jews and Christians are ashamed of these things and endeavour to give them somehow an allegorical signification'.[87] We previously noted Origen's pre-eminence among the early teachers who wrote in Greek (the language of the New Testament). Origen also learned his Hebrew from living sources, and so his comments are of special interest when he states:

> In the Hebrew language Adam signifies man; and that in those parts of the narrative which appear to refer to Adam as an individual, Moses is discoursing upon the nature of man in general. For 'in Adam' (as the Scripture says) 'all die;' and were condemned in the likeness of Adam's transgression, the word of God asserting this not so much of *one particular individual* as of the *whole human race*.[88]

We saw earlier that Augustine was no more a crude literalist than Origen. We also noted, however, some of his novelty in theology due to Manichaean influences. One of these was an idea that all babies are born inheriting the guilt of Adam (which he thought was washed away in physical baptism). This would obviously necessitate a literal single man from whom all present people descended. Augustine's supposed biblical basis for this was a mistranslation in his Latin version of Romans 5:12: 'death passed on all men *for in him* all sinned'.[89] It should of course have read: '*inasmuch as* all sinned.' Theologically conservative scholarly commentaries (eg that of Sanday and Headlam) have long ruled out Augustine's interpretation, and Cranfield's more recent work, even though written from a fairly Augustinian position, states that it 'should surely be rejected'.[90] Augustine bolstered this with various other verses taken out of context.[91] Though many of his ideas were adopted by the Calvinism of the Reformation, they have been decisively rejected by many spiritual movements in church history, eg the Wesleyan and Finneyan evangelical revivals. Our own reasons for firmly rejecting such ideas are purely biblical, and in no way depend on the question of whether we all descend from one human pair.[92]

Those who accept, then, the Augustinian/Calvinist doctrine that we inherit guilt because we were 'in Adam' when he as an individual sinned, would logically find in this a good reason to insist on a literal Adam. To those of us who, for theological reasons unconnected with science, believe their doctrine mistaken, it can form no such basis of belief. Whether there may be *other* biblical reasons to support a view that Adam must have been a literal single individual we shall presently consider.

In Genesis 3 we read of the snake. Taken strictly literally, the story would imply:

1. Before man's Fall there was only one serpent and he walked upright, had great wisdom and talked.
2. After man's Fall that particular serpent was cursed and made to crawl (note that no ban on walking was put on his descendants if we take it literally).
3. Also, the serpents would be particular enemies to man, and would bruise their heels and eat dust as part of their diet.

To take it thus would not only be absurd, but would miss its point. New Testament writers make explicit the consistent Jewish interpretation which sees the serpent as Satan — though Satan is not literally a serpent since in the same breath he can be spoken of as a 'dragon' (Rev 20:2). The 'seed' of Satan are his followers — a 'brood of vipers' as the

Gospels say (Mt 12:34; Lk 3:7). Just as the serpent denied that God had really spoken, so his 'seed' denied that God had really spoken or acted through Jesus (Gen 3:4; Mt 12:24). The serpent Satan lied because the truth was not in him (Jn 8:44), his offspring spoke falsely because of what was in them (Mt 12:34). The word 'seed' can, of course, be taken either as singular or plural, and we take the 'seed' of the woman to refer to Christ.[93] There was, then, enmity between the 'brood of vipers' and 'seed of the woman', the bruising of whose heel may speak of the crucifixion, during which a nail was driven into it. The church, as Christ's non-literal body, also enters into the conflict (Rom 16:20).

If, then, we take the New Testament as our guide, we see the snake as the embodiment of Satan. It could, of course, have been a literal embodiment, but whether or not it was is irrelevant. It is, however, more difficult to accept an approach like that of E J Young to read into the account two separate characters (a physical snake and Satan). Not only is it a highly artificial interpretation, but Young himself is inconsistent in his argument, slipping inadvertently into speaking as though the snake is Satan and at times taking a highly allegorical view.

Were Adam and Eve literal people or nothing more than personifications of Man and Woman? We noted Paul's ambiguity, and that sometimes he speaks as though 'Adam' is 'Man'. In Romans 5 he speaks of the coming of sin. He tells us that unless a moral law is recognised (either explicitly or in one's conscience), there is no sin (Rom 5:13). In Eden Man recognised that law, broke it, and so fell into sin. In doing so they had grasped an experiential 'knowledge of good and evil', but at a cost predicted by God. This cost was death (Gen 2:17), but what kind of death? Paul pictures death first entering through one man (Rom 5:12). This is logical enough, as there must have been a very first individual to recognise the authority of a divinely revealed moral law. In this sense there surely must have been an

'Adam': an individual whose experience first began the experience of Man with sin and death. Paul goes on (5:12) to picture death as spreading to all men, because all men sinned. Neither the spreading of the sin nor the parallel spreading of salvation through Jesus is automatic – both involve choices of the individuals.[94] Paul later reflects in his own experience this spreading of sin and death. In Romans 7:9 he relates how before he felt the authority of moral law he was alive, but on recognising it and committing sin for the first time 'sin sprang to life and I died'. This indicates, very clearly, that he refers to spiritual death, and presumably thinks that we should take Genesis to do so too.

## The dating of Eden

Can Genesis be used to date Eden? Genesis 5 contains a list of genealogies, but again the New Testament can guide us as to how to interpret these. When Matthew 1:7–11 repeats the genealogies of 1 Chronicles 3:10–16, but omits several of the names, this was neither a mistake nor a deception, but a deliberate use of an accepted literary convention of the times. Matthew's readers recognised that Hebrew genealogies did not have to be strict father-son relationships, so no misunderstandings could arise. The same, of course, applies to the genealogies of Adam's descendents. When it gives the age at which 'X begat Y', the word 'begat' could mean (as evidently in Matthew) that X begat the forebear of Y at that point. The early church did tend to believe that the time since Adam was in thousands of years. Most actually gave it as earlier than Ussher's famous 4004 BC in the seventeenth century. Thus, for example, Theophilus placed it at 5529 BC,[95] Clement of Alexandria c 5590 BC,[96] Julius Africanus at 5531 BC,[97] etc. But the difficulties of any certainty, bearing in mind the difficulties of interpreting the genealogies, were often noted. What does seem clear is that the time since the time of Adam is to be seen in terms of thousands rather than hundreds of thousands of years.

## The Flood

We have seen that, if we take guidance from the New Testament, the Genesis accounts of creation and Eden are historical but couched in allegorical language, and even Adam himself is at times taken as 'Man'. What, then, of Noah and the account of the Flood?

Unlike Adam, the Bible always seems to regard Noah as an individual within a particular historical context. The Flood passages of Genesis describe historical events in a normal observer style rather than an allegorical one. If, therefore, we accept the inspiration of the Bible, we must believe that there was an individual called Noah, and there was a physical flood.

To be faithful to Scripture, however, we still need to ask two important questions:

1.  What did the actual words mean to the writer, ie to what concepts in his mind did they relate?
2.  In what way is the language being used, eg as literal, sarcasm, hyperbole, etc?

On 1, the point of departure for interpreting any biblical passage must be to try to understand what the writer intended by the language he used. To do this, one needs first to understand the concepts in the mind of the writer. Some have suggested that the Genesis writer believed in some kind of primitive cosmology, but we know of no evidence that this was so. On the other hand, there is no indication that the Genesis writer had a concept of a spherical planet earth. The Hebrew word *eretz*, which is translated 'earth' in Genesis 1:1 and various verses in Genesis 6, does not mean 'planet earth' as we now think of it. Though we may choose to read this into, say, Genesis 1:1, this is a modern reinterpretation. The writer simply meant 'earth' as distinct from the heavens or as distinct from the sea (Gen 1:10). No particular cosmology, either primitive or modern, was implied.

It is, in fact, unlikely that any early Old Testament writer had in mind a globe when he used the word *eretz*. Elsewhere the word is actually more commonly translated 'land' (1476 times) or 'country' (140 times) or 'ground' (96 times).[98] Thus to translate, for example, 'the whole *eretz*' as 'the whole earth' is really misleading to the modern reader, for he or she thinks of 'earth' in terms of 'globe'. To translate it 'the whole land' would much better convey the kind of concept in the mind of the writer.

This can amply be illustrated from some of the other places in which similar phrases are used. In virtually every case to render it 'globe' in any literally implied sense would make it nonsense. Thus in Genesis 41:57 when 'all the *eretz* came to Egypt ... because the famine was severe in all the *eretz*', we are surely not to take this as literally global or even as the whole of the inhabited world. In Exodus 10:5 the locusts are said to have covered 'the face of the whole *eretz*' — but meaning the whole land in question. In Numbers 22:5, 11 Israel were said to 'cover the *eretz*'. In 2 Samuel 15:23 (AV) 'all the *eretz* wept with a loud voice', whilst in 2 Samuel 18:8 (AV) the battle was 'scattered over the face of all the *eretz*'. In 1 Kings 4:34 and 10:24 'all the *eretz*' sought to hear Solomon's wisdom. King Cyrus, in claiming 'all the kingdoms of the *eretz*' in 2 Chronicles 36:23, was quite aware of other kingdoms beyond his boundaries. Jeremiah 12:11–12 (AV) reads: 'The whole *eretz* is made desolate, because no man layeth it to heart ... for the sword of the Lord shall devour from one end of the *eretz* even to the other end of the *eretz*: no flesh shall have peace.'

The meaning of phrases like 'the whole *eretz*' (as 'for any flesh') must be taken from the context. Generally, the use of the phrase elsewhere would not allow any modern reinterpretation of it to mean 'all the globe'.

The use here of the word 'reinterpretation' may seem strange to some, who have always thought that this was what the Noah account literally said. But this is precisely what it is: a reinterpretation. It involves reading into the word *eretz* a concept which it never contained in its Old Testament usage.

There may possibly be some justification for such a reinterpretation of the word *eretz* in Genesis 1:1, and we would not rule it out for 6:1, 6:5, etc, though it may not be the most natural reinterpretation to make. What we have to recognise, however, is that if we ask whether the Flood was global or non-global, we are asking a question which the language of Genesis was not intended to answer – and either conclusion is a reinterpretation into modern terms of the original concepts.

On the point 2, to fail, for example, to recognise the hyperbole in Jesus' teaching in Matthew 23:24 or Luke 14:26 could lead to some strange ideas! Of the way in which language is used in the Old Testament, G B Caird writes: 'Overstatement is . . . characteristic of the Hebrew style, and the Old Testament abounds in examples of it.'[99] Thus when, for example, there is a reference to the 'nations that are under the whole heaven' in Deuteronomy 2:25 (AV), this is exaggeration or hyperbole. This may also apply to very similar expressions in Genesis, as when it says that 'all the high hills . . . under the whole heaven were covered' (7:19 AV).

So what did the writer mean? Clearly, he was referring to a cataclysmic event for Noah and his contemporaries. Their known world was evidently destroyed. But need it have been the whole planet as we now know it? This question has been asked by Christians since the global nature of the planet was known. We may wonder if any light is thrown on this question by the reference to the Flood in 2 Peter 3:5–7 (AV) which reads:

By the word of God the heavens were of old, and the earth (Greek: *ge*) standing out of the water and in the water: whereby the world (*cosmos*) that then was, being overflowed with water, perished: but the heavens and the earth (*ge*), which are now, by the same word are kept in store, reserved unto fire against the Day of Judgement.

The New Testament uses *ge* 248 times, mainly to mean the soil or land.[100] What does the word *cosmos* mean? In classical Greek it could mean 'world order' or 'created universe'. In the Greek Old Testament (LXX) it can be translated as 'world' (in *any* sense) only in the late apocryphal books of Maccabees and Wisdom. Apart from the created universe, it can mean the human order[101] or be used in the sense of honoured 'throughout the world' (Mk 14:19; Rom 1:8). It never seems to imply a globe.

In the New Testament, Paul uses the word to the sophisticated Greeks to say, 'The God who made the world (*cosmos*) and everything in it is the Lord of heaven (*ouranos*) and earth (*ge*)' (Acts 17:24). Although the idea was rejected by more philosophical Greeks, the old myths had held Uranus and Ge to be the primal sky and earth gods — and Uranus long survived in popular cult along with other deities. Paul asserts that everything (ie the universe or *cosmos*) was created by God — and heaven and earth are created things under his rulership. In this context Paul's background would have made him well aware that his hearers believed the earth to be a globe, though whether it was or not is irrelevant to his point about God's lordship. By the word *cosmos*, however, Paul here surely means 'the sum total of everything linked to space and time', as in, say, Aristotle.[102] He does not mean the globe.

The word *cosmos* can be used to mean the inhabited area of possession (as in 'gain the whole world'), but most commonly in the New Testament it means the system of human affairs.[103] Interestingly, even then Luke in Luke 4:5

replaces the word *cosmos* (used by Matthew and Mark) with the word *oikoumene* (inhabited earth), which elsewhere he uses in a more restricted sense to mean the 'civilised world' of the Roman Empire (eg in the census of Luke 2:1).[104]

Where does this leave us? When 2 Peter 2:5 says that God destroyed 'the ancient *cosmos*' or '*cosmos* of the ungodly' in a flood, the reference is most likely to the evil system of human affairs (as Peter also uses the word in 2 Pet 1:4 and 2:20). When in 2 Peter 3:5–8 he says that the *ge* which was formed out of water was destroyed with water, he means the 'land'. To make either verse refer to a globe is to reinterpret his words in a way the language simply does not imply. To insist that he must mean total planetary coverage is to force his words way outside their real meaning.

If Peter's language does not necessarily imply literal universality, what of his context? He was arguing against 'scoffers' who 'followed their own evil desires', ie who rejected God. The point at issue was not whether or not the Flood was global, but whether or not God was active in his own world. Our God is a God of morality and judgement who acts in history — this is central to Christianity. But whether the judgement was applied to the 'land' meaning a limited area or literally across the planet is relevant neither to Peter's point nor to Christian faith.

It could, perhaps, be objected that if it were only a local flood, then the ark would have been unnecessary because Noah and the animals could have been saved through migration. Whilst this is, of course, true, the ark would have been just as purely symbolical if the Flood were literally universal, for God could quite easily have saved Noah and all the animals by putting them into suspended animation. He could, indeed, have vapourised the wicked without using a flood at all. Perhaps God chose this method in order to emphasise mankind's stewardship over the animal creation. As for Noah, his motivation for building the ark and collecting animals was not some kind of modern ecological enthusiasm. He did it in obedience to God. Whatever point God intended by working this way remains unchanged whether literally all species or just species in the region concerned were thus preserved.

When, therefore, we ask today whether or not the Flood was global, we are asking which of two ways to reinterpret the language of Genesis. Since the time when scientific knowledge raised the question, people have taken it to mean (a) global and all-covering, or (b) global but not all-covering, or (c) local to 'the land'; and its language could plausibly be reinterpreted to fit with any of these. Interestingly, there have been scholars throughout at least the last three centuries who have believed it more localised. Before any geological theory — before even any geological theories of universal floods — a local flood was advocated by the learned Bishop Edward Stillingfleet in 1662,[105] followed by Revd Matthew Poole, an Anglican of Presbyterian sympathies in 1670.[106]

Because the Genesis language is open to the different interpretations, later Christians more commonly took scientific knowledge into account in deciding how it should be taken. In the late eighteenth century, for example, there was a common belief in a worldwide (though not necessarily all-covering) flood. André Deluc, a careful scientist working consciously in the Baconian tradition, was one sincere Christian who constructed one of the best known theories. He believed that Noah's Flood was worldwide, but that some animals were left on uncovered mountain tops. Thus he asserted of Genesis 6:13:

> The more literal translation of the latter part of the verse is: 'I will *destroy them*, and the *earth with them*.' We see that the term 'earth' does not here signify the 'terrestrial globe', but the 'land' inhabited by man; conformably to this we read in Chapter I, verse 10: 'And God called the dry land *earth*.'[107]

Almost identical arguments were used by some of the leading evangelical British and American geologists and theologians in the last half of the nineteenth century. Evangelical geologist and theologian Hugh Miller wrote *The Testimony of the Rocks* in 1849, with clear arguments for interpreting the Bible to mean a local flood. The Congregationalist John Pye Smith wrote his influential book *Relation Between the Holy Scriptures and Some Parts of Geological Science* in 1839, which included detailed arguments for a local flood.[108] Later, American geologists J W Dawson[109] and G F Wright[110] wrote similar strong lines of argument, linguistic and geological. As a valid interpretation, this received further support from scholars such as the great Hebrew commentator F J Delitzsch.[111] There were, of course, some who continued to interpret the Flood as global, but its interpretation as local was widespread among evangelicals during this period.

Some modern writers have argued strongly that Genesis must mean a universal flood.[112] Yet most of their supposed biblical arguments are merely emotional, eg:

> So frequent is the use of universal terms and so tremendous are the points of comparison ... that it is impossible to imagine what more could have been said than actually was said to express the concept of a universal deluge.[113]

The problem with this is that it is an insistence on pressing the narrative (in a manner both Morris and Whitcomb do constantly elsewhere) to answer modern questions it was never intended to answer — at the cost of an almost cavalier disregard of the actual language and intent of the writer. Morris and Whitcomb then back this up not with clear biblical exposition, but by appeals to points of their supposed modern science (eg on the depth necessary to cover mountains in the Sumerian region).

We believe, therefore, that the Bible implies there was an

individual Noah, and a physical flood throughout all the land. It leaves it open to modern reinterpretation whether or not that 'land' implied the whole globe, though the actual language would tend on the whole to imply not. There is, then (if the expression may be pardoned!), no question here of watering down the Flood account. It is a question of understanding what it actually meant as written, and to which modern concepts this relates.

The question of whether it was universal as far as mankind was concerned is a different issue. The language of Genesis 6:6 would seem to offer the strongest indication that it was, ie that all of existing human population was involved. The problem is that, again, we wonder how far this is pressing the language to answer questions it was not intended to answer. Even this, therefore, we would still wish to leave open.

## Conclusion

This section has had very little to say about modern science, but has been basically concerned with using other parts of the Bible — especially the New Testament — as guidance on how to interpret the Genesis accounts of creation and the Flood. No serious Christian commentator (ancient or modern) has ever taken the Genesis 1-3 accounts totally literally, even though some have said that they did. In actual fact to do so would be absurd, subvert its meaning, and deny the New Testament. The Flood accounts do refer to an actual individual and a physical flood. The language, however, leaves it open as to whether we should take it in our terms as global or not.

## Notes

1. C S Lewis, *Miracles*, p 73.
2. E J Young, *Studies in Genesis One* (1964), p 105.
3. H M Morris, *The Genesis Record* (1976), p 31.

4. Morris, *Evolution and the Modern Christian* (First published, 1967; second edition 1977), p 55.

5. Morris, *The Biblical Basis for Modern Science* (1984), p 116.

6. Ie the non-apostolic *Epistle of Barnabas*, xv (*Ant Nic Fath*, i, 146).

7. Irenaeus, *Against Heresies*, XXVIII (*Ant Nic Fath*, i, 557).

8. Hippolytus, *Fragments on Daniel* (*Ant Nic Fath*, v, 179).

9. Methodius, *Fragments on Things Created* (*Ant Nic Fath*, vi, 381).

10. Lactantius, *The Divine Institutes*, VII, 15 (*Ant Nic Fath*, vii, 211).

11. Theophilus, *To Autolycus,*, xiv-xvii (*Ant Nic Fath*, ii, 101–4).

12. John of Damascus, *Exposition of the Orthodox Faith*, II, 1 (*Nic & Pos Nic Fath*, ix (part 2), 18).

13. Basil, *The Hexameron*, Homily 2 (*Nic & Pos Nic Fath*, viii, 64–5).

14. Chrysostom, *The Fathers of the Church* (translated by R C Hill, 1985), p 199.

15. *Encyclopaedia Britannica* (1987), vol 8, p 997.

16. Origen, *First Principles*, bk iv, chap 3 (this translation by G W Butterworth, 1936). The translation from the Latin is quoted, but the Greek is similar.

17. *Encyclopaedia Britannica* (1987), vol 14, p 386.

18. See R T Forster and V P Marston, *God's Strategy in Human History*.

19. Augustine, *City of God* (translation by J Healey, 1945), vol 11, p 6–7; also in *Nic & Pos Nic Fath*, 1, i, 208.

20. Augustine, *De Genesi ad Litterum* (c 401–15), 8.1.

21. *Ibid*, 1.2, 4.29–33.

22. *Ibid*, 8.47.

23. H M Morris and J Whitcomb, *The Genesis Flood* (1961), p 255, and elsewhere.

24. Morris, *The Genesis Record*, p 61.

25. *Ibid*, p 76.

26. *Ibid*, p 100.

27. *Ibid*, p 94.

28. Morris, *The Beginning of the World* (first edition, 1965; second edition 1977), p 76.

29. *The Genesis Record*, p 119.

30. *Ibid*, p 121.

31. *Ibid*, p 139.

32. *Ibid*, p 119.

33. *Ibid*, p 90; *The Beginning of the World*, p 38.

34. *The Genesis Record*, p 84; *The Biblical Basis for Modern Science*, p 127.

35. *The Beginning of the World*, p 24; *Evolution and the Modern Christian*, p 60; *The Biblical Basis for Modern Science*, p 117.

36. E J Young, *Studies in Genesis One*, p 105.

37. E J Young, *In the Beginning*, (1976), p 41.
38. *Studies in Genesis One*, p 56.
39. *In the Beginning*, p 43.
40. *Studies in Genesis One*, p 104.
41. *In the Beginning*, p 44.
42. *Ibid*, p 69.
43. *Studies in Genesis One*, p 74.
44. *In the Beginning*, p 109.
45. E J Young, *Genesis 3* (1966), p 64.
46. *In the Beginning*, p 106.
47. *Genesis 3*, p 116.
48. *Ibid*, p 98–99.
49. See Davis A Young, *Creation and the Flood* (1977) and *Christianity and the Age of the Earth* (1982).
50. E H Andrews, *Christ and the Cosmos* (1986), p 80.
51. *Ibid*, p 81.
52. *Ibid*.
53. Andrews, *God, Science and Evolution* (1985 edition; first published, 1980), p 101.
54. Andrews, *From Nothing to Nature* (1978), pp 111–12.
55. *Christ and the Cosmos*, p 87.
56. F Schaeffer, *Genesis in Space and Time* (1972), p 57.
57. Morris, *The Genesis Record*, p 127, etc; A E Wilder-Smith, *Man's Origin, Man's Destiny* (1974), p 282.
58. *God, Science and Evolution*, pp 82, 87.
59. See, for example, Mary Hesse, *Models and Analogies in Science* (1966); also I G Barbour, *Myths, Models and Paradigms* (1974).
60. C S Lewis, *Miracles*, p 78.
61. Morris, *Beginning of the World*, p 24.
62. *Ibid*, p 23.
63. Eg Young, *Genesis 3*, p 8.
64. Andrews, *From Nothing to Nature*, p 5.
65. Spanner, *Biblical Creation and the Theory of Evolution* (1987), p 59, etc.
66. See H Blocher, *In the Beginning* (1984; translated from French, 1979), p 30, or E J Young in *Studies in Genesis One*, p 59, etc, D Kidner, *Genesis* (1967), p 23, etc.
67. See Blocher *op cit*, p 30.
68. See M G Kline, *The Structure of Biblical Authority* (1975), also followed by astronomer Howard J Van Till in *The Fourth Day* (1986).
69. Quoted from H M Morris, who strongly defends 'plenary verbal inspiration' in *Many Infallible Proofs* (1974), p 168.

70. See, for example, Kidner, *Genesis* and Blocher, *op cit*. F A Filby, *Creation Revealed* (1964), chap 2, sets it out in particular detail.
71. See Blocher, *op cit*, pp 54–5.
72. *Ibid*, p 32.
73. See Origen, *Against Celsus*, vi, 1 (*Ant Nic Fath*, iv, 596).
74. Morris, *The Genesis Record*, p 84.
75. Young, *Studies in Genesis One*, p 104.
76. Augustine, *City of God*, xi, 7 (*Nic & Pos Nic Fath*, 1, i, 209).
77. *Genesis Record*, p 81.
78. See J W Dawson, *The Origin of the World According to Revelation and Science* (1890), p 142; also modern writers such as M Kline, 'Because it Had Not Rained', *Westminster Theological Journal*, vol 20 (1958): p 15; and Blocher *op cit*.
79. Young, *In The Beginning*, p 70.
80. *Ibid*; also *Studies in Genesis One*, p 74.
81. Andrews, *Christ and the Cosmos*, p 82.
82. See Alexander Heidel, *The Babylonian Genesis* (1951), or Howard J Van Till, *The Fourth Day* (1986), chap 2.
83. Augustine, *On the Trinity*, iii, 9 (*Nic & Pos Nic*, 1, iii, 62).
84. See V Paul Marston, *The Biblical Family* (1981) or *God and the Family* (1984).
85. Blocher, *op cit*, pp 98–100.
86. Spanner, *op cit*, p 65.
87. Quoted by Origen in *Against Celsus*, iv, 38 (*Ant Nic Fath*, iv, 514).
88. *Against Celsus*, iv, 40 (*Ant Nic Fath*, iv, 516).
89. Augustine, *On the Forgiveness of Sin and Baptism*, i, 10 (*Nic & Pos Nic Fath*, 1, v, 26, etc).
90. C E B Cranfield, *Romans* (1980), vol 1, p 276.
91. A favourite is Psalm 51:5, which says no such thing and is anyway no more intended literally by David than is Psalm 51:4.
92. See the Appendix of our *God's Strategy in Human History*. We would, of course, emphatically assert the biblical doctrine that all people are sinners and are in need of a Saviour.
93. Paul in Galatians 3:16, 29 makes use of a similar ambiguity.
94. See also *God's Strategy in Human History*.
95. Theophilus to Autolycus, iii, 24–8 (*Ant Nic Fath*, ii, 118–120).
96. Clement, *Stromata*, i, 21 (*Ant Nic Fath*, ii, 332–3).
97. Julius Africanus, *Fragments of Chronography*, iii (*Ant Nic Fath*, vi, 130).
98. These numbers are given in F Filby, *The Flood Reconsidered* (1970), p 83.
99. G B Caird, *The Language and Imagery of the Bible* (1980), p 133.
100. See C Brown, *The New International Dictionary*, vol i, p 517.

101. *Ibid*, pp 521–6.
102. *Ibid*, p 521.
103. *Ibid*, p 524.
104. *Ibid*, pp 518–9.
105. E Stillingfleet, *Origines Sacrae* (1662), bk 3, chap 4.
106. M Poole, *Synopsis* (1670).
107. A Deluc, *An Elementary Treatise on Geology* (1809), pp 389–90; Deluc is essentially a late eighteenth-century figure.
108. Smith's letters on this to geology Professor John Phillips (in the Oxford Geology Museum) show his care to check his scientific facts.
109. J W Dawson, for example, in *The Origin of the World According to Revelation and Science*, (2nd Edn 1880).
110. G F Wright, for example, in *Scientific Confirmations of Old Testament History* (1896).
111. F Delitzsch, *A New Commentary on Genesis* (translated 1899).
112. Ie the followers of Morris and Whitcomb in *The Genesis Flood*.
113. *Ibid*, p 57.

## 12

# RELATIONSHIPS BETWEEN BIBLICAL FAITH AND SCIENTIFIC KNOWLEDGE

## Introduction: scientific and religious minds?

THE PRESENT CHAPTER SEEKS TO look at several issues. Firstly, it asks if the mental approach and frame of mind found in faith and that in science are contrasting, similar, or complementary. Secondly, it considers the nature of scientific and of religious knowledge, and whether or not either are subjective or objective. Thirdly, it considers the proper relationship between theology (the interpretation of the Bible) and science (the interpretation of nature).

In the late nineteenth century Francis Galton, a cousin of Darwin and scientist in his own right, put forward a new thesis that 'the pursuit of science is uncongenial to the priestly character'.[1] Rejecting the Christian views of the Christian home (happy by his own admission) in which he had been brought up, he advocated the 'improvement' of the human race by scientifically controlled selective breeding, ie eugenics. Ironically, as he was using his scientific mind to explore his main interest of genetics, the real breakthrough in that area of science was being made by an Austrian priest, Abbot Gregor Mendel![2]

But, ironical as the particular circumstances may be, Galton's contention is one which many today may intuitively feel. Is it plausible? Are the attitudes of mind needed for faith and science so different that conflict is inevitable?

Two separate questions may be asked here. Firstly, have great scientists in history been, on the whole, irreligious? This is a question we shall take up in our next chapter. Secondly, is the kind of thinking involved in science similar to or a contrast to that involved in Christian faith? Before we consider this, which is a subject for this present chapter, we must consider the nature of scientific knowledge itself.

## Scientific knowledge

Christians (like anyone else) often simply assume that it is obvious what is the nature of science and scientific truth. Alternatively, they choose the latest fashion in the philosophy of science (empiricism, Popper, Polanyi, Kuhn or whatever) and show that Christianity has always said almost the same thing.

The problem is that the nature of science is far from obvious, and the nature of knowledge and of science have been and still are topics of intense debate among scientists and philosophers. As it happens, philosophy of science is one of Paul Marston's specialist interests, and he began his study of it under the teaching of Popper, Lakatos and Fyerabend in the LSE in the late 1960s. The next few paragraphs attempt to portray something of recent thinking, though those who find it heavy going might want to skip to the conclusions!

To begin with, an unreflective view of scientific methodology might be something like this:

1. A scientist first observes objectively, making sure he or she has no presuppositions or prejudice.
2. His or her observations accurately represent what really is 'out there', and general patterns of cause and effect which necessarily operate.
3. These patterns are formulated into scientific laws, which, once verified, are certain truth.

In actual fact the logical positivism (or more moderate logical empiricism) which dominated secular Western philosophy in the 1940s-1950s was not much removed from this. The movement's basic tenets might be summarised thus:

1. Any statement (other than a definition) had meaning only if it were capable, at least in principle, of complete verification.
2. Verification implied specifying an observation which demonstrated its truth.
3. Neutrality of observation and the language used to describe it was a desirable aim.
4. Knowledge was actually about human sensations. A table was real in the sense that it expressed a continual possibility of a sensory experience. Non-directly observable concepts, like atoms, were real only in the sense that they were words useful as a shorthand way of speaking of possible sensations (eg of seeing chemical reactions).[3]

Actually positivism was something of a crusade: all religion, metaphysics, etc, was not simply wrong but literally meaningless and to be abandoned forthwith.

The whole system, however, simply did not hold water, as is shown by the experience of the leading English positivist, A J Ayer. In 1936 Ayer wrote his *Language, Truth and Logic*, setting out in great clarity this wonderful new system. One of its chief critics, Sir Karl Popper, soon raised a fundamental problem. Scientific laws are generalisations (eg 'Electric current *always* produces a magnetic field'); but we never observe generalised laws as such, we observe only specific instances of them (eg 'In 1,000 observations, in each case an electric current produced a magnetic field'). How, then, can we make the logical jump from specific instances — however numerous — to the universal statement that it *always* happens? To do so we need to make two assumptions.

The first is that nature always behaves uniformly or consistently. The Christian, of course, has good reason to assume this, as he or she believes in a consistent Creator-God behind nature. But why should the atheist believe it? Early attempts such as that of J S Mill to defend it rationally look very much like circular arguments.[4] Science, of course, cannot be done at all unless nature does behave consistently, but for the atheist the belief that it does so must be an act of faith.

The second problem is that we can never be sure that there is not some qualifying condition which we have missed. Inevitably, in making observations we are selective: we could not note the total state of everything in the universe at the moment of observation. Thus, for example, electricity might behave differently under conditions of super-cooling.

Problems like these led Ayer in the second edition of his book in 1946 to a long preface, full of special pleading and tortuous logic, in which he tried to argue that 'single observations' might be totally objective, neutral and verifiable with certainty, whilst universal scientific laws were 'weakly verifiable' rather than strongly so. It was unconvincing. By 1956 (in *The Problem of Knowledge)* Ayer was fighting to preserve any sense for knowledge, and by 1978 he said of positivism: 'I suppose that most of the defects were that nearly all of it was false.'[5]

Logical empiricism's demise had also been caused by a further problem. This was, in essence, that all *seeing* also involves *interpreting* — there is no such thing as pure objective observation. Books by Hanson (1958), Polanyi (1958) and Kuhn (1962) emphasised this and heralded a new phase in the philosophy of science,[6] but it had been explored in some depth over a century earlier by William Whewell. Whewell was a Cambridge don whose sermons show a real depth of Christian commitment, but who had a high reputation in scientific circles and actually invented the word 'scientist'. Whewell was critical of the naïve empiricism derived from Locke and Hume, which viewed the mind as a kind of blank sheet passively receiving objective reflections of reality. 'There is,' wrote Whewell, 'no sensation without an act of the mind.'[7] The mind is active. In observing we interpret, though we may not be aware that we are doing so. A modern illustration might be to imagine Aristotle, Newton and Einstein all watching an apple fall. Aristotle sees a piece of solid matter returning to its natural place. Newton sees the acceleration effects of mutual force of gravity between the earth and the apple. Einstein sees the stable behaviour of an apple in the warp in the time-space continuum introduced by the presence of the earth. In seeing the event each also interprets it not as a separate act but as part of the perception. An implication of this recognition that observation is not purely passive is that scientific discovery is creative. It actually involves a mixture of painstaking methodical work together with creative intuition and imagination.[8]

Major figures in the development of such ideas were pragmatist C S Peirce, and in the early twentieth century the Catholic physicist and philosopher of science Pierre Duhem.[9] Logical empiricism was in many ways an anachronism. Its proponents' naïvety on questions discussed so profoundly by the Christian Whewell nearly a century earlier is hard to explain, except on the grounds that their anti-religious fervour blinded their eyes. The criticisms of Hanson and Kuhn restated these old insights, and contributed to the demise of logical empiricism.

By the end of the 1960s logical empiricism was dead, but what was to replace it? Karl Popper offered falsificationism. Laws of Science could not, he said, be verified, but they could be tested. A theory was scientific if, and only if, it made predictions specific enough to test. It must, therefore, be possible to specify a set of conceivable observations which would be deemed to have refuted the theory. For example, a general law that 'all electricity produces a magnetic field' would be refuted if we ever found an instance where it didn't happen.

It was, of course, pointed out (eg by Braithwaite, in *Scientific Explanation* in 1953) that no theory can be tested in isolation, for other theories are assumed in testing it. Popper argued for a convention to regard particular observations (and therefore background assumptions) as not in question.[10] To many this seemed somewhat arbitrary and unrealistic — in practice scientists do not in any case regard a single counter-instance as a refutation. Others took Popper's ideas just to mean that one was testing a set of theories for consistency.

T S Kuhn began from quite a different standpoint. Instead of beginning, as had the positivists and Popper, from a logical construct, he began from a consideration of the way in which science had actually advanced in history. A key Kuhnian term was 'paradigm'. Initially he used this word 'paradigm' very vaguely, but later took two main meanings: (a) examplars: results and ideas known and explicitly recognised in that scientific discipline; (b) disciplinary matrices: a more subtle idea meaning a 'conceptual framework' within which phenomena are perceived. Kuhn portrayed 'normal science' as development of ideas routinely within a scientific specialist area or discipline. Periodically, however, he suggested that anomalies built up to such a degree that the whole disciplinary matrix had to be changed in a revolutionary way, and phenomena viewed from a new perspective. An example of this might be the change from thinking of the earth as stationary to thinking of the sun as stationary — the whole way of perceiving the world changed. Similarly, in the twentieth century the change from Newtonian mechanics to those of Einstein involved a major change in the way of looking at things. Those with such radically different paradigms may use the same words, but they view them so differently that a simple test cannot decide between the competing paradigms: they are incommensurable.

Many criticised Kuhn because scientific development does not fall neatly into 'normal' and 'revolutionary' science, but there was a more fundamental question. He had portrayed science as being unlike a building programme, where each new brick is added on to those already built up. Rather he had seen it as a process of building (normal science), but with a periodic demolition and entire reconstruction from a different perspective (revolutionary science). But in what sense, then, could one speak of 'scientific progress', and in what sense could any scientific concepts refer to 'real' things which were 'out there', since they might always be changed by a new perspective? The implication of Kuhn seemed to be that science must ultimately be subjective.

Reactions to this varied. Fyerabend and his school thought Kuhn not radical enough. Science, he said, did not develop 'logically' and no ideal methodology was possible. Whilst Fyerabend believed in basing science on observation, he did not believe this would lead, even ultimately, to a single 'One True Theory'.[11] Later this view became more extreme. Science was, they said, simply an 'ideology' like any other, with no special claim to truth. In this school of thought 'objectivity' is simply institutionalised belief.[12] This kind of view has cut little ice with real scientists, and other philosophers of science have heavily criticised it.[13] One of its basic problems is that it leads logically to pure relativism: the assertion that any set of beliefs is as true as any other. The internal inconsistency of this approach is seen precisely in the fact that it makes an apparently absolute assertion concerning the relativity of truth — yet it denies that assertions can be absolute! The apparent inability of its proponents to live with the logical implications of their approach (ie that no objective statements at all would be possible) is not surprising. In practice it *is* unlivable.

In opposite reaction to Kuhn has stood various realist schools of thought, reasserting (though usually redefining) objectivity and the view that science follows a reality external to ourselves. Thinkers like H Brown, I Hacking, H Putnam, D Shapere, and F Suppe have argued along lines roughly as follows:

1. Scientific theories are typically approximately true, and more recent theories are closer to truth than older ones.
2. There are real entities out there which correspond to both the directly and indirectly observable terms in a mature science.
3. Later theories contain earlier ones as 'limiting cases', ie the earlier ones are instances of later ones under special conditions.
4. Scientific theories are confirmed through their power to explain and predict.

Issues of realism have set the agenda for debate since the 1970s, though we are still far from a consensus.[14] The concept of 'domains' as areas of science was introduced by Shapere in 1969 as 'fundamental conceptual tools for illuminating the nature of science',[15] and taken up by Suppe, Brown and others. They seem, however, even more vague than Kuhn's paradigms, and after ploughing through much of the literature one feels little the wiser about how to recognise a domain which is truly scientific. Other criticisms of realism have been made, for example, by Laudan (who is also critical of Kuhnian relativism),[16] and by Van Fraassen.[17] The latter is actually an instrumentalist, ie he believes that scientific theories are *nothing more than* instruments used for prediction which are *useful* or *less useful* rather than *true* or *false*.[18]

Realists themselves today tend rather to fudge the question of how we recognise true science or true knowledge,[19] but they have stimulated useful discussion on the nature of observation. Human beings are viewed as able to perceive only a small range of electromagnetic waves. Much, then, of our ordinary descriptive language is dependent on how our sense organs happen to be constructed; but the entities deduced by processes of scientific inference (eg atoms, neutrinos) would eventually be deduced by intelligent Martians starting with very different kinds of sense organs. In an ironical sense, then, the logically deduced entities of science (neutrinos, electrons, etc) are more fundamentally real than human observational sensations like black and white or loud and soft.

Can we draw out any commonly agreed features of science? This is not easy, but the following might be suggested:

1. Nothing guarantees the uniform behaviour of nature, but such uniformity is necessary for science and has to be accepted as an act of faith which 'seems to work'.

2. Though everyday objects are real in an everyday sense, the language of immediate description relates to human organs of sense and is insufficient for science. If there are ultimately real entities, then they are (like atoms and neutrinos) known only through elaborate chains of reasoning. Their description, in most cases, is ultimately in the language of mathematics.

3. Scientific theories may be regarded in three basic ways:
   (a) *instrumentalism*: as nothing but instruments for predictions
   (b) *falsificationism*: as conjectures about truth which are testable, but can never be verified
   (c) *new realism*: as mature theories in a converging road to truth in a particular domain.

   Under any view, however, there is no guarantee than any particular theory is true in some absolute sense.

4. Scientific discovery comes not by pure observation, but by a combination of creative intuition, imagination, and logical thinking. Competing paradigms, or theories within a domain if you prefer this terminology, may involve different and on some points irreconcilable perspectives. In some cases apparently conflicting models may be applied to the same phenomena. But this does not mean that any theory is as good as any other, unless a more extreme subjectivism even than that of Fyerabend is adopted.

## Scientific and religious thinking

Clearly, there are great differences between the thinking relevant to the spiritual and that to the material world of science. Nevertheless, we might list points which are parallel to those just given:

1.  There is no ultimate proof of the reality of the spiritual dimension: any historical, miraculous, or inner experience can always be explained away. Belief in its reality is based upon an act of faith in something which seems to work and to make a coherent sense of our totality of experiences.
2.  The scientific unseen world of atoms, etc, is, in a sense, more real than the human perceptions from which it is inferred. Likewise, the Christian believes that the unseen spiritual world is, in a sense, more real than the human experiences from which it is inferred.
3.  Any reflective person will recognise how statements, for example, like 'God is our Father' show the high extent to which theological language contains implicit metaphor. Evangelicals will be realists in believing that their language, however metaphorical, refers to 'really existing' entities. Nevertheless, none of us can have an absolute guarantee that our particular interpretations are true. As with science, our present knowledge is 'partial' (1 Cor 13:12) and may later prove to be a limiting case of a wider reality.
4.  Different language and perspective may be applied to the same reality of God, and in some instances different models of language (eg concerning providence and the divine relationship in space-time) may be apparently irreconcilable perspectives. This does not mean, however, that extreme religious existentialists have been right in asserting that any view of God is as good as any other, or that people are free to make up whatever view they like about God.

Robert E D Clark has made a valuable short commentary on some of these issues.[20] More recently, Russell Stannard usefully compared the processes involved in his own discovery of 'charm' in physics, with those involved in Christian faith.[21]

More fundamentally, recent thinking in epistemology (ie the question of obtaining and testing knowledge) emphasises, in the words of D L Wolfe, 'the production of a system of assertions which makes sense out of final experience'.[22] Wolfe recognises that an interpretive belief system 'constitutes the spectacles through which one experiences',[23] but that in any such interpretive schema we search for:

1. *consistency*: freedom from self-contradiction
2. *coherence*: internal relatedness of statements in the interpretive schema
3. *comprehensiveness*: applicability to all experience
4. *congruity*: appropriateness to the experiences covered.

This covers both scientific and religious schema and, indeed, the mixture of the two, which virtually all of us hold. Scientific thinking can never be independent of all metaphysical and religious beliefs.

Both scientific research and religious (more specifically, Christian) thinking involve a mixture of subjective and creative thinking and objective realities. Both work from the seen to the unseen in human experience, and regard, in some sense, the unseen as more real. Both involve the confession that our knowledge is partial. Neither, therefore, should have a dogmatic spirit — though in neither case does this mean that extreme scientific or religious relativists are right to suggest that any theory is as good as any other. There may, of course, be different perspectives of the same reality, but this does not mean that rational beings are free to believe whatever they like about such things, on grounds that any theory is equally true. If there is a certain measure of what is called incommensurability between the different perspectives within competing scientific viewpoints, or within competing religious viewpoints, this does not rule out rational discussion about what is mutually inconsistent, and what is illogical or logical.

## Theology and science

In considering the basic relationships between nature, the Bible, science and theology we need to establish what the mainstream position of Bible-believing Christians has been. We maintain that, on the whole, it has been to seek a synthesis between theology based on the Bible and science based on observation. It has been to recognise that the Bible was not designed to answer scientific questions, and should not be pressed to do so. Having said this, however, it must be recognised that this approach was sometimes implicit rather than explicit (especially before the seventeenth century) and was not always followed consistently even by its advocates ('to err is human'![24]). We would, however, wish to defend this classical Christian approach against both the sceptic who may falsely portray Christians as naïve obscurantists, and against any kind of new theology which seeks to try to alter this Christian consensus.

The essential basis of science is a belief in an orderly, law-like world of nature. The Greeks either took it on trust, or (sometimes, but not often) believed in a rational Creator-God or demiurge. Even then, the followers of Plato thought that nature's resistance to order might make exact science impossible! But the Hebrews had a logical basis to believe in the rationality of nature, since it was created by a consistent God. God, to the Hebrews, was supremely the consistent Lawgiver. He had spoken, and the physical world followed the regularity he set for it (Gen 1:3, 6, etc). His spoken moral laws revealed true moral order (Gen 2:17). Thus Psalm 19, having stated how the skies and sun 'proclaim' the glory of God, went on to praise his moral statutes. The root of the whole concept of 'laws of nature' in our culture goes back to ideas of the supreme Lawgiver.

For whatever reasons, it was Greek rather than Hebrew thinkers who went on to explore the regularities of nature in more detail. Yet we must remember that Greek philosophy included not only elements of what we would call experimental science, but also speculation, rhetoric, and ethics. When educated Christians (from Paul onwards) looked at Greek philosophy, they therefore had mixed reactions. Paul himself was uninterested in scientific questions, but could not have believed their systems totally anti-Christian, as he sometimes quoted their words even on the nature of God (Acts 17:28; Tit 1:12).

The early Greek Fathers were positive towards secular learning about nature, though aware of its deficiencies. Justin Martyr (c100–c165) was a man deeply learned in Greek philosophy who became a Christian. Though modern accounts sometimes misrepresent his thinking, anyone who reads his works finds a man deeply committed to Christ, to the Pauline theology of the Atonement through faith, and to the teaching of John that Christ was the expression of that eternal Word of God, which 'gives light to every man' (Jn 1:9). Justin abhorred the Greek gods,[25] but believed men like Socrates partially enlightened through that eternal Word.[26] Actual scientific issues are not the concern, of course, of his works.

Clement of Alexandria (c150–c215) wrote that philosophy had 'been given by divine providence as a preparatory discipline for the perfection which is by Christ'.[27]

The saintly scholar Origen (c185–254) wrote that philosophy was 'ancilliary to Christianity', but added 'study first of all the divine Scriptures'.[28] Origen's own preoccupation with theological issues did not preclude an awareness and acceptance of current secular teaching on, for example, the four supposed elements of matter.[29] There was no indication that he supposed one should somehow begin from the Bible on such scientific theories. Origen's influence on the best of later Christian thinkers prevailed even through slander and false accusation.

In second century North Africa began the tradition of Latin Fathers. The lawyer Tertullian (c160–c225) believed that pagan philosophy was 'the rash interpreter of nature and the dispensation of God', the source of heresy, the 'wisdom' rejected by Paul in Corinthians,[30] and anything good in the philosophers was copied from Hebrew writings anyway![31] Any synthesis of theology and secular learning was, he thought, unacceptable. Tertullian's intolerance and legalism led him to break with orthodoxy, joining the rigorously moralistic Montanists. The *Encyclopaedia Britannica* comments,

> Even the Montanists, however, were not rigorous enough for Tertullian. He eventually broke with them to found his own sect. In antiquity, most Christians never forgave him for his apostasy (rejection of his earlier faith) to Montanism ... Later Christian writers mention him only infrequently, and then unfavourably. Somewhat grudgingly, however, they acknowledge his literary gifts and acute intelligence.[32]

Tertullian, then, was a key formative figure in the literary style of the Latin church (which is why modern scholars find him so interesting), but that church did not follow the extremes of his theology.

Tertullian's famous contemporary, the more orthodox Minucius Felix, by way of contrast portrayed Greek natural philosophy from Thales onwards as pointing to the one true God.[33]

Lactantius (c240–c320) is sometimes pilloried for apparent disbelief in a spherical earth, but his objections were common sense rather than theological.[34] He did not attempt to construct a cosmology from the Bible. As to secular philosophy, he showed a positive attitude to it in citing a wide range of philosophers (eg Orpheus, Thales, Anaxagoras, Cleanthes, Chrysippus, Plato, Cicero, Ovid, Seneca) in support of belief in a Creator-God. He also held that: 'the philosophers touched upon the whole truth and every secret of our holy religion' though were unable to defend it against criticism.[35]

Ambrose of Milan (c339–97) found in Genesis a harmony with the standard Greek thinking on characteristics of elements.[36]

We have already commented on the most influential of the Latin Fathers, Augustine of Hippo (354–430). Augustine, though himself tinged with neoplatonism, was fairly critical of Greek philosophy. He does not, however, appear to wish to construct what we would call science from the Bible. Thus in, for example, his commentary on Psalm 104, Augustine shows no inclination to build a cosmology, but takes a highly allegorical approach.[37] When he tentatively advances biblical reasons for believing the antipodes uninhabited, he specifically prefaces this by pointing out that it is a question on which 'scientific conjecture' can offer no evidence.[38]

Basil the Great (c330–79) insists of Scripture: 'I take all in the literal sense.'[39] Yet he keeps an open mind on scientific questions:

> Let us admit that the earth rests upon itself or let us say that it rides upon the waters; we must still remain faithful to the thought of true religion and recognise that all is sustained by the Creator's power ... Grand phenomena do not strike us the less when we have discovered something of their wonderful mechanism.[40]

Gregory of Nyssa (c330–c395) presumes that man discovers anatomy 'by his experiences of sight, and light and perception' — proceeding to sum up empirical medical science as it stood in his day.[41]

We cannot here follow through the whole history of interactions between theology and science.[42] From the eleventh century onwards, Christian scholars, particularly in the newly established universities, sought ways to assimilate the rediscovered scientific works of Aristotle to Christian theology. Christians like Albertus Magnus were explicit that they would sooner follow secular sources on scientific matters, but equally in that truths of science and faith could never be opposed.[43]

Men like the pious Bishop of Lincoln, Robert Grossteste (c1175–1253) led a reawakening of interest in Greek thought, and a flowering of observational science, carried on by Roger Bacon, William of Ockham and others. The fourteenth century was an era of particular excitement in Oxford and Paris, with men like Bradwardine, Ockham, Albert of Saxony and Oresme carrying on the traditions of observational science within a Christian belief system. Steneck takes Henry of Langenstein as typical of the continuation of this approach, emphasising observation in a way which 'with some modifications becomes the foundation of modern experimental science'.[44]

In the sixteenth century Vesalius' *Anatomy of the Human Body* and Copernicus' *Revolutions of the Heavenly Spheres* marked new phases in biology and astronomy. Neither, in fact, were saying anything new in supposing that scientific study should be based on reason and observation. If Copernicus feared anything, it was the mockery of the common people, not any backlash from anyone who might have preferred him to begin his astronomy from the Bible.

In general the Reformers seem to have been more literalist than the New Testament or the earlier phases of Christian scholarship. Calvin, however, whilst he accepted the inspiration of the Bible, believed that Moses 'adapted his writing to popular usage' and 'he who would learn astronomy and other recondite arts, let him go elsewhere'.[45] The Bible was not a source for science.[46]

Though modern science developed on a continuum and did not start at any particular time, the first half of the seventeenth century was important for it. Both Kepler (1609) and Galileo (1633) put forward theories which required a physically moving earth adrift in space. Kepler was a devout Lutheran, whose astronomical works actually contained much Christian symbolism. Kepler, however, argued that when 'the sacred writings' speak concerning ordinary matters in which 'it is not their normal function to instruct men, they do this in a human manner so that they may be understood by men'. Some, he says, are mistaken in thinking 'Psalm 104 to be wholly concerned with physics, since it is wholly concerned with physical matters ... the psalmist is a very long way from speculation about physical causes'. Rather he is unfolding a hymn 'in which he runs through the whole world as it appears to our eyes'.[47] This echoes Origen, Augustine, and the early Christian Fathers.

Galileo, a confirmed Catholic, cited Augustine in support of his basic tenet that:

> The Holy Bible can never speak untruth — whenever its true meaning is understood. But ... it is often very abstruse, and may say things which are quite different from what its bare words signify ... This being granted, I think that in discussions of physical problems we ought to begin not from the authority of scriptural passages and from sense experiences and necessary demonstrations; for the Holy Bible and the phenomena of nature proceed alike from the divine Word.[48]

Stillman Drake, an authority on Galileo, sees Galileo's position as reflecting historic Christianity, and his conflict as with Aristotelianism not Christianity.[49] In fact, Galileo's early opponent on the moving earth, the scholarly Cardinal Bellarmine, believed something not much different. Noting that the Council of Trent forbad any teaching contrary to the early Fathers, he wrote to Galileo's disciple Foscarini:

> If there were a real proof that the sun is in the centre of the universe ... that the sun does not go round the earth but the earth round the sun, then we should have to proceed with great circumspection in explaining passages of Scripture which appear to teach the contrary, and rather admit that we did not

understand them ... But as for myself, I shall not believe that there are such proofs until they are shown to me.[50]

Bellarmine was clearly not saying here that he could prove the earth stationary from Scripture. He was open to the possibility that it might one day be proved that it was not, and took it for granted that scientific observation would be the means of that proof. We will consider in our next chapter the issues involved in his insistence that scientists should wait for proof rather than teach speculation as fact.

## The rise of Baconianism

Coppleston's famous *History of Philosophy* spoke for many modern scholars in stating: 'Modern philosophy is generally said to have begun with Descartes (1596–1650) or with Francis Bacon (1561–1626) in England and with Descartes in France.'[51] In 1620 Francis Bacon published his *Novum Organum*, a radical book which had a profound effect on the thinking of scientists. Bacon taught that the ancient Greeks, when treated as 'authorities', became 'idols'. Beliefs about nature should be based on experimentation and observation. The following passage sets out key ideas of Bacon on theology and science (though note that in his day 'science' was referred to as 'natural philosophy', and the word 'scientist' had not been invented):

> The school of Paracelsus, and some others ... have pretended to find the truth of all natural philosophy [ie of science] in the Scriptures; scandalising and traducing all other philosophy as heathenish and profane. But there is no such enmity between God's word and his works. Neither do they give honour to the Scriptures as they suppose, but embase them. For to seek heaven and earth in the word of God, whereof it is said, 'Heaven and earth shall pass away but my word shall not pass,' is to seek temporary things amongst eternal; and as to seek divinity in philosophy is to seek the living among the dead, so to seek philosophy in divinity is to seek the dead amongst the living ...

the scope or purpose of the Spirit of God is not to express matters of nature in the Scriptures, otherwise than in passage, and for application to man's capacity and to matters moral or divine. And it is a true rule: 'What a man says incidentally about matters not in question has little authority'; for it were a strange conclusion, if a man should use a similitude for ornament or illustration sake, borrowed from nature or history according to vulgar conceit, as of a basilisk, an unicorn, a centaur, a brierus and Hydra, or the like, that he must needs be thought to affirm the matter thereof positively to be true . . . In this vanity some of the moderns have with extreme levity indulged so far as to attempt to found a system of natural philosophy on the first chapter of Genesis, on the book of Job, and other parts of sacred writings; and repression of it the more important, because from this unwholesome mixture of things human and divine there arises not only a fantastic philosophy but also an heretical religion.[52]

Bacon says that God has laid before us 'two books or volumes to study if we will be secured from error; first the Scriptures revealing the will of God, and then the creatures expressing his power'.[53]

Descartes' *Discourse on Method* was published in 1637. Though he emphasised reason where Bacon emphasised observation, the differences between them are fewer than often supposed.[54] Though God was central to his whole system, knowledge of the physical world was to be based on observation and reason.

One could hardly exaggerate the standing and influence of Bacon, both on Western science and on the thinking of Bible-believing Christians in their attitude to it. Newton, for example, whilst by no means uncritical of Bacon, himself wrote of 'two books' which should be read separately, though he believed them to have similarities since God was author of both.[55] Other early members of the Royal Society tended to see themselves as Baconians, and his approach was standard to scientist Christians in the seventeenth and eighteenth centuries. In fact, mainstream scientist Christians in Western Europe for well into the nineteenth century (if not later) saw themselves as following the traditions of Bacon, Descartes or both. George Marsden presents Bacon as 'the pre-eminently revered philosopher' in dominant evangelical colleges in America for much of the nineteenth century, and indicates that a version of Baconianism (albeit sometimes rather simplified) was influential into early twentieth century.[56] Interestingly, H M Morris cites Bacon as a 'great creationist scientist' and the 'originator of the scientific method'.[57]

The Baconian 'two books' idea is explicitly repeated by many modern scientist Christians too, eg Professor Douglas Spanner in 1987.[58] Put briefly it is this:

| Two Divine 'Books': | BIBLE | NATURE |
| --- | --- | --- |
| Human Interpretations: | THEOLOGY | SCIENCE |

Both the 'book of God's word' (the Bible) and the 'book of God's works' (nature) are true and infallible, but human interpretations of them are not.

It might be useful to make clear what this is not saying. Firstly, Bacon was not saying that the Bible speaks only spiritual truth and never refers to historical or physical facts. The fact of the Resurrection, for example, is not incidental to the truth of the account, but basic to it. The Bible relates God's dealings with men in actual history and in the physical world, and any attempt to 'spiritualise' away all space-time references is an illogical innovation.

Secondly, to say that the Bible is not a textbook of science does not mean that it contains wrong science. Neither Bacon nor his followers implied this. To say, moreover, that the language of the Bible is often 'observer language' rather than 'technical language' (eg on the Flood) is not to say that what it described was mistaken.

Sadly, however, this basic 'two books' approach has been

much misunderstood and misrepresented by some modern writers, particularly among young-earth creationists. Morris' associate J C Whitcomb attacks what he calls the 'double-revelation theory', which he summarises:

> The theologian is the God-appointed interpreter of Scripture and the scientist is the God-appointed interpreter of nature, each having specialised lenses for reading the true message of the particular 'book of revelation' which he has been called upon to study.[59]

The only reason Whitcomb seems to give for his rejection of the principle scientist Christians have accepted for at least 300 if not (implicitly) nearly 2,000 years, is that he feels science has limitations in exploring past events, and that there are particular problems with some modern theories about origins. He does not mention the problems or limitations of theology and biblical interpretation.

Theologian E J Young quotes Whitcomb and adds that the double-revelation theory entails a low estimate of the Bible because: 'Whenever "science" and the Bible are in conflict, it is always the Bible that, in one manner or another, must give way.'[60]

This is, of course, incorrect. It is not 'the Bible' but the fallible human interpretations of it made in theology which must 'give way'.

Morris also says that the double-revelation theory must be 'unequivocally rejected by Bible-believing Christians'. He argues that whilst nature needs interpreting, 'the Scriptures, in fact, do not need to be "interpreted" at all, for God is well able to say exactly what he means.'[61] In view of the various theological controversies throughout history among Bible-believing Christians, not to mention disagreements between young-earth creationists themselves, this is breathtakingly unrealistic. Its inconsistency is amply confirmed when, as we have seen, Morris' own writings contain numerous allegorical interpretations of Genesis.

In Britain, young-earth creationist E H Andrews recently attacked the historic Christian and Baconian position, under the term 'complementarity'. Andrews actually attacks the modern versions of it by Christians such as Ramm, Mixter and MacKay, seemingly unaware that what he is rejecting is not some modern aberration, but the thinking of Bible-believing mainstream Christianity for centuries. He says they are 'at a loss to know what to do with the doctrine of creation, and dare not mention miracles'.[62] This is most strange, since the great majority if not all those listed by H M Morris as 'Bible-believing creationists' held this Baconian view, and so have the vast majority of Christians who have analysed and defended the miraculous. More fundamentally, however, he seems not to understand the logical relationships of nature, Scripture, science and theology. Thus he says, 'The error of complementarity is that it places Scripture alongside science',[63] and emphasises the 'fallibility' and 'shortcomings' of 'human wisdom'.[64] Neither Bacon, Ramm, Mixter, MacKay, nor anyone we know places the Bible and science on the same level. It is the Bible and nature which are on the same logical level as self-revelations of God, and theology and science which are human interpretations of them. It is not the Bible but theology which needs adjusting as science progresses. Of course, human wisdom is fallible, but this is no more true in science than in theology or in writing young-earth-creationist literature. Andrews' own work differs on key points in interpreting Genesis from Morris or Young, so why should we accept *his* interpretation as infallible and free from 'human wisdom'?

We would, then, defend the classical Baconian approach, which was rooted in earlier Christian ideas and has shaped the whole of Christian and scientific thinking on relationships of science and theology. Many of the greatest scientific minds in history have accepted it, and it is unrealistic for sceptics to view it as naïve or obscurantist. On the other hand, two kinds of new theology should also be resisted. The

Bible is neither to be 'spiritualised' out of all reference to the world of space-time, nor to be used as a source-book for scientific theory. Neither liberalism nor young-earth creationism have any claim to represent the historic mainstream of Bible-based Christianity.

## Objectivity, theology and science

As we have seen, neither objectivity nor knowledge in science can ever be absolute. On the other hand, there is a reality, which means that scientists are not free to make up whatever laws they like. There are experiences of our world which are real, and though they may later be reinterpreted or seen as part of a larger truth, they remain undeniable experiences. Disagreements or uncertainties in present science do not imply it to be unreal or lacking any objectivity.

As science is the systematic human interpretation of God's 'book of nature', so theology is the systematic human interpretation of God's 'book of his word', the Bible. Theology too is about realities, and theologians cannot make up whatever theories they like. There are experiences of God which are real, and though they may later be reinterpreted or seen as a part of a larger truth, they remain undeniable experiences. Disagreements or uncertainties in present (or past) theology do not imply that it is unreal or lacking any objectivity.

To say all of this is to deny neither the God-givenness of nature nor the God-givenness of the Bible — but it is to affirm human fallibility in interpreting both.

In general, science and theology are concerned with different issues: the respective realms of the physical and the spiritual. They are not, however, totally independent realms, because God has acted in space-time. Thus on some things, such as specific events in the past, both nature and the Bible have something to say. The main point of a biblical account may be clear, but on details incidental to its main purpose it may not be. At any given state of human knowledge we have to study the two accounts (nature and Scripture) together, reaching whatever tentative harmony currently fits best. Thus, for example, in the Renaissance it may have been a harmony of Aristotelian science and theology. There should be nothing embarrassing for Christians in this when later science changed and a new synthesis of science-theology emerged — *providing that we recognise clearly the tentative nature of the synthesis in any given period.*

Science (the interpretation of nature) and theology (the interpretation of Scripture) have spheres of interest which are different, but which overlap on some issues of events in space-time. On these issues, we have suggested, neither theology nor science should dominate. Rather Bible-believing Christians of each generation need to seek the harmony which best fits all the current information — but without dogmatism, because points in either current theology or in current science may later turn out to be mistaken.

When, however, a new scientific idea is put forward, it may conflict both with previous scientific ideas and with current ideas of how to harmonise in areas of overlap between theology and science. Important new scientific ideas do not simply add facts, like bricks to an existing wall. Often they involve quite new perspectives. Sometimes (eg the motion of the earth) when first suggested, they face apparently overwhelming physical objections, and lack any conclusive evidence. Existing science tends by nature to be conservative. Students, for example, expect particular results to experiments. If things turn out otherwise, they usually presume something has gone wrong rather than reject the textbook theories. Against this proper conservatism must be set a tolerance of new hypotheses. Scientists sometimes do become blinkered — though very often this is only our own hindsight evaluation. An example of this is cited by atheist Richard Dawkins, speaking of the indignant disbelief of Zoologists in 1940 when Galambos first reported that bats use sonar.[65] No religious issue was involved here — just a quite natural reluctance to believe what seemed preposterous. But no one would use this to proclaim that there is a conflict between zoologists and science!

## Objections to concordism

A final point worth discussing is the relationship between our suggested approach and that of Christians at Calvin College, Michigan. This is reflected in works of astronomer Howard J Van Till (1986)[66] and geologist Davis A Young (1987).[67] We have much sympathy with their viewpoint, but wonder how far it is possible to divide up past geologists/theologians into 'literalists' and 'concordists' as they do, with 'predominantly literalist' Christian naturalists in the seventeenth and eighteenth centuries followed by concordists from then on.

It is doubtful whether the term 'literalist' means anything at all, for not even avowed modern literalists like Morris do, in fact, take Genesis literally. Ancient writers classed by Young as 'literalists' did not pretend to any literalism — Burnett being markedly allegorical, and Whiston denying that the 'days' were literal. Among supposed concordists, some were more literal than others on various particular issues. To divide people up into 'literalists' and 'non-literalists' is artificial and misleading.

What is meant by 'concordist'? Those Young cites were Baconians, they did not try to derive their science from Genesis, nor, in the main, did they believe that it was written in scientific language. They did, however, believe that the accounts of the creation and Flood referred to actual historical events. Were they wrong in this?

Van Till emphasises the identification of Genesis 1 as 'a preamble and prologue to the covenant' between God and Israel which 'addresses ... the question of the identity of God and the issue of how he is related to humanity'. We have sympathy with this, but it needs treating with care. Which is the covenant and which the preamble? Is it the covenant with Noah, with Abraham or with Israel? There is no simple covenantal structure, and at times Van Till treats the preamble as Genesis 1–11, at others as all of Genesis. Moreover, he himself mentions a 'historical prologue' as part of a covenantal preamble. Is he claiming that this can be fictional? Surely a historical prologue cannot *only* refer to timeless 'eternal verities', but must have some relationship with actual past events? But if this is so for, say, the Flood, then surely concordists have been right to try to synthesise the few details it gives with what is known from archaeology and geology? Its supposed position as a covenantal preamble would not tell us *a priori* which parts were in allegorical and which in historical observer language.

We can, then, share Young's criticisms of a view that the Bible provides 'high quality data' about 'details of the internal structure of the planet'.[68] We are, however, only half sympathetic to his statement that 'we will be on the right track if we stop treating Genesis 1 and the Flood story as scientific and historical reports'.[69] Whilst Genesis 1-3 bear clear marks of some allegorical language (confirmed by New Testament and early church teaching as we have seen), the Flood account seems to be the same kind of observer-language history as the rest of Genesis or Exodus. The terms used relate to the concepts and observational perspective of the writer, and are not high-quality scientific data in the sense of direct correspondence to modern scientific terms. It is, however, an historical account, and as such it is quite proper to consider whether some of the observational terms used may be reinterpretable into our modern concepts and understanding.

Hugh Miller, for example, rightly regarded the Flood as an actual event, rightly refused to derive his geology from Genesis, but rightly sought a synthesis of understanding of the event from the observer perspective of Genesis and the scientific perspective of geology. How is this different from the enterprise Young suggests for interdisciplinary teams? Why does he seem to think it novel to suggest that theologians and scientists should work together or that the cultural background of Genesis be taken into account?[70] The supposed concordists have been doing this for centuries.

It is true that some of the concordists may have tried to make too close an equivalence between biblical terms and current scientific ones. He shows clearly how much such rather more literalistic correspondences have varied one with another. This might be a problem to someone who puts forward their system as the only possible interpretation of Genesis and denounces others as apostate. We do not, however, believe that many past concordists did this. Perhaps Young's judgement is coloured by his 1987 perception of the inadequacies in his own rather oversimplified age-day theory in his 1977 *Creation and the Flood*. It is, however, perfectly proper for each generation to suggest systems harmonising current scientific and theological knowledge, provided that it is recognised that these may later need amending or replacing. It makes no sense to proclaim that the necessity of such changes makes concordism a failed enterprise that evangelicals should abandon, any more than it would make sense to say that science is a failed enterprise because various scientific theories are later replaced or amended. The nature of human knowledge remains that we 'know in part' (1 Cor 13:9) and all human-knowledge systems remain liable to be amended.

We need not be over critical of past concordists in order to set before us for our own generation the task of synthesis of current scientific and theological knowledge. We should recognise the tentative nature of our systems, and that the data both of Scripture and of nature may be misread. But in making such syntheses in this spirit we will be following the mainstream of Bible-believing Christians and scientists throughout history. Davis A Young and his colleagues at

Calvin College may well be able to play a valuable part in establishing a concord of knowledge in our own generation.

## Notes

1. F Galton, *English Men of Science: Their Nature and Nurture* (1874), p 24; also F M Turner, 'Victorian Conflict Between Science and Religion', *ISIS*, vol 69 (1978): pp 356–76.

2. Mendel's papers were published in 1865 and 1869; reprinted in C Stern and E R Sherwood, *The Origin of Genetics: A Mendel Source Book* (1967).

3. See A J Ayer, *Language, Truth and Logic* (1936), or summaries, for example, in F Suppe, *The Structure of Scientific Theories* (1977) or H Brown, *Perception, Theory and Commitment* (1979).

4. J S Mill, *A System of Logic* (1843).

5. Interview in *The Listener*, 2nd March 1978.

6. N R Hanson, *Patterns of Discovery* (1958); M Polanyi, *Personal Knowledge* (1958); T S Kuhn, *The Structure of Scientific Revolutions* (1962).

7. W Whewell, *The Philosophy of the Inductive Sciences* (1840, 1847), p 28.

8. See, for example: W I Beveridge, *The Art of Scientific Investigation* (1968); A Koestler, *The Act of Creation* (1964); or P B Medawar, *Induction and Intuition in Scientific Thought* (1969).

9. P Duhem, *The Aim and Structure of Physical Theory* (1906).

10. K Popper, for example, in *The Logic of Scientific Discovery* (First published 1934; this edition 1968), p 106, where Popper calls them 'basic statements'.

11. See analysis, for example, in P H Nidditch (ed) *The Philosophy of Science* (1968).

12. See D Bloor, *Knowledge and Social Imagery* (1976). See also the religious perspective in Derek Stanesby, *Science, Reason and Religion* (1985), chap 3.

13. See, for example, W H Newton-Smith, *The Rationality of Science* (1981).

14. See, for example, T Nickle (ed), *Scientific Discovery, Logic and Rationality* (1980) and J Leplin (ed), *Scientific Realism* (1984).

15. F Suppe (ed), *The Structure of Scientific Theories* (1977), section vii.

16. J Leplin, *op cit*, chap 11; R Laudan, *Science and Values* (1984), chap 5.

17. Leplin, *op cit*, chap 12.

18. On general issues of philosophy of science the second editions of F Suppe, *op cit*, and A F Chalmers, *What is this thing called Science?*

(1982) are useful, though now a little dated. Ian Hacking's *Representing and Intervening* (1983) is useful, but less comprehensive. Also useful (though having little on the new realism) is the Christian perspective in Paul Helm's *Objective Knowledge* (1987) and Del Ratzsch, *Philosophy of Science* (1987). Derek Stanesby's *Science, Reason and Religion* (1985) contains a good summary of historical movements in philosophy of science and their relationship to Christian religion.

19. See Paul Marston's review of H I Brown's book *Observation and Objectivity* (1987) in *Nature*, vol 331 (April 1988).

20. R E D Clark, *Christian Belief and Science* (1960).

21. R Stannard, *Science and the Renewal of Belief* (1982), chap 10.

22. D L Wolfe, *Epistemology* (1982), p 51. This is a useful short introduction from a Christian viewpoint.

23. *Ibid*, p 60.

24. This famous epithet from Pope's An Essay on Criticism (1711), based on older sources, so strikes a chord with most people that it has passed into proverbial use — and the second part of it, 'to forgive is divine', might in this instance have a deeper meaning!

25. Justin, *First Apology*, vol XXV, (*Ant Nic Fath*, i, 171).

26. Justin, *Second Apology*, vol X (*Ant Nic Fath*, i, 191).

27. Clement, *Miscellanies*, VI, 27 (*Ant Nic Fath*, ii, 516).

28. Origen, *Letter to Gregory* (*Ant Nic Fath*, x, 295–6).

29. Origen, *First Principles*, II, 1 (*Ant Nic Fath*, iv, 269).

30. Tertullian, *On Prescription Against Heretics*, vol VII (*Ant Nic Fath*, iii, 246).

31. Tertullian, *Apology*, vol XLVI (*Ant Nic Fath*, iii, 51).

32. *Encyclopaedia Britannica*, 1987, vol 11, p 653.

33. Minucius Felix, *Octavius*, vol XIX (*Ant Nic Fath*, iv, 183).

34. Lactantius, *Divine Institutes*, III, 24 (*Ant Nic Fath*, vii, 94 and 237).

35. Lactantius, *Epitome of the Divine Institutes* vol XXXIX (*Ant Nic Fath*, vii, 204).

36. *The Fathers of the Church*, vol 42 (translated by J Savage, 1961), day three.

37. Augustine, *On the Psalms*, civ (*Nic & Pos Nic Fath*, 1, viii, 510).

38. Augustine, *City of God*, XVI, 9 (*Nic & Pos Nic Fath*, 1, ii, 315).

39. Basil, *Hexameron*, Homily IX (*Nic & Pos Nic Fath*, 2, viii, 101).

40. *Ibid*, Homily I (*Nic & Pos Nic Fath*, 2, viii, 57).

41. Gregory of Nyssa, *On the Making of Man*, vol XXX (*Nic & Pos Nic Fath*, 2, v, 422).

42. Some references are in Hooykaas, *Religion and the Rise of Modern Science* (1972).

43. See, for example, D C Linberg, *Science in the Middle Ages* (1978), p 96, etc.

44. N Steneck, *Science and Creation in the Middle Ages* (1976), p 144.

45. Calvin, *Commentary on Genesis*, vol i, p 15.

46. See also Hooykaas, *Religion and the Rise of Modern Science*, p 117, etc.

47. Kepler, *Astronomia Nova* (1609).

48. Galileo, *Letter to the Grand Duchess Christina* (1615).

49. S Drake, *Galileo* (1980), p 59.

50. From a letter of Bellarmine in April 1615 to one of Galileo's associates. Details are given in A Koestler, *The Sleepwalkers* (1959).

51. F Coppleston, *A History of Philosophy* (1960), vol 4, p 13.

52. F Bacon, *Of the Advancement of Learning* (1605), bk 11; see also *Novum Organum* (1620), vol lxv.

53. Quoted from Bacon, *Valerius Terminus* (published 1734), though similar comments are in other works.

54. See R M Blake et al, *Theories of Scientific Method* (1960), especially chap 3 on Bacon and chap 4 on Descartes.

55. See F E Manuel, *The Religion of Isaac Newton* (1974).

56. G M Marsden, *Fundamentalism and American Culture* (1980), pp 55–62, 111–12, 169, 214–5, etc.

57. Morris, *A History of Modern Creationism* (1984), p 26.

58. D Spanner, *op cit* p 16 etc.

59. J C Whitcomb and D B DeYoung, *The Moon: Its Creation, Form and Significance* (1978), p 54.

60. E J Young, *Studies in Genesis One*, p 53.

61. H M Morris, *The Biblical Basis for Modern Science*, p 47.

62. E H Andrews, *Christ and the Cosmos*, p 71.

63. E H Andrews et al (eds), *Concepts in Creationism* (1986), p 10; see also in *Christ and the Cosmos*, p 71.

64. *Christ and the Cosmos*, p 71.

65. R Dawkins, *The Blind Watchmaker* (1986), p 35.

66. Howard J Van Till, *The Fourth Day*.

67. Davis A Young, 'Scripture in the Hands of the Geologists', *Westminster Theological Journal*, vol 49 (1987): 1–34, pp 257–304.

68. *Ibid*, p 294.

69. *Ibid*, p 303.

70. *Ibid*, p 302.

# 13

# CONFLICT THROUGHOUT HISTORY BETWEEN CHRISTIANITY AND SCIENCE?

## The conflict thesis

'EXTINGUISHED THEOLOGIANS LIE ABOUT THE CRADLE of new science as the strangled snakes beside that of Hercules.'[1] This graphic picture was given by T H Huxley in the late nineteenth century, but it is often the picture which the media and person in the street still has. Theology and science are seen as somehow naturally in conflict with each other.

In general, historians of science today have abandoned the Huxleyan conflict thesis of science and religion. But why did Huxley put forward his viewpoint, and why has it proved so popular? To Huxley, free scientific enquiry was an end in itself to be pursued with the vigour of a military campaign, regardless of socio-religious consequences. In 1864, Huxley and eight fellow scientists formed a dining club, The X-Club. They were united in what one member called: 'devotion to science, pure and free, untrammelled by religious dogmas.'[2] Colin Russell has shown how The X-Club fitted into a context in which it sought independence for science, and to establish scientists (rather than any other group) as leaders in society to whom people looked for answers.[3] Though Huxley also had (as we shall later see) Christian associates who shared some of these aims, the agnostic members of this Club would naturally want to portray organised religion in a bad light in any science-religion issues. Yet they did not represent the greatest scientists of the period, which included the illustrious Faraday and Maxwell, and it seems unlikely that they reflected the views of the majority of the common run of scientists. A contemporary survey by Galton is cited by Moore, who asserts: 'Most scientists were religious men.'[4] Huxley was, however, a brilliant publicist, active in science education at all levels, and for a time the X-Club dominated the Royal Society and British Association for the Advancement of Science.

Two books in particular added to the conflict thesis. J W Draper, a Lancashire man who became a science professor in New York, published *History of the Conflict between Religion and Science* in 1875. He set out to portray history as a 'narrative of the conflict of two contending powers', adding, 'No one has hitherto treated the subject from this point of view.'[5] Developing his novel approach, he supposes that with the breakdown of the old religion of the Roman Empire, religious affairs 'fell into the hands of ignorant and infuriated ecclesiastics, parasites, eunuchs and slaves'. All Draper's work was then seen through this novel distorting medium of a conflict thesis. Early Christians (eg Bede) who speculated on cosmology were dismissed as 'preposterous' and ignorant, with no real attempt to understand the observational base of what they thought. Others (eg Lactantius) were portrayed as rejecting as 'heretical' what actually they rejected on quite good common-sense grounds. Draper's book was effective propaganda, but not history.

The second book was the 1895 *A History of the Warfare of Science with Theology in Christendom* by A D White, first President of Cornell University. Ecclesiastical opposition to his liberal policies at Cornell seemed to lead him to see science and dogmatic theology as locked in a struggle. Admitting his debt to Draper, White's own work is more temperate, but still fails to come to terms with the thinking of earlier ages. It fails (in terms of the great modern historian

Collingwood) to understand the thinking of those studied, and it suffers from a triumphalist tendency to assess all ideas with the hindsight presumption that they are 'good' only if they correspond with present ideas.[6]

As a tool to achieve particular ends, the conflict thesis was effective but as history, it is unacceptable and it has come under increasing criticism from historians during the twentieth century.[7] As so often, however, popular opinion and the clichés of the media have lagged behind informed opinion.

## Religious scientists

Before looking at specific issues of supposed conflict, we might well mention the numbers of prominent scientists throughout history who have been deeply religious — even in eras when apathy or unbelief was common.

One must, of course, recognise various problems or dangers in this. Firstly, there are sometimes difficulties in identifying religious convictions of scientists — the potted biographies in encyclopedia may fail to mention even the most profound evangelical commitment.[8] Secondly, there may be a problem in assessing exactly where in the theological spectrum a person's convictions should be placed, and how deep those feelings run. A person who is nominally orthodox may actually be less profoundly Christian than someone with a deeply felt and thought-through personal faith which includes elements of unorthodoxy. A third problem concerns selectivity, ie to generalise whilst ignoring counter-examples. Some of these pitfalls are illustrated in a book of H M Morris'.[9] Morris excludes the devout evangelical Asa Gray (perhaps because Gray accepted evolution) and includes the Arian Whiston, the broad churchmen Owen and Herschel, and the unitarian Agassiz — all without any indication of their theology. He cites as 'creationists' figures like Cuvier, Buckland, Owen and Agassiz, who were important figures in the rise of a geology, which he elsewhere claims is anti-biblical and crypto-evolutionary.

What exactly, then, can be asserted? Firstly, we do believe that there is truth in the arguments of Professor Hooykaas and others, that biblical Christianity was itself a contributory medium for the growth of modern science.[10] Many great scientists connected their faith in the rationality of nature with their faith in the rationality of the Creator-God. There were, of course, *some* great scientists who were not markedly religious (like Huygens and Helmholtz[11]), but two points can be made about this. Firstly, their outlook was generally moulded by the Christian heritage of belief in a rational God and rational universe. Secondly, there seem to have been markedly *more* scientists who were outrightly religious (and markedly *fewer* who were outright materialists or sceptics) than one would have expected from the general times and societies in which they lived. In almost any age philosophers have been more impious than scientists! We are not able here, however, to substantiate these assertions in rigorously statistical terms. All that we are prepared to do is to illustrate it by listing some of the really great scientists who have been deeply religious. We will cite the *Encyclopaedia Britannica* (*EB*) or the *Dictionary of Scientific Biography* (*DSB*) in indicating their importance:

1.   *Johannes Kepler (1571–1630)*

   [He] transformed the old geometrical description of the heavens into dynamical astronomy ... also founded modern optics ... best known for his discovery of the three principles of planetary motion ... the first to declare that the other planets resemble the earth as being material bodies (*EB* vol 6, p 809).

   Kepler was a deeply sincere Lutheran, whose system of astronomy was written with a deep symbolism of the divine presence built into it.

2. *Blaise Pascal (1623–62)* Pascal 'laid the foundations for the modern theory of probabilities' (*EB*, vol 25, p 452). He experienced a profound religious awakening and became a Jansenist.

3. *Robert Boyle (1627–91)* 'Boyle was noted for his pioneer experiments in the properties of gases ... a devout Protestant, took a special interest in promoting the Christian religion abroad, giving money to translate and publish the New Testament' (*EB*, vol 2, p 447).

4. *John Ray (1627–1705)* Ray was a 'leading seventeenth-century English naturalist and botanist who contributed significantly to progress in taxonomy' (*EB*, vol 9, p 961). He was a very sincere Christian who wrote about God in creation.

5. *Isaac Newton (1642–1727)* Newton needs no quotation to be recognised as one of the most towering scientific intellects in history. His thinking was profoundly religious, and a personal God was essential to his system. His orthodoxy has been a subject of debate, but he certainly had a deep belief in the inspiration of Scripture.[12]

6. *John Dalton (1766–1844)* He 'developed the atomic theory of matter and hence is known as one of the fathers of modern physical science' (*EB*, vol 3, p 861). Dalton was a Quaker.

7. *Georges Cuvier (1769–1832)* Cuvier 'established the sciences of comparative anatomy and palaeontology' (*EB*, vol 3, p 815). A sincere Protestant, he 'undoubtedly rediscovered his faith sincerely each time a new period of mourning cast gloom on his existence' (*DSB*, vol III, p 523).

8. *Michael Faraday (1791–1867)* 'one of the greatest scientists of the nineteenth century', his membership in the Christian sect of Sandemanians was 'the single most important influence upon him and strongly affected the way in which he approached and interpreted nature' (*EB*, vol 19, p 83).

9.  *Asa Gray (1810–88)* A 'botanist whose extensive studies of the flora of North America did more than the work of any other botanist to unify the taxonomic knowledge of plants of this region ... one of the few persons whom Darwin kept fully informed concerning the publication of his *Origin of Species* ... Gray was a devout Christian' (*EB*, vol 5, p 436).

10. *Louis Pasteur (1822–95)* He made 'scientific contributions among the most varied and valuable in the history of science and industry ... brought about a veritable revolution in the nineteenth-century scientific method' (*EB*, vol 25, p 465).

    'Although he was reared and died a Catholic, religious ritual and sectarian doctrine held little attraction for him — he described his own philosophy as one "entirely of the heart". Thoughout his life he distained materialists, atheists, freethinkers and positivists ... never doubted the existence of the spiritual realm or of the immortal soul' (*DSB*, vol X, p 354).

11. *Lord Kelvin (William Thomson) (1824–1907)* He was 'foremost amongst the small group of British scientists who helped to lay the foundations of modern physics' (*EB*, vol 22, p 503). Both Lord Kelvin and the others of the group (including Maxwell, Lord Rayleigh and Stokes) were Bible-believing Christians.

12. *James Clerk Maxwell (1831–79)* 'Regarded by modern physicists as the scientist of the nineteenth century who had the greatest influence on twentieth-century physics, he is ranked with Sir Isaac Newton and Albert Einstein for the fundamental nature of his contributions' (*EB*, vol 23, p 725). Maxwell had an evangelical conversion while at Cambridge in the early 1850s, and attended a Baptist church in the 1860s.

13. *Max Planck (1857–1947)* He was the 'originator of the quantum theory', and 'revolutionised our understanding of atomic and subatomic processes, just as Albert

Einstein's theory of relativity revolutionised our understanding of space and time. Together they constitute the fundamental theories of twentieth-century physics' (*EB*, vol 25, p 869). A church-warden from 1920 until his death, Planck professed his belief in an almighty omniscient God (although he did not personify him). Planck said science and religion, although starting from different standpoints, wage a 'tireless battle against scepticism and dogmatism, against unbelief and superstition' with the goal 'toward God' (*DSB*, vol XI, p 15).

14. *Albert Einstein (1879–1955)* Einstein was 'one of the most creative intellects in human history'. He was a believer in 'Spinoza's God, who reveals himself in the harmony of what exists' (*EB*, vol 8, p 197).

We may mention others in the course of this section, but what all this does indicate is the frequency with which seminal thinkers in the history of science have been profoundly religious, and often Bible-believing Christians.

## The true relationship between science and belief

If, then, we reject as unhistorical the conflict thesis, how should we characterise the historical interaction of theology and science? We are going to suggest a number of generalisations:

1. Where new scientific theories met opposition, there have usually been strong physical reasons for this.
2. In any scientific controversy there have usually been Christians of equal sincerity on both sides.
3. The use of biblical verses to settle scientific questions has been common only where no observational evidence existed, as a part of a synthesis of known facts. Its use to reject observational science has been rare among acknowledged Christian leaders.

4.  Scientific speculation itself has not been outlawed, but there may have been objections to presenting speculation as 'fact' to those whose faith might thereby be damaged.
5.  Objections have sometimes been made to scientific theories which, in fact, contain their own religious metaphysics.
6.  Whatever the disagreement, scientists have very rarely, even in times of shocking and unChristian religious intolerance, had life or liberty threatened for purely scientific speculation.

It may be useful to make a few general comments on these. Obviously, Christian leaders have sometimes been mistaken over physical details of the world — but then so have most scientists as well, so this is of no great surprise or significance. Clearly, too, there have been exceptions to 3, ie where individuals have tried to fit science and observation into preconceived schemes they think they find in Scripture. We are arguing only that the mainstream of Christian thought has not believed that the language of Scripture was specific enough to dictate points of physical science. On 6, we are not denying that there has sometimes been deplorable religious intolerance. But it is possible for Koestler as a non-Christian observer, to write:

> Giordano Bruno and Michael Servetus (burned in 1553 by the Calvinists in Geneva) seem to be the only scholars of repute who became victims of religious intolerance in the sixteenth and seventeenth centuries — not, of course, because of their scientific but because of their religious opinions.[13]

Koestler sees scientists as a kind of species of sacred cow, ambling unmolested through the bazaar of religious persecution. Ironically, there are instances of persecution by irreligious authorities. During the avowedly anti-Christian French Revolution, one of history's greatest chemists, Antoine

Lavoisier, was guillotined on a trumped up charge — reputedly with the words 'France does not need men of science'.[14] In modern Soviet Russia there was a more overt clash of science and 'religion', as eminent adherents of the scientific Mendelian genetics were mercilessly persecuted because the theories were thought to contradict Marxist ideas.[15] Atheistic systems do not regard scientists as sacred cows.

We could not hope in the present work to demonstrate the aforementioned suggestions comprehensively. What we are going to do is to illustrate them with three particular issues: the structure of the universe, the development of geology, and the theory of evolution.

### Cosmology: the structure of the universe

Everybody today is brought up to know that the earth is a tiny sphere, rotating in space and orbiting the sun. If they are told anything about the history of this idea, it is probably that the church persecuted Galileo for proving it. But what are the facts? How did we come to have this kind of cosmology?

The scientific history may be outlined thus. In the fourth century BC, the ancient Greeks put forward various suggestions for the earth, including that of Aristarchus, which suggested that the earth went around the sun. The one which generally triumphed was that based on Aristotle and Hipparchus, modified by Ptolemy in the mid-second century AD. The earth was held to be a small stationary sphere, at the centre of the universe. Below the moon the four elements of earth, air, fire and water each had a natural place to which they sought to return. Above the moon it was, they thought, observably different, with sun, stars, and planets going around in complex systems of circles in which the centre of one circle moved on others.

Copernicus, in 1543, put forward the suggestion that the

sun was stationary and the earth went around it and rotated. Mathematically his new calculations were accepted, though actually he centred the earth's orbit not on the sun but a point in empty space; as a physical system, however, the idea that the earth could rotate at that speed without flinging everyone off was too absurd for the theory to make much headway. Around 1600, Tycho Brahe was completing his great series of accurate observations, and suggested a system with the earth stationary, but with some planets circling the sun as it in turn circled the earth.

In 1609 Kepler published his *New Astronomy*, containing the 'true' elliptical orbits of the planets around the sun, together with a suggested physics and nascent ideas of gravity. In 1632 Galileo published his *Dialogue on the Two World Systems*, a thinly disguised argument for the Copernican system.

Finally, in 1687 Newton published his *Principia*, clearly laying out ideas of gravitational force and inertia, and deriving Kepler's elliptical planetary orbits from these assumptions. By this time, there was little doubt that the earth orbited the sun, though followers of Descartes did continue for a time to doubt the 'mystic' idea of a gravitational force acting at a distance — an idea which only disappeared in the twentieth-century physics of Einstein.

## Early Hebrew and Christian attitudes to cosmology

How did Hebrew and Christian believers react to this down through history? Let us begin with the Old Testament concepts. In various books one finds fanciful schema of supposed Hebrew cosmology, with a flat earth standing on pillars and a dome-shaped firmament.[16] It is, of course, possible to build this kind of picture from selected verses, but other verses could equally fancifully be used to build up a modern picture. Thus in the same book of the Bible, Isaiah, it refers to the 'circle of the earth' (Is 40:22) and to the 'four corners (literally "wings") of the earth' (Is 11:12). The compiler of Isaiah intended neither phrase as a statement of science, and it is foolishness to press either into more than the normal observation of everyday appearances.

Early Christian leaders frequently made two points of criticism of Greek philosophers. The first was that there was much disagreement among them over basics, and many of their ideas were speculative and offered no means to determine whether or not they were true. Today this is hard for us to understand, for we are brought up to recognise a huge body of scientific facts based on observation. Secondly, natural philosophy (ie science) had no moral use, little practical use, and questions of faith and ultimate destiny were far more important. Again, today we automatically link science with technology and with improving the physical welfare of mankind, and often fail to understand how recent is this link. At the time they were made, these criticisms were both reasonable and valid.

In the last chapter we argued that the classic Christian approach based its beliefs about specifics of nature on observational study rather than on the Bible. But did early Christian teachers ever oppose *particular demonstrable concepts of cosmology on biblical grounds*? Actually, this happened surprisingly seldom. Let us take, for example, Lactantius, who has frequently been criticised on this count. Thus J W Draper wrote about Lactantius' reference to 'the heretical doctrine of the globular form of the earth',[17] and A D White wrote: 'Lactantius referred to ideas of those studying astronomy as "bad and senseless," and opposed the doctrine of the earth's sphericity both from Scripture and reason.'[18] In our last chapter we noted Lactantius' generally positive attitude to secular learning. Let us turn now to the passage of Lactantius to which White referred.[19] Actually, his phrase is '*mad* and senseless', and he refers it to the attempts to settle astronomical questions by 'disputation and conjecture'. The whole passage could in fact be read as a plea to concentrate on observation rather than speculation, in a complex and knowledgeable assessment of philosophical schools. As for the earth's sphericity, we can find no argument against it based on Scripture: his objections are to its absurdity.[20] Of course, he got it wrong, but there were mistakes about particular points in the physical world in the beliefs of Copernicus, Galileo, Darwin and most great scientists. It is absurd to single out Lactantius to blame for making such a mistake.

What of Augustine, who is also sometimes criticised on this issue? His actual argument was that 'although it be supposed or scientifically demonstrated that the world is of round or spherical form', even if the other side were inhabitable, it did not 'immediately follow that it is peopled'.[21] This was a question not of scientific but of historical evidence — and there was none! Regarding it as 'absurd' to suggest that people (presumably descendants of Adam) travelled all round the world by boat to get there, he thought the antipodes uninhabited. He was mistaken, but certainly not obscurantist, silly or antiscientific.

Augustine's great contemporary, the Latin Father and translator Jerome (whose Vulgate version was adopted by the Catholic Church) assumed in his commentary on Ezekiel 1:6 that the antipodes were inhabited with human supplicants, just as in our own hemisphere. Augustine's view was based on reason, not religious orthodoxy.

We already mentioned in our last chapter the view of Basil, that the Bible said nothing about the shape of the earth, and there is no evidence that any Christian orthodoxy developed which said otherwise.

Much reference is made by conflict theorists to the sixth-century Alexandrian monk Cosmas Indicopleustes, who thought the great tent made by Moses (the Tabernacle) a picture of the cosmos. Cosmas saw the earth as a rectangular plain, with the sun revolving around a conical mountain. Even the more mild form of conflict theory suggested by Dijksterhuis states that Cosmas 'became the prevalent opinion again for several centuries'.[22] Recent scholarship, however, discounts this, the *Encyclopaedia Britannica* stating: 'His idiosyncratic work is not representative of the general state of cosmographic theory among Christian philosophers of his day, and had small influence on later writers.'[23] The preponderant Christian scholarship of the period (such as Boethius and Bede) was Greek, and the recovery of further ancient Greek works in the tenth to twelfth centuries led to the fusion of Aristotelian science and Christian thought known as scholasticism.

This whole movement was founded on a harmony of observational science and faith, and its early leaders were men of great breadth of vision and intellectual ability. In the much later opposition of remnants of this great movement to 'new' ideas such as the motion of the earth, we must remember both the natural conservatism of *all* scientific establishments, and the great physical objections to a moving earth.

## Believers and the growth of belief in a moving earth

Actually, one of the first works arguing in detail for the possibility of a moving earth was written in 1377 by Oresme, Bishop of Lisieux, by order of the King of France. In *Le Livre du Ciel*, Oresme counters physical objections, and says of Bible verses which appear to imply a stationary earth:

> One can say that [the Bible] conforms in this part to the manner of common human speech, just as it does in several places, as where it is written that God repented and that he became angry and calm again and things of the same kind, which are not in fact at all as the letter puts it.[24]

On issues such as that of the long day of Joshua 10:12, or the sun going back in the time of Hezekiah (Is 38:8), he suggests it more in line with God's general working to 'disturb the common course of nature' in a small local way (ie in the earth) than in the whole universe.[25]

Copernicus (1478–1543) was actually a conservatively minded devotee of Greek science, yet it was he who created the first mathematical system based on a moving earth. A canon of the Catholic Church, he received nothing but clerical encouragement during his lifetime. The first résumé of his system was given in 1532 by the Pope's private secretary in the Vatican gardens.[26] In 1535 Cardinal Schoenberg (a confidant of the Pope's) urged Copernicus to publish. Copernicus' most immediate disciple, Rheticus, stood high in the Lutheran camp when he published a *Narratio Prima* in 1540 summarising his mentor's views. Copernicus' reluctance seems to have been from fear of common ridicule rather than religious persecution — coupled with the knowledge that he had no evidence for the truth of his system, which was at least as mathematically cumbersome as the old one. His *Revolutions of the Heavenly Spheres* was published in 1543.

White's conflict thesis, predictably, asserts: 'All branches of the Protestant church . . . vied with each other in denouncing the Copernican doctrine as contrary to Scripture.'[27] Actually, Luther appears not to have referred to the question in any published work; the story often related of his supposed opposition comes from someone else's recollection twenty-seven years later of an after-dinner remark.[28] Calvin seems to mention it in only one sermon, and then his rejection is on 'common-sense' rather than biblical grounds.[29] Melanchthon rejected Copernicanism, but numbered admirers of Copernicus among his friends. The absence of scientific intolerance here is all the more remarkable if we remember that these Reformers were steeped in an Augustinian view of God which encouraged persecution of dissenting Christians (such as the Mennonites or Anabaptists) and led to them being burned, imprisoned, or exiled.

A generation later the pious Lutheran Johannes Kepler published in 1609 the true elliptical orbits of planets (including the earth) about the sun. Koestler suggests that the reason why Kepler (like Rheticus in the generation before) could move so freely in Catholic Europe was that scientists were sacred cows — in Kepler's case perhaps under a secret protection of the powerful Jesuit order.[30] Kepler's great reputation led to his appointment as imperial mathematician to the Catholic Emperor Rudolph II!

Perhaps the most well-known persecution is that of Kepler's famous contemporary Galileo. Whilst preparing this chapter, we bought in a local newsagent a popular publication called *Discovery*, which proclaims of him:

> Through his observations, he made many discoveries and proved that the earth and the planets of the solar system revolved around the sun. This, though, brought him into conflict with church leaders of the day, for the Scriptures taught that the earth was at the centre.[31]

Is this accurate? Galileo was a man who revelled in debate, and ridiculed opponents in it. This was a good way to win debates but also to make enemies. Though he claimed to have long been a Copernican, his public interest came only after his improvement of the telescope (around 1609), and the telescopic discoveries which he tried to portray as relevant to the issue. In 1615, following some after-dinner conversation, he launched himself into the controversy with a *Letter to the Grand Duchess Christina*. We quoted in the last chapter from the response of the leading Cardinal Bellarmine in a letter to Galileo's disciple Foscarini. If a physical proof of the earth's motion could be produced, then the church would be prepared to rethink its biblical interpretation (ie rethink the current synthesis of theology and science). Until that time, Galileo was, he said, prudent to speak only hypothetically about earth motions.

In 1632 Galileo published a *Dialogue on the Two World Systems*. This was supposed to present 'both sides', but was a thinly disguised argument for the earth's movement. In its final section the favourite argument of the Pope on the issue was put into the mouth of the dunce in the *Dialogue*, and the Pope (who had previously been an admirer of Galileo) was not pleased! Scientifically, Galileo's book would have been out of date even if published fifteen years earlier. He ignored Kepler's elliptical orbits (published twenty-three years earlier) and gave the impression of circular ones, which would have been absurdly inaccurate. He ignored Tycho's system (then accepted by leading Jesuits, because it fitted best the data and lack of observed parallax) and pretended the choice was between his own and Aristotle's. All the physical proofs presented in his book were either wrong (eg his key theory of the tides) or would apply equally to Tycho's system. It was a popular book rather than a real academic contribution — written in pithy Italian rather than academic Latin.

So what was the fuss? In today's terms the real issue might be seen as one of the social responsibility of a scientist rather than one of academic freedom. Do scientists have a duty to publish any and all discoveries or ideas they have, irrespective of the social effects of such publication? Should Galileo have popularised a system for which he had no proof and premature publication of which might have had an destabilising effect on ordinary people? Bellarmine, rightly or wrongly, had thought not, and in Galileo's later trial 'the only real issue was whether or not he had received and disobeyed a specific personal order' from Bellarmine in 1615.[32]

Galileo was never thrown in the dungeons, but placed under comfortable house-arrest. He was not pronounced heretical, but was made to recant and his book placed in the prohibited Index. (Copernicus' book had been on the Index from 1616–1620, pending very minor corrections.) Three of the ten Cardinals refused to sign the sentence anyway.[33] Ironically, it was after the Inquisition turned him away from his rather sterile astronomical speculation that Galileo did some of his really useful work on dynamics in the last years of his life — fêted and honoured by all!

Throughout all this period Galileo had many supporters in all branches of Catholicism, though he had also made personal enemies. When, however, a young firebrand denounced Galileo from a pulpit somewhere, more than one leading member of the order might express to Galileo their regret that such ignorance existed.[34]

We hold no particular brief to defend the Catholic Church. Of course, there were individual bigots (there still are, both religious and secular) and there were power contests. But as a matter of history, it is inaccurate to present the Galileo affair as a simple one of science versus religion.

Isaac Newton was born in the year (1642) that Galileo died, and by his publication in 1687 of *Principia* virtually all Protestant scholars and many Catholic ones accepted Copernican ideas.

There was, to be sure, a small group of Hutchinsonian Christians who held out against Newton until the early nineteenth century. They believed that Newton's system was against both the Bible and nature — and thus occupied an intellectual position much like young-earth creationists today. They were never, however, regarded as mainstream or orthodox. John Wesley, for example, was himself interested in scientific literature and encouraged his preachers to be. He read (with them) various books on Hutchinson's system, and his growing criticism culminated by 1758 in saying: 'I am more and more convinced that they have no foundation in Scripture or sound reason.'[35]

## Later developments in cosmology and summary

We now believe the universe to be inconceivably vast, but this vastness has served only to increase the sense of awe felt by believers at the greatness of their God. The earth had long been thought small in comparison with the universe. When, in the nineteenth century, its extreme minuteness became known, many evangelicals such as eminent scientist David Brewster concluded that God must have created other life elsewhere in it.[36] Others, such as the evangelical geologist Adam Sedgwick had no biblical objection to such other life forms, but argued that, since God was a free agent, whether or not he had in fact made them was a matter for observation.[37]

The twentieth-century development of concepts of galaxies, the expanding universe, and the big-bang theory of origins, was, in its time, quite uncontroversial with Christians. Any present controversy — for example, the age of the universe — has arisen from the young-earth creationists whose theology has developed over the last twenty-five years.

In summary, on issues of cosmology it is, of course, possible to find Christians who 'got it wrong'. It is also possible to find Christians who confused their theology with their science. What we are arguing is that, in general, the mainstream of Christian thought — early church, Renaissance, Catholic and Protestant — took a basically Baconian approach and did not build scientific cosmologies from Scripture nor oppose clear scientific facts because of their theology. The fact that occasionally individual Christians 'got it wrong' is no more reason to be critical of Christianity than the fact that individual scientists 'got it wrong' would lead us to be critical of science.

## Geology, evolution and conflict theory

It is popularly supposed that the church long fought against geological ideas that the earth was very ancient, and led the assaults on Darwin's theory of evolution in the late nine-teenth century. Professional historians of science, of course, have long since recognised that the first of these suppositions is virtually a myth, and the second needs substantial modifi-cation. It is, however, important to promote a wider knowledge of the truth about the history of geology and evolution in relation to faith, because this affects the perception of important current issues in the minds both of Christians and of the uncommitted. In fact, we shall see that Bible-believing Christians generally led in the rise of strati-graphic geology and the establishment of the geological column, and in the Darwinian debate there were evangeli-cals prominent on both sides.

We have already noted how classical conflict theory started with agnostic propaganda, and there are similarly motivated popular modern conflict-theory productions which are critical of Christianity. Sadly, however, there are also modern works by young-earth creationists which, in the words of one excellent article on the history of creationism, are 'the warfare model with the role of cowboys and indians reversed'.[38] Though we do not doubt the sincerity of the writers, these are full of demonstrable historical mistakes and highly improbable speculation, and they leave an impression as misleading as the agnostic versions.

The comment made above was actually referring to M Bowden's book, *The Rise of the Evolution Fraud* (1982). Bowden is not a trained or accredited historian of science, and relies heavily on early books by Irving (1956) and Himmelfarb (1959).[39] These particular secondary sources were interesting in their day, but would not be taken as reliable by serious historians of science in the 1980s. His other main source is L Wilson's biography of Lyell (1972), which makes some untenable assumptions about geology in the period.[40] As we shall see, much of Bowden's historical account is demonstrably mistaken or is highly improbable speculation. H M Morris, however, has copied many of

Bowden's ideas in his own *A History of Modern Creationism* (1984). Apart from the specific historical errors, Morris (and to some extent Bowden) tends to take a 'big man' approach to the history of science. An individual is identified as 'Father of X-ology', obscuring the essential continuity of the development of science, and creating the myth that an individual 'superhero' (or villain) can change the course of science.

There have also been more popular pamphlets, such as Sylvia Baker's *Bone of Contention* (1976). On this particular one, Paul Marston wrote both to authoress and publisher in 1977, listing numerous primary sources to show that nearly all its key historical assertions about the history of science and evolution were demonstrably incorrect. The regrettable repeated reissue (in several languages) of the uncorrected pamphlet since that time, illustrates the tenacity of the demonstrable historical errors it contains.

## Key points of terminology

We need first to look at the terms 'evolution' and 'creation'. The word 'creationist' properly refers to the belief that something has been designed by a personal being. It implies a belief about the existence of an idea in the mind of a personal God, before the idea came to embodiment in the physical realm.

The word 'evolution' can, of course, mean many things. Some have indeed tried to include in it metaphysical or religious connotations.[41] As we shall use it, however, it implies no more than a theory about the purely physical realm, ie present species are descended from one or a few original life forms.

In this sense, then, evolution and creation cannot be opposed, as they refer to different dimensions of reality. Grammatically, either could be used either as adjective or noun, thus 'evolutionary creationist' actually means the same as 'creationary evolutionist' (or 'theistic evolutionist'). From a Christian viewpoint, however, the fact that someone believes in creation is more important than the mechanism they happen to believe was used. For this reason, it seems better to keep 'creationist' as the noun and put the method used in creation as the adjective.

With this convention, we might distinguish among believers in the physical theory of evolution:

1. *Evolutionary creationists* believe that God created through a process of evolution.
2. *Evolutionary mystics* believe that there is some mystic meaning behind the evolutionary process.
3. *Evolutionary materialists* believe that only matter exists, and evolution is nothing but its laws working out.
4. *Evolutionary progressivists* believe that a meaning is to be found in progress: a metaphysical process behind evolution.

Among believers in the religious (or metaphysical) doctrine of creation, there would be included:

1. *Evolutionary creationists* believe that God created organic life through a process of evolution: a type-i miracle in religious terms.
2. *Age-day fiat creationists* believe that creation of organic life involved type-ii miracles, but in separate acts over a long time span.
3. *Gap-theory creationists* believe creation was a re-creation after a disaster, and occurred by type-ii miracles.
4. *Young-earth creationists* believe that creation involved type-ii miracles over a period of 144 hours about 6–8,000 years ago.

Though terms can be defined as authors wish, we believe that this particular suggested schema is clearer than some others which have been used, eg distinguishing young-earth creationists by a capital 'C',[42] by using inverted commas,[43] or by distinguishing 'Creationist' from 'Creationism'.[44] In each of these other three approaches consistency has proved impossible. Likewise, attempts to distinguish evolutionism (meaning what we call evolutionary progressivism) from general evolutionists is too confusing.[45] Our own schema, to some extent following earlier writers like Bernard Ramm and Alan Hayward, is longer but we believe it to be clearer.[46]

It is, indeed, vital to be clear. Morris' use of terms, for example, disguises a very basic self-contradiction. In one of his books Morris asserts:

> The evolutionary model of origins and development is itself fundamentally atheistic . . .
> A popular semantic variation of theistic evolution is a system called progressive creationism . . . it is almost impossible, either scientifically or biblically to distinguish progressive creation and theistic evolution . . . the progressive creationist . . . visualises a bumbling sort of god.[47]

Both progressive creationism and gap-theory creationism are, according to Morris, just semantic variations of evolutionary creationism — and belief in evolution is itself inherently atheistic. One might, therefore, expect him to argue that progressive and gap-theory creationists were really crypto-atheists. Actually, as we will see, virtually all those he cites as great 'creationist scientists' and all those he acknowledges as spiritual giants of the century 1850–1950 were progressive, gap-theory, or evolutionary creationists; there were virtually no important advocates of young-earth creationism. By using the term 'creationist' in a woolly way, he disguises the fact that at times he writes as though young-earth creationists were the only real ones, and at others implies the opposite.

Morris' actual argument that evolution is inherently atheistic (although, paradoxically, he admits that most evolutionists are probably theists) is just that it makes God redundant.[48] If, of course, we see God only in type-ii miracles, then this might be true — but this has never been the mainstream Christian view. As we have seen, when the Bible speaks of God 'creating' the wind in Amos 4:13, this in no way implies he would be redundant when scientists discovered its natural causes. Ironically, Morris accuses the progressive creationists of a 'god of the gaps' mentality, with a progressively smaller role as science removes the gaps. Yet he himself sees it as vital for God to operate in a big series of 'gaps' in natural processes (ie type-ii miracles of creation) over an initial 144-hour period. If God really did operate only in these gaps (though concentrated in 144 hours instead of across millennia), then there would be a risk that future physical theory might put him out of business. For those of us, however, who stand with the Bible-believing church throughout history and believe that God is behind *all* natural processes as well as operating in type-ii miracles, science is not seen as a threat as any gaps may be filled in, but as testimony to the contrivance of God.

Evolution, in itself, is no more atheistic than belief in the earth's rotation — though there have, of course, been atheists who believed both!

A final point about terminology concerns the term 'uniformitarian'. It is unfortunate that the literature (secular and religious) contains such divergences of use of this term that it is inadvisable to use it as a term on its own. As a physical theory (and so aside from any religious meanings, eg a scepticism of the supernatural), it has two basic meanings: (a) a belief that present fundamental natural laws of physics and chemistry are similar to those of the past; and (b) that rates of geological processes, which are produced by particular combinations of the laws of physics and chemistry, have always remained the same. This distinction was made in the

1830s by Professor of Geology Adam Sedgwick,[49] and it has been repeated in different forms since by Hooykaas,[50] Stephen Jay Gould,[51] and others. Unfortunately, there is no consistency about which of the two meanings the term 'uniformitarian' properly has. The often cited phrase 'the present is the key to the past' could, of course, equally be cited of either of these two meanings, and only muddles the issue further. For this reason we will call (a) 'actualism', and (b) 'rate-uniformitarianism'.

Put simply, young-earth creationists often state that modern geology is based on uniformitarian principles, and find no shortage of secular geologists (most of them poorly informed on the history of geology) to cite to prove it. If they mean actualism, then the claim is true — and it is true for all branches of science. Science itself is possible only if it may be assumed that nature behaves in a law-like way. This is not to say that scientists rule out type-ii miracles, but just that science as such can deal only in regularity. If, on the other hand, it is asserted that modern geology was built on rate-uniformity, then the claim is demonstrably false, as we shall see.

## Geological history

Earth science based on observation basically dates from the mid-seventeenth century.[52] We might distinguish three main important areas of actual fieldwork:

1. Structure (ie recognition that strata had a structure)
2. Composition (ie mineralogy, what the rocks were made of)
3. Fossils (in the modern sense of living remains turned to stone).

On structure, Steno (1631–86), who later entered holy orders, was one of the first to suggest the study of strata on the obvious presupposition that they indicated an order of deposition.

In the systematic study of the structure of mineralogy and rock composition John Woodward (1665–1728) founded a system which, though not profound, makes Porter describe him as 'remarkable' and 'prophetic' in pointing the way forward.[53]

Fossils had long puzzled observers. Some looked like living creatures, others didn't, and opinions on their origins varied. Xenophanes (c570–480 BC) seems to have believed they originated from living creatures, and Avicenna (AD 980–1037) certainly did so and was followed by scholastic scholars like Albertus Magnus. The idea of their connection with the Flood was emphasised by D'Arezzo in 1282. Important studies included Hooke's *Micrographia* (1665), Martin Lister's article in the Royal Society *Transactions* in 1671 (which first noted that different kinds of rock yielded different fossils), and Lhwyd's *Lithophylacii*, in 1699. Woodward also began a useful collection of fossils and minerals, still intact in Cambridge. At that time there was no obvious reason why living creatures should 'turn to stone', and no obvious reason why fossils should not (like minerals and crystals) be chemical products of the rocks themselves.[54] Nevertheless, the consensus view by the early eighteenth century was that fossils were the remains of once living creatures.[55]

Naturalists at that time also faced the wider problem of constructing a theory to explain how strata formed, why fossils were found on tops of mountains and how — since they were all Christians of varying orthodoxy and piety — this fitted Genesis. It should, however, be noted that they all generally took a Baconian approach, not 'tailoring nature to the Scriptures', nor feeling any great theological pressure to do so, but simply developing their theology and science together in seeking an ultimate unity of knowledge.[56] Though, of course, individuals sometimes failed in the application of this approach to which they were committed, science 'confirmed' Scripture but did not begin from it.[57]

One suggestion was that most of the earth's surface structure was laid down during the one Noachic Flood. Two Cambridge scholars on what Porter describes as 'the liberal and rationalistic wing' of the church put forward such theories.[58] Both Burnet's (1681) and Whiston's (1696) theories proposed non-supernatural mechanisms, though neither were practical naturalists. Theologically, Whiston was unorthodox, whilst Burnet took Genesis very allegorically. They found few followers — scientific or theological.

A third Flood geology was that of Woodward, *Essay Toward a Natural History of the Earth* (1695). Woodward suggested that in the Flood the stone, minerals, chalk, etc, 'lost their solidity' and were 'sustained in the water', eventually resettling in the order of 'different specific gravity'.[59] Contemporary Christian naturalists like the pious Ray, Lhwyd, Nicholson, Baker, etc, found this to make neither scientific nor theological sense. They pointed out that neither the strata nor fossils are in order of specific gravity, it would have required far more water than the Bible implied, the shells would also have dissolved (leaving no fossils), etc. Woodward was forced to introduce the type-ii miracle — supposing that normal gravity was suspended, etc. This — though modern Flood geologists usually resort to similar stratagems — all rather defeats the original object of constructing a scientific theory of the Flood: given enough miracle, *any* theory can be made compatible with observation.

More biblically minded critics also pointed out that the Bible referred to the same rivers before and after the Flood, that the curse dated from the Fall of Adam and not the Flood, and that the Bible implied a longer period than the fourteen days in May suggested by Woodward to account for fossil leaves.[60] Woodward was a pioneer in observational geology, but his actual system was scientifically impossible and biblically unsound.

There was also another important model which gained some support, due to Robert Hooke (1635–1703). Though Hooke believed in the Bible and the widespread effects of Noah's Flood, he believed that marine fossils were found on mountains because the earth's surface was in a constant cycle of uplift and fall: a series of catastrophic earthquakes over a long period of earth history. His system prefigured the later one of Hutton (whom some have suggested knew of it) and also some ideas of William Smith.[61]

It should actually be noted that in general (Woodward was an exception) 'most theorists were not fieldworkers, and most fieldworkers did not write theories'.[62] Fieldworkers, like Ray and Lhwyd, were all too aware of the shortcomings of theories. Davis Young rightly portrays how Ray puzzled about how to construct one.[63] Earthquakes might raise sea-floors, but not to the extent needed for mountains. A single flood of short duration could not account for distributions of rocks and fossils without great ad hoc introductions of miracles. Thus, though most naturalists suspected that a worldwide flood might have something to do with fossils on mountains, ideas (like Woodward's) that all the strata were laid down in one universal flood were never part either of scientific or of Christian orthodoxy. Men like Hooke, Ray and Lhwyd believed no less in the Flood than Woodward, but could not believe it the sole agent for laying down the strata.

Apart from Woodward, Morris cites two key Bible-believing naturalists from this early period: the 'founder of natural history' and 'strong Christian' Ray (1627–1705) and the 'founder of systematic biology' Linnaeus (1707–78). Linnaeus is also cited as a 'creationist' by Bowden and as a 'man of great piety and respect for the Scriptures' by Morris.[64] Linnaeus, like Ray, specifically rejected the possibility that all the fossils could have been laid down in the Genesis Flood.[65] Such, in fact, was the effect of accumulating evidence that one modern study states that by 1750

Woodward's theories 'were so undermined that they could no longer be accepted, even by those geologists who emphasised the Flood's role'.[66] One of the few prominent eighteenth century Flood-geology naturalists was Alexander Catcott, who held a tense mixture of Woodwardian and Hutchinsonian ideas.[67] Hutchinson rejected Woodward as insufficiently 'literalist', and Hutchinsonians continued as a minority (much as modern young-earth creationists), though were rejected by mainstream evangelical leaders.

By the late eighteenth century, all schools of geology had concluded that the world was much older than previously thought. There were, however, two major areas of controversy:

1.  *Aqueous versus igneous* Neptunism held that virtually all rocks had been laid down by the agency of water, except relatively recent volcanic rock. Vulcanism held that a number of rocks (eg basalt) were formed from molten lava, ie were igneous in origin.
2.  *Progressivism versus steady state* This concerned whether the process showed a beginning (primitive rocks which contained no fossils) or was simply endlessly cycling, with no trace of any beginning.

Neptunism was generally progressivist, vulcanism could be either. In these movements the figureheads (though not the founders) came to be Werner and Hutton. Hutton argued that even granite was igneous, and was a strong advocate of a steady-state theory. Though he is cited as a founder of uniformitarianism by Morris,[68] by Bowden,[69] and by Baker,[70] he merely shared the universal actualism of geologists and was not particularly a rate-uniformitarian in the later sense of Lyell.

Hutton himself was deistical, but there was no lack of Christians (eg Revd Playfair) among his most prominent supporters. His steady-state system merely says there is no *apparent* trace of a beginning; God could, of course, have created the whole thing instantaneously as an ongoing system. It was never a simple issue of theological differences, and — though many were also interested in theology — the arguments were, with few exceptions, based on observational evidence.

In the early nineteenth century there were two further developments. The first was the recognition by English engineer William Smith, that particular strata could be systematically identified by their fossils. The written dissemination of this idea owed much to the writings of Brongniart and Cuvier,[71] and it is interesting that both Bowden and Morris cite Cuvier as a 'famous creationist scientist' who 'discovered' comparative anatomy and vertebrate palaeontology.[72]

It was also Cuvier who developed a second influential idea, based mainly on data from around the Paris Basin, that there had been successive widespread floods. In England, William Buckland developed this into a notion of successive worldwide floods, of which the Flood of Noah might be the last.[73] This form of catastrophism (ie successive catastrophies) became popular. A leading advocate for it was the Cambridge Professor of Geology, Adam Sedgwick. Its leading opponent was probably the Scottish naturalist John Fleming, who rejected it (in favour of a tranquil flood) on both geological and biblical grounds![74] Both were highly competent scientists. Theologically, Sedgwick identified his views with those of Charles Simeon — acknowledged as one of the foremost evangelical leaders of his generation[75] — whilst Fleming was part of the evangelical revival which split the Church of Scotland. On both sides of the debate, then, leading protagonists were firm evangelicals!

By the 1830s, various controversies had become settled among serious geologists:

1. Neptunism had been right in believing the rocks to show a one-way history rather than an endless cycle (as Hutton had thought).

2. Neptunism was wrong in supposing that mineral type indicated age of rock: granite, for example, was fossil-free not because it was primitive (ie before organic creation), but because it was igneous (ie solidified from molten rock, which could be of any period).

3. Neptunism had been wrong, and vulcanism right, in the igneous origin of basalt, granite, etc, and igneous rocks played a major part in earth history.

4. The association of fossil type with age was accepted.

5. The successive worldwide Flood theories were abandoned. Sedgwick's own fieldwork, for example, led him to a public admission in a Presidential Address to the Geological Society in 1831 that his former views on 3 and 5 had been wrong. Dean Buckland, Reader in Geology at Oxford, made the same admission in footnotes in a work of natural theology of 1836.[76]

In this period Charles Lyell put forward two distinctive theories:

(a) *Rate-uniformity* He assumed that rates of all processes had been constant, and actually tried to work out time spans based on it.[77]

(b) *Steady-state* Lyell assumed that all the genera of animals had always existed in a steady cycle of species change: there was no progression of animal forms.

On (a), his sympathisers never numbered more than a small minority of geologists — the general view (well expressed by Sedgwick) was that it was a gratuitous assumption. Lyell's attempts at actual time spans were never accepted, and by the 1860s even he admitted it was hopeless.

Lyell's steady-state theory fared even worse, he won no notable converts, and this has led Michael Bartholomew in his detailed studies to call Lyell a 'singular figure'.[78] Lyell's famous *Principles of Geology* (1830–3) was a best-selling introduction, but neither of his distinctive ideas convinced the geological world. What was more influential was its version of geological history — a version which was really propaganda. Porter calls it 'mythic history'.[79] His praise of Hutton and criticism of Werner as heads of two supposedly warring factions in the earlier period is misleading, as are his exaggeration of the importance of Hutton and of himself in geological development. Unfortunately, his version of history passed into folklore, copied in the historical works of Whewell and Geikie and down to modern ones like D H Hall in his 1976 *History of Earth Sciences During the Scientific and Industrial Revolutions*.

Young-earth creationists like Bowden, Whitcomb and Morris (and some secular writers too) seem to make several basic mistakes about the geology of this period. Thus they assume that:

1. Flood geology had become orthodox, and Cuverian multiple catastrophes overthrew it.
2. Geology in the 1830s was a bit of amateur dabbling by gentlemen, without much empirical base or history.
3. Lyell was a kind of Hercules figure, taking the feeble geological establishment by storm to establish uniformitarian principles.
4. Lyell himself was a secret evolutionist, dedicated to overthrowing Genesis.
5. The geological column was then developed on Lyellian principles, preparing the way for evolution.

All these points may be shown to be demonstrably historically mistaken. On 1, Morris and Whitcomb state: 'Throughout the eighteenth century and well into the nineteenth, most theologians and scientists of the Western world believed that the Deluge was responsible for the major fossiliferous strata of the earth.'[80] Morris extends this mistaken idea even to the nineteenth century, and so makes a quotation (actually taken from a secondary source dated 1946) referring to Buckland's 1820 work, to show that Buckland 'abandoned' Flood geology for Cuvier's multiple floods.[81] The quotation is made out of context, and a scientist of Buckland's generation would have been little more likely to have ever believed in Flood geology than to have believed that the world was flat.

Points 2 and 3 are clear in Bowden's portrayal of a supposed group of 'amateur gentlemen', and his citation of Himmelfarb's assertion (long since discredited) that geology was 'in so feeble a state that it could not resist the determined assault' of Lyell's theory.[82] A similar, but more detailed perception due to Laudan is considered at some length in Paul Marston's PhD thesis. Laudan's suggestions are misleading because there is, in fact, a breadth of continuity in observational work, a point not very clear in her more recent work.[83] Morris, however, follows Bowden's misunderstanding on this, listing a supposed circle of 'untrained' geologists (inexplicably including Chambers, whom no one regarded as a competent geologist and who contributed nothing).[84] Neither explains what kind of training they would have expected geologists to have. In the 1830s, of course, there were no 'professional' scientists in the modern sense, and the modern route into science of specialist degree, PhD research, etc, did not exist.[85] Nevertheless, there were ways for researchers to be recognised as competent and genuine contributors to the ongoing advance in observational science.[86] Geologists trained by studying the literature on the observational results which had been accumulating since about 1700, and by working with experienced geologists.

Morris and Whitcomb too claim that the view of Cuvier and Buckland were 'eclipsed by the Lyellian school of uniformitarian geology'.[87] Ascribing to Lyell's influence both widespread use of fossils for dating, and 'uniformitarianism', Morris asserts: 'Lyell is, then, a figure of key importance in the sudden conversion of the world from creationism to evolutionism.'[88]

Lyell's effect was not really crucial. The evangelical Fleming had been leading an assault on Bucklandian catastrophism in 1825–6 when Lyell was still a catastrophist,[89] and Fleming was justifiably angry when Lyell later tried to claim the credit for its demise.[90] Fleming, Scrope and Prevost were probably at least as influential as Lyell on professional geologists like Sedgwick. Sedgwick's own field observation was the real reason for his change of mind, which occurred between 1827 and 1830, before Lyell's book was published.[91] In any event, what was distinctive in Lyell's system remained an oddity, and some modern evangelical geologists have doubted if even Lyell himself fully accepted it.[92] Certainly, many key geologists retained either the neo-catastrophist ideas of Elie De Beaumont on mountain building (as did Sedgwick), or the neo-catastrophist glacial theories of Agassiz (as did Buckland).

Bowden seems to misunderstand not only Lyell's effect on geology, but also his religious motivation. He cites a letter of Lyell's referring to 'freeing the science from Moses' and to the harm of 'Mosaic systems', and applauding Bishop Sumner's castigation of Ure.[93] Bowden takes 'Mosaic systems' as 'a typically oblique reference to the accounts of creation and the Flood, as given in Genesis'. Not so. Lyell did not mean to attack Genesis, obliquely or otherwise, and in his inaugural lecture in the orthodox King's College in 1832 he included the classic argument from design and consistency of geology with Scripture.[94] By 'Mosaic systems', he was referring to those who tried to found systems of geology on Genesis rather than observation. There were a number of these during the period, and they may be characterised as follows:

1. They are by people with little or no field expertise in geology; they do not stand in the tradition of observational research.

2. Each is individualistic — none founded a school.
3. None is strictly literalistic anyway.
4. None won support from the evangelical (or any other) Christian leaders of the time.[95]
5. Most were quite respectful to geologists, seeing themselves as reinterpreting what the geologists were finding.

Ure was the only one of them in the Geological Society, though he was really a chemist and had joined in early days of laxer membership. Actually, both Ure's religious orthodoxy and his personal life failed to win the respect of his contemporaries, whilst Bishop Sumner, in contrast, was one of the leading evangelicals of his generation.[96] On Ure's geology, the evangelical Professor Sedgwick wrote a stinging review. Lyell's attitude to Ure, then, was unexceptional. Bowden's suggestion, moreover, that 'Lyell's sole purpose in rapidly befriending Darwin and promoting his interests was in order to use him as a means of propagating the theory of evolution' borders on fantasy.[97] Darwin's main mentors during his famous 1830s Galapagos trip were Adam Sedgwick and J S Henslow — an emphatically orthodox Anglican, rightly described by Bowden as 'deeply religious'.[98] Darwin was a pleasant and promising naturalist — and Lyell's interest in him was no more remarkable than theirs. Throughout the 1850s, Lyell opposed even progression of forms (let alone evolution) and was still (as his notebooks show) thinking in terms of a supernatural origin of new species.[99] Though we feel one modern expert on Lyell may be going too far in stating, 'Lyell feared evolutionary ideas in part because they contradicted . . . Christian theology,' nevertheless, we do find him even in the late 1860s, struggling to come to terms with a true Darwinism.[100] It would be ludicrous to see him as secret evolutionist in the 1830s.

Several important points need to be made about the construction of the geological column. Firstly, it was in no way based on assumptions of evolution, hidden or otherwise.

Most orthodox geologists rejected Lyell's idiosyncratic no-change-at-all system, and held that different orders of creature came into being at different stages; but this did not imply progression at any more detailed level. The basic column structure was established by 1855 (later changes were largely verbal or detail). During this whole period not one person who contributed to the column (including Lyell) believed in evolution. Important in establishing the correlation of fossils with strata was the Protestant Christian Cuvier — lauded, as we have seen, by both Bowden and Morris. The early circle included Buckland, a dean who wrote on the design of God in creation and whose wife attended an evangelical church.[101] The standard 1820s textbook was co-authored by W D Conybeare (whose 1839 book on the Christian Fathers shows a highly orthodox theology) and Phillips (who held to the orthodox gap theory of Genesis). In the 1830s, Lyell himself was a contributor mainly to the study of later strata. The evangelical Sedgwick made major contributions to Cambrian, Ordovician (by another name), Silurian, and Devonian. Later, the evangelical Hugh Miller made great contributions on the Carboniferous, and unitarian Agassiz (lauded as a creationist by Morris) on glacial theory. Sedgwick, Miller and Agassiz all vigorously opposed evolution in written critiques of works by Chambers and/or Darwin. But Morris and Whitcomb assert in their *The Genesis Flood* (1961) that fossil dating of rocks was based on 'the two assumptions of uniformity and evolution'.[102] Actually, fossil dating did not depend on rate-uniformity and was developed by anti-evolutionists, though Morris and Whitcomb's mistake has been endlessly copied by their followers.

A final point showing misunderstanding about the building of the geological column is the often repeated accusation of circularity, ie that the rock strata are dated using the fossils, but the fossils in turn are dated from their place in the strata. Morris made this in 1961 and in numerous books since, and many of Morris' followers have repeated the charge.[103] So what actually happened? In many places the layers which make up the strata are fairly flat and similar over wide local areas. The similarity of fossils within similar strata had been noted by various engineers, scientists and landowners, but it was William Smith who first developed the idea systematically. Smith, a surveyor, worked at a time when quarries and mines all over the country were opening geological sections to view. In pioneering work around Bath (where the layering is clear), and then nationwide, he found similar fossil correlation. Smith was not a theoretician, and his approach was structural rather than thinking in terms of dating.[104]

The lower/older strata are, of course, often much more contorted and not in simple layers. Adam Sedgwick, probably the major pioneer of the stratification of older rocks, wrote in 1846 of his method:

> In every country which is not made out by a pre-existing type, our first labour is that of determining the physical groups, and establishing their relations by natural sections. The labour next in order is the determination of the fossils found in successive physical groups; and, as a matter of fact, the natural groups of fossils are generally found nearly co-ordinate with the physical groups.[105]

Sedgwick claimed that his method, which he saw as the classical method of William Smith, began by finding the rock succession in a particular locality using three dimensional mathematics and the tracing of rock types up from a baseline. The *initial* identification of fossil types must be made on the basis of their position in some local succession. Only then do they become a useful tool to correlate rocks in far-apart localities. There is no more circularity involved here than in any other area of science.

## The church and geology

We have seen that Christians, and in particular evangelicals, were highly involved in the rise of historical geology. But how did leaders of the church react to geology and the geologists in their midst?

In Paul Marston's PhD thesis there are details of a study on this for the crucial 1820s and 1830s.[106] The evidence is that mainstream geology was accepted by leaders in the high church, among the theologically liberal, and in both Anglican and non-Anglican evangelicalism. This point is important, for it seems not always to have been well understood, even in some modern historical works.[107] In this period, the mouthpiece of the moderate evangelical Anglicanism of Simeon, Wilberforce, Sumner, and the so called Clapham Sect was the *Christian Observer*. Though it would print letters from 'Scriptural Geologists', and even from the more extreme Hutchinsonians, its editorial line consistently supported mainstream geology and the position of clerics like Conybeare and Sedgwick who were geologists. On the other hand, it equally clearly rejected any suggestion (such as that made by Powell at Oxford) that the Bible might contain historical or scientific mistakes. Among Church of Scotland evangelicals, key leaders like Thomas Chalmers, and geologist Hugh Miller, were equally clearly committed to the value of geology. Among leading non-Anglicans (or Dissenters), John Pye Smith wrote his book on the *Relation Between the Holy Scriptures and Some Parts of Geological Science* in 1839. His acceptance of mainstream geology was continuous (his correspondence with John Phillips is extant) and a final version was issued just after his death in 1854.

This is not, of course, to deny that support for eccentric geological schema was apparent in some sections of the less educated Christian public. Support was given to this by the Calvinist editor of the weekly paper *The Record*, whose dour controversial tone was deeply distasteful to many evangelicals.[108] Its attitude was abhorred by major evangelical leaders like Simeon, Sumner and Henry Venn.[109] In any event, a modern study can state: 'The following of the Scriptural geologists, for all their vociferousness and the plenitude of their tracts, was small and consistently so.'[110]

Evangelicals supported two main schema for the reconciliation of Genesis and geology during this period, though there were variations on them. The first of these is generally called 'age-day creationism', in which the 'days' of Genesis 1 were held to be long periods of time. The second is generally called 'gap-theory creationism'; this held that at some point in the first two verses of Genesis 1 there was a very long gap, and the rest of the chapter described a process of re-creation or restitution of the world. Rather than, 'The earth was without form and void' (1:2 RSV), it was suggested that it meant: 'The earth became without form and void'. Variations on these two ideas generally held sway among evangelicals between about 1815 and the date of the publication of Darwin's evolutionary theory in his *The Origin of Species* in 1859.

The origins of these two views are hard to discover. Some claims have been made that the early Fathers taught one or other, but we doubt there is any real evidence for this. Though, as we have seen, literalism on the 'days' was never a part of orthodoxy (and an age-day theory would be entirely compatible with their approach to the term), early Christians had no evidence for an ancient earth and would have found no immediate reason to speculate from Genesis, as they knew it was not intended to deal with such questions. It was by the eighteenth century that the ancient earth had come to be generally accepted. The age-day theory can be traced back to Buffon in *Époques de la Nature* (1778), but was influentially revived by evangelical G S Faber in his *Genius and Object* (1823), and had its most illustrious pre-1859 geological advocate in Hugh Miller in his *The Testimony of the Rocks* (1857). Miller actually portrays the 'days' as visionary or prophetic, but argues that they are also indicative of time periods in history.

The gap theory is traced by Ramm to some figures in the seventeenth century,[111] but in the nineteenth century it owed its popularity to Chalmers in *The Evidence and Authority of the Christian Revelation* (1814), John Pye Smith's *Relation Between the Holy Scriptures and Some Parts of Geological Science* (1839), and later works like G H Pember's *Earth's Earliest Ages* (1876). Influential geological advocates were Buckland in *Geology and Mineralogy Considered With Reference to Natural Theology* (1836), supported by high-church scholar Pusey; Hitchcock supported it, and Sedgwick also tended towards it, though later was more wary of committal.[112]

Variants of the age-day and the gap theory dominated evangelicalism in the years before Darwin. Two other ideas, however, caused reaction without achieving popularity as systems. In J H Kurtz's *Bible and Astronomy* (1842) a form of gap theory was combined with the idea that the six 'days' were visions given to Moses rather than intended to have any real reference to time periods.

Secondly, in 1857 the evangelical naturalist P H Gosse published his *Omphalos*. The word means 'navel', and Gosse drew attention to the obvious fact that Adam did not need a navel as he had no mother — yet surely God would have created him with a navel. In other words, Adam, as an instantaneous mature creation, bore marks of a history which did not in fact occur. All of what we have called type-ii miracles actually involve creating an apparent history. Thus, for example, changing water into wine gives it an apparent history of fermentation, etc. Gosse carried this to its logical (or some thought illogical) conclusion, and suggested that all the fossils, etc, had been placed there as part of an apparent age — the earth might really be only a few thousand years old. Philosophically this is, of course, unassailable; it is just that to most people going to quite that extreme seems rather far-fetched! On the other hand, Gosse's point about apparent age does have to be taken into account for any creative acts performed as type-ii miracles.

## Darwin's theory: introduction and history

Darwin's *Origin of Species* was published in 1859. In this section we will look at the scientific issues, and make the following basic points:

1.  The observational evidence was against Darwinian evolution at that time.
2.  Scientists actually fell into a whole range of views, from anti-evolutionists (like Sedgwick and Agassiz), through evolutionists who played down natural selection (like neo-Lamarckian Samuel Butler and the later Mivart), to those (like Darwin, Huxley and Galton) who saw natural selection as the main agent in evolution, and finally those (like Wallace) who saw it as virtually the only agent.
3.  Twentieth-century developments in evolutionary theory have involved extensions and modifications to Darwin's theory rather than its rejection — and the nature of the evidence has radically changed.

Darwin's evolutionary theory can be summarised briefly as follows:

(a)  There are variations (for reasons not then known) among the offspring of any living creature.
(b)  These variations will mean that some of these offspring are better able than others to survive and reproduce.
(c)  There will, in turn, be differences among the offspring of these successful reproducers — the most successful, in turn, reproducing.

(d) This process will imply what may be called 'natural selection', in which competition to survive in successive generations' organism produces a cumulative evolutionary trend.

This theory began to emerge in Darwin's unpublished sketches in the 1840s. In 1858 A R Wallace independently arrived at it and sent Darwin a paper about it (not knowing that Darwin had already reached this conclusion). This forced Darwin's hand, and eventually Wallace's paper was read together with the earlier sketches of Darwin in the Linnean Society for that year. The real publicity about it, however, began with the publication the following year (1859) of Darwin's *The Origin of Species*.

Darwin's main arguments for the theory could be divided into two. The first was by analogy. He noted how breeder selection could produce a Great Dane and a Pekinese from the same dog stock — and made the analogy to 'natural selection' as a source of change in the wild. He presumed that there was no limit to the changes which could occur by this selection.

The second was based on a kind of 'what would we expect if I am right' argument. Darwin did this very well — though critics suspected that given sufficient ingenuity, he could have explained almost anything!

These two kinds of argument made evolution plausible, but did not show it was true. *Darwin had little or no positive evidence that it had actually happened.*[113] He had explicitly to admit ignorance of: the laws governing inheritance, the cause of particular variations, the reasons for hybrid sterility, the reasons for rarity or extinction, the conditions favourable for new species, the means of transport, and the reasons for embryo variation. The fossil record, except in very broad outline, was an embarrassment to be explained away rather than a proof.[114] It showed little or no evidence of gradation from one species into another, and Darwin had to argue that it was very incomplete, failing to convince his old mentor Sedgwick, among others. Positive evidence against the theory was produced by physicists like Kelvin and Jenkin.[115] This was that the cooling rates of the sun and earth did not (on known laws of physics) allow enough time for evolution. The physicists were open to suggestions for possible sources of energy, but found none plausible — and could not at that time have known that a nuclear source of energy would later be identified.

On a scientific level, then, the debate was not one between unprejudiced Darwinians and obscurantist conservatives. On a basis of observation alone, any rational person would have had to reject Darwin's theory as the observable evidence was against it. Science, however, is a search beyond immediate observation for a coherent overall view, and it was a belief that they had found this (in spite of contrary evidence) which motivated the evolutionists.

Darwin presented the debate in *The Origin of Species* as though it was between simple flash-bang creationists, on the one hand, and his own theory on the other. This was misleading. Those (eg Sedgwick and Agassiz) who rejected evolution often veered towards a complex concept of 'arche-types' — a kind of variations-on-a-theme approach, which might also be held by non-Darwinian evolutionists (which probably included the leading anatomist Richard Owen).

On the actual laws of inheritance Darwin had speculated unconvincingly, but formed no viable theory. Around the turn of the century Mendel's ideas were rediscovered, producing some further problems for Darwinian theory. Gradually, however, over the course of several decades, a reconciliation between the ideas of Darwin and those of Mendel was affected, largely through the mathematical work of Haldane and Sewall Wright. This resulted in what has become known as the synthetic theory or neo-Darwinism, with which Julian Huxley is also associated. By the 1930s, this was generally accepted outside a few religious circles.[116]

In more recent years the idea of a smooth flow of evolutionary change (gradualism) has been challenged by a group centred around Stephen Jay Gould and Niles Eldredge.[117] They suggest that there may be long periods of stability with little change and many fossils, alternating with brief periods of comparatively rapid change (ie rapid evolution over thousands of years rather than millions). A further emphasis comes in the work of Richard Dawkins which portrays the inherited 'codes' (genes), which determine physical characteristics of living things, to be the real units struggling for survival.[118] All apparent altruism, all acts of self-sacrifice of the individual, are to be explained as unconscious stratagems of the genes in their 'struggles' to survive. Yet another line of thinking questions the use of the word 'random' and the extent of natural selection at molecular level, arguing for the possibility of occasional 'jumps'.[119]

It must be emphasised that all these developments are movements within neo-Darwinism — not attacks on it. The neo-Darwinian assumption remains overwhelmingly predominant among biological scientists, and no one should be misled on this by the careful selection of quotations (often out of context) which appears in some anti-evolutionary literature.

### The church in a post-Darwin age

The supposed rantings against Darwin of ignorant contemporary clerics is a classic part of the conflict-theory folklore. Classically portrayed as a supreme example of this is the June 1860 British Association debate at Oxford, where the 'ignorant gibes' of Bishop 'Soapy Sam' Wilberforce were supposedly silenced by the cool scientific precision of T H Huxley in what is taken to be a turning-point of the evolution debate. Actually, Wilberforce (the high churchman son of the famous evangelical anti-slavery campaigner) was a competent amateur naturalist, had been primed by Owen, the greatest comparative anatomist of the age, and (by Darwin's own admission) made all the most telling points against Darwin in an article in the *Quarterly Review* of July 1860.[120] It seems highly unlikely that this was any kind of turning-point, or, indeed, that many people thought Huxley to have won the debate. The gleeful undergraduate uproar was probably more to do with the fact that Huxley had been publically rude to a bishop.[121]

In the light of modern historical scholarship, a number of points may be made about the religious aspects of the evolution debate in the century after Darwin:

1.  At times Darwin's own work read in a reductionist way, going beyond scientific theory to imply a lack of design.
2.  Religious objections were usually (even when made by those, like evangelicals, committed to a high view of biblical inspiration) to this reductionism rather than to any conflict with the theory itself based on a supposed biblical literalism.
3.  Virtually all the main evangelical scientists and spiritual leaders during the period accepted an ancient earth, being divided between evolutionary creationists, age-day creationists, and gap-theory creationists. Evolutionary creationists, those who believed in instantaneous creations over a long time span, and to some extent age-day theorists, tended to accept elements of framework theory, ie that Genesis 1 embodied a literary framework rather than being strictly chronological.
4.  Evangelicals were to be found in Darwin's closest circle of scientific supporters on both sides of the Atlantic. A number of evangelical theologians also came to support his theory soon after its publication, and this continued throughout the early fundamentalist movement.

Some of these points may be startling. Though they can be illustrated only very briefly here, two modern books of careful scholarship have examined the reactions of Christians to Darwin's theories: those of James R Moore and David N Livingstone.[122] Also of great interest is Henry Morris' *A History of Modern Creationism* (1984). On the religious views of twentieth-century figures (many known personally to Morris) there is no reason to doubt its accuracy. What, however, we shall see is that the perspective Morris takes seems inconsistent. Having shown that virtually all those he accepts as spiritual Christian leaders between 1859 and 1940 were gap-theory, age-day or evolutionary creationists, he elsewhere proclaims all such ideas to be equivalent to evolution, which he says is inherently atheistic and 'pictures God as a sadistic ogre'.[123] Having accepted that all these evangelical leaders saw no inconsistency in interpreting the Bible in harmony with their views, he, nevertheless, maintains that theories like the age-day one are in 'flagrant contradiction' with Genesis, and that he has 'conclusive proof' that the 'days' were literal and speaks of 'pervasive theological apostasy' among the major evangelical figures of the late nineteenth century.[124]

What Morris implies, therefore, is that all the spiritual giants of the church over a period of a century or more followed a sadistic ogre, believed in theories in flagrant contradiction with the Bible and were theologically apostate. Only with the light of his own movement (mainly post-1961) has the self-evident biblical truth been re-established. The reader — Christian or non-Christian — will have to make his or her own assessment of the plausibility of such extreme claims.

Was Darwinism itself anti-Christian? As we shall see, the term itself has caused some confusion, and may be best avoided. Darwin's own religious views are still hotly debated. From a unitarian background, he briefly became more orthodox when at Cambridge (perhaps under Henslow's influence). Darwin's *Autobiography* suggests that, even at the time of writing *The Origin of Species* in 1859, he saw himself as a believer in God. Later, in 1887, he denied he had ever been an atheist, though accepted the term 'agnostic'. John Hedley Brooke, however, argues that Darwin meant this in a sense rather different from Huxley — in actual fact Darwin wavered, was undecided, and could speak differently on different occasions, not from deception but from uncertainty.[125] Darwin struggled over the question of design. On the one hand, natural selection seemed to open the door to the possibility that creatures could have evolved purely accidentally, and he felt a moral revulsion against the idea that suffering and death could form a part of a design plan. On the other hand, he found it hard to escape a conviction that the universe as a whole must be more than a product of undesigned chance.

In the late 1850s and early 1860s Darwin's inner circle actually included a number of highly religious men. Adrian Desmond rightly remarks that even the crusade of The X-club was never 'simply a matter of church-baiting rationalists triumphing over religious obscurantism, but a more subtle attempt, jointly undertaken by "agnostics", deists and some Christians, to professionalise science and put it at the disposal of the mercantile middle classes'.[126] A R Wallace, who independently formulated and consistently supported the theory of evolution by natural selection, was a lifelong spiritualist. In England, the circle of close supporting naturalist friends around Darwin and Huxley included the unitarian W B Carpenter (1813–85), who proposed Huxley for his FRS, and the broad churchman W H Flower (1831–99). There was the Methodist W K Parker (1823–90), whose 'lifelong almost rustic piety was reminiscent of Faraday's' with an 'exuberant belief in Old Testament miracles'.[127] There was J W Hulke (1830–95), a 'deeply religious Calvinist' who was Huxley's 'formidable ally'.[128] Then, in those early years, there was Professor of Zoology St George Mivart (1827–1900), an evangelical who became a Roman Catholic in 1844 during the revival of Anglo-

Catholicism. A keen Darwinian, he was almost one of Darwin's inner circle, and a close friend of Huxley.[129] His later move to belittling natural selection was a bitter blow to the group.[130] In America, the foremost supporter of Darwin was indubitably the botanist Asa Gray (1810–88), who was the first one outside the English circle to whom Darwin revealed his theory. The *Encyclopaedia Britannica* says of Gray: 'Gray was one of the few persons whom Darwin kept fully informed concerning the publication of his *Origin of Species* (1859). Gray was a devout Christian, however ...'[131] Livingstone states of Gray: 'His convictions were thoroughly evangelical. He stated that the Nicene Creed encapsulated the heart of his faith.'[132] Moore states: 'A moderate Calvinist and an adherent of the fundamental doctrines of evangelical Christianity.'[133]

Darwin's leading American proponent, then, was an evangelical. On the other hand, the leading scientific anti-Darwinian in America was probably J Agassiz (1807–73). Agassiz was a theist, but no evangelical, and Livingstone suggests that he found unitarianism congenial to his views.[134] Agassiz believed so strongly in special creation that he opposed racial intermarriage, because he thought the different races had been made separately. This is ironical since Morris, Bowden and Baker all laud Agassiz as a creationist and Bible-believing champion of orthodoxy, and Morris decries evolution for its supposed connection with racism and imperialism.[135] But let us note that in America the foremost scientific figures on both sides believed in God *and* accepted orthodox geology, but Darwinian evolution was defended by the evangelical and attacked by the theologically liberal racist.

An associate of Gray was the evangelical Congregationalist minister G F Wright (1838–1921). A linguist and philosopher as well as a theologian, Wright also became an expert on glacial geology in the region.[136] Both his orthodoxy and intellectual stature were generally recognised, and he 'allied himself with those who became fundamentalists in the twentieth century'.[137]

A second geologist was J D Dana (1813–95). Morris says that he was one 'of the most prominent American geologists', and 'at first opposed Darwinism, but eventually accepted evolution. Nevertheless, he continued to be a firm believer in biblical Christianity.'[138] This is true (even though on Morris' premises it should be impossible!), and is confirmed both by Livingstone[139] and the *Encyclopaedia Britannica*.[140]

The Revd George Macloskie, a Presbyterian and Princeton Professor of Biology, held to inerrancy but came to an evolutionary view of creation — being troubled that some churchmen had sanctified the position of Agassiz, who was 'not a theologian and scarcely a Christian'.[141]

Alexander Winchell 'played a major role in organising geology as a science in the United States', and stood in the tradition of the evangelical Arminian Methodism of John Wesley.[142] Though Winchell tended to the neo-Lamarckian end of evolutionism, his commitment was clear.

Morris cites three 'Creationist geologists' who 'fought evolutionism'.[143] The first was Benjamin Silliman (1779–1864), who reconciled the creation statements in Genesis with orthodox geology. The second was the evangelical Congregationalist Edward Hitchcock (1793–1864), an advocate of orthodox geology who favoured age-day or gap theory. In 1859 Silliman was eighty and Hitchcock sixty-six — neither lived long to reflect on the new theory and both would have thought ludicrous Morris' brand of young-earth creationism. The third of Morris' anti-evolutionary geologists was J W Dawson (1820–99). Dawson was actually a good friend of Lyell. He adopted the age-day theory and firmly accepted orthodox geology.[144] In his later work he accepted 'that there may be a theistic form of evolution ... It necessarily admits design and final cause'.[145]

What is obvious to anyone familiar with the period is that it is highly unlikely that any one of Morris' supposed 'Creationist geologists' would have thought credible his young-earth creationism, or accepted his views on the relationship of science and the Bible. Even those who were against evolution would not have accepted Morris' kind of supposed literalism. The issue was not literalism, but the place of design. Paul Marston's PhD thesis has shown a similar pattern for the evangelical geologist Sedgwick who, like Dawson, objected to evolution as such on scientific rather than theological grounds. On the other hand, Moore and Livingstone show just how many scientists, of various theological views including evangelicals, did accept some form of evolution; and Moore argues that the more orthodox Christians were the more orthodox Darwinians!

Turning from the evangelical scientists to the evangelical theologians, we find the same pattern. Morris' reconstruction of events is a strange mixture of fact and myth. He writes:

> As long as the scientists believed in creation, Christian leaders were quite content to believe in the inerrancy of Scripture and the literal historicity of the biblical accounts of creation and the Flood ... But as soon as the scientists turned to evolution, theologians and church leaders in almost every denomination scurried in a hasty retreat to the old compromising types of exegesis used by early theologians, such as Origen and Augustine, in order to accommodate evolution and the geological ages in Genesis.[146]

But Christian leaders before 1859 did not take Genesis literally in Morris' sense, and evolutionary theory was in no sense a watershed in the development of biblical interpretation. Lamenting their failure to stand on the word of God, Morris bewails that:

Certain very popular religious leaders of the day who were believed to be orthodox Bible believers, such as Frederick Farrar, James Orr, Charles Kingsley, and Henry Drummond, were tremendously influential in persuading rank-and-file Christians to accept theistic evolution. The same was true in the United States, where even such stalwarts as B B Warfield and A H Strong — known as strong defenders of the faith — capitulated to evolution.[147]

The only notable exceptions cited by Morris are Spurgeon, Moody and Charles Hodge of Princeton. Spurgeon (1834–92) was a leading South London Baptist, a renowned preacher rather than a theologian or profound thinker. He remained against evolution, yet in one review wrote: 'We look upon evolution as a questionable hypothesis. It is not yet an ascertained or acknowledged truth of science, and assuredly the time has not come to incorporate it with our faith in revelation.' Colin Russell, who cites this review, gives a more balanced view of Spurgeon's undoubted anti-Darwinism.[148] Moody (1837–99) was a mighty preacher, much used by God in British universities and elsewhere, but was neither theologian nor philosopher — and made no claim to be. Moody was a close friend of evolutionary apologist-theologian Henry Drummond, and also of R A Torrey — of whom more presently. Only the third of Morris' supposed exceptions, Charles Hodge, carries any real theological weight — and he was very influential on Calvinism of the whole period. Unfortunately, Morris quite misunderstands him. Hodge actually accepted a form of age-day theory, emphatically denying that the 'days' of Genesis must be literal and fully accepting orthodox geology. What of evolution? In his book *What is Darwinism?* he concluded, 'It is atheism,' but this is misleading. He defined Darwinism as including the three elements: (i) evolution, (ii) natural selection and (iii) rejection of design. Obviously if this third point is included in a definition of Darwinism, then Darwinism is atheism. But Hodge was quite clear that someone could believe in evolution by natural selection (like Asa Gray) and still be a Christian, though not a 'Darwinist' in Hodge's sense of that word. In other words, Hodge saw no particular problem in reconciling the purely scientific theory of evolution by natural selection with Christian faith.[149] What he then went on to argue was that Darwin and Wallace had, in fact, added to this system the metaphysical concept of 'pure chance' as an alternative agent to God.[150] Unfortunately, Hodge's use of terms has left many confused about his real position. G M Marsden in his interesting recent work on fundamentalism, leaves the definite impression that Hodge saw all evolution as incompatible with the Bible.[151] In actual fact Hodge's book shows clear sympathy with what Marsden presents as the most general view at the 1873 Evangelical Alliance, in which Hodge participated. Some, like the respected evangelical theologian James McCosh, accepted evolution. Others thought it difficult to accept, though even then there was no apparent support for literal recent creation in six days.

Finally, M B Anderson, in a popular speech, pointed out the two ways of using evolution: either as God's method of development or as pure chance.[152] Evolution, however, was not a 'verified law' but only a 'working hypothesis'. Hodge's later book said just the same. Hodge's position is, however, also left unclear by J R Moore and in some earlier papers of Livingstone, but is clear in Livingstone's *Darwin's Forgotten Defenders*.[153]

Morris is, however, correct in his assessment that major theologians of the period, such as B B Warfield and A H Strong, mainly moved to accept evolution. Moore and Livingstone add numerous other leading evangelicals, including A A Hodge, S Van Dyke, James McCosh, Landey Patton, W T Shedd, and a number of others. Their attitudes varied from total acceptance to acknowledging its compatibility with evangelicalism, but questioning its inductive base (with good reason as we have seen!).

## The twentieth century

What about the twentieth century? What views were taken by the key evangelical figures? It is instructive first to run through the views of all those cited by Morris as key Bible-believing theologians and spiritual leaders — in particular, for example, those in the movement which gave the name to 'fundamentalism'. The quotations are from Morris' *A History of Modern Creationism*:

1. *R A Torrey (1856–1928)* 'A highly successful evangelist' and 'one leading figure' in the fundamentalist movement, his book 'served as one of the key "textbooks" motivating the fundamentalist movement'. Torrey actually states that anyone who tries to insist that the 'days' of Genesis must be literal 'displays a hopeless ignorance of the Bible. Anyone who is at all familiar with the Bible and the Bible usage of words knows that the word "day" is ... frequently used of a period of time of an entirely undefined length'.[154]Ironically, in view of these strong words, Torrey reputedly took the infant Henry Morris in his arms in 1919 and prayed that the Lord would use him in his service.[155] Torrey himself accepted the orthodox geology of Dana, under whom he studied, and was a gap-theory creationist. He also followed earlier evangelical teaching on the existence of pre-Adamic man.

2. *W B Riley (1861–1947)* He was 'one of the most outspoken fundamentalists and creationists of the period' and a 'key personage in the fundamentalist revival'. Riley was an age-day creationist.

3. *H Rimmer (1890–1952)* 'The most widely known creationist of this period,' he was 'recognised by fundamentalists as the greatest Christian apologist of his generation.' Rimmer was a gap-theory creationist, believing Noah's Flood only regional, although he did also (inconsistently) refer favourably to G M Price.

4. *W H Griffith-Thomas (1861–1924)* Griffith-Thomas was 'another key leader of the fundamentalist movement . . . a scholarly writer and speaker, publishing many outstanding volumes of biblical and apologetics studies . . .' He was an age-day creationist.

5. *I Brown* 'Perhaps the most godly, gracious Christian gentleman I ever met, as well as one of the finest Bible teachers and creationist scientists.' Brown was a gap-theory creationist.

6. *Carl Schwarze* 'Obviously a fine scientist and also a fundamentalist.' Schwarze was a gap-theory creationist.

7. *L Allen Highley* 'Another fundamentalist . . . a very gracious Christian gentleman.' He was a gap-theory creationist.

A few points are worth spelling out in more detail here. First, by Morris' own admission, most of the founding fundamentalists accepted either the age-day or the gap-theory form of creationism, and he can cite none who were young-earth creationists. The actual term comes from a restatement of *The Fundamentals* edited by R A Torrey as a twelve volume paperback series in 1910–1915, and later reissued in a four volume set. The volumes, several million of which were issued, stood firm for biblical Christianity and gave rise to the term 'fundamentalism'. Volumes 4 and 6 contained work by the renowned Scottish theologian James Orr (1844–1913), who contended for a moderate Calvinist form of historical evangelicalism in Britain and America. Orr asserts:

The Bible 'does not profess to anticipate the scientific discoveries' of the nineteenth and twentieth centuries. Its design is . . . to reveal God and His will and His purposes of grace to men, and, as involved in this, His general relation to the creative world . . . Natural things are taken as they are given, and spoken of in simple, popular language, as we ourselves every day speak of them.[156]

Orr adopted an age-day theory, regarding it as certain that the world 'is immensely older than 6,000 years', and that whilst 'evolution is not yet proved, there seems to be a growing appreciation of the strength of the evidence for the fact of some form of evolutionary origin of species . . .'[157] In keeping with general scientific thinking of the period, Orr tended more to a neo-Lamarckian form of evolution — also holding (as did other contributors to *The Fundamentals*) that mankind was a sudden 'jump'.

In volume 7 there was a contribution from Professor G F Wright, giving a version of Darwinian evolution, though again making mankind an exception. [158]

Though in these later volumes there are a couple of anti-evolutionary (or at least anti-'natural selection') articles by little-known figures, it should therefore be remembered that the roots of early fundamentalism are in an acceptance of organic evolution. Perhaps 'original fundamentalist creationism' should be regarded as an alternative name for 'evolutionary creationism'!

The present writers would be proud to be called 'fundamentalists' in the tradition of men like Torrey, Wright, Orr, and other eminent contributors.

Critics of evolution in the years between 1859 and 1920 did not reject orthodox geology. They believed in a very ancient earth, and usually accepted that the 'days' of Genesis might not be literal. In actual fact it would seem that the origins of modern young-earth creationism may be traced back to Ellen White (1827–1915), a prominent early leader and prophetess among the Seventh-day Adventists.[159] In her character studies *Patriarchs and Prophets* she had written of the geological efficacy of the Flood, burying immense forests, which turned to coal. As a young man, Adventist George McCready Price (1870–1962) read these and, although untrained in any area of science, began in 1906 (though mainly in the 1920s) a series of books advocating a form of Flood geology in which all strata were laid down in the Flood. Morris admits:

Almost the only writers to advocate literal recent creationism during this period, however, were to be found among the Lutherans and Seventh-day Adventists — no doubt partly because their respective founders, Martin Luther and Ellen G White, had taught six-day creationism and a worldwide flood.[160]

Morris then lists Adventists like H W Clark, F L Marsh and E S Booth, etc, all of whom were taught by Price, and then cites various Lutherans (Byron Nelson, Graebner, Rehwinkel, etc), none of them scientists, who based their views on a strict reading of their sixteenth-century founder. One of the very few with scientific training who accepted Price's theories in the mid-1920s was D J Whitney (1884–1964). Morris judges that from his letters: 'Whitney . . . was irascible and highly impatient with anyone who disagreed with him about almost anything.'[161]

What we find, then, is that Price's appeal was to his fellow believers in the prophetess Ellen White, to some Lutheran pastors without scientific training or knowledge, and to the very occasional irascible person with scientific training. The bulk of critics of evolution did not accept Flood geology. Even the famous lawyer/politician William Jennings Bryan, who led the abortive attack on evolution in the infamous 1925 Scopes trial, or Tennessee Monkey Trial as it became known, was (by Morris' own admission) an age-day theorist who rejected Price and accepted orthodox geology.[162] In England, the Evolution Protest Movement was founded in 1932. Its founder/President was Sir John Ambrose Fleming, called by Morris 'one of the century's foremost scientists, but also a strong creationist'.[163] Fleming accepted orthodox geology and the existence of pre-Adamite men. The Evolution Protest Movement member called by Morris 'the most prolific creationist writer in England' was ornithologist Douglas Dewar — a gap theorist who rejected Flood geology.[164] Morris accepts that virtually the only 'Britisher' in the period to accept young-earth creationism was Major

E C Wren, whose style was 'marked by pungency and impatience ... much like that of D J Whitney'.

It is, then, clear that fundamentalism of the 1930s and 40s, in Britain and America, was characterised by an acceptance of orthodox geology, an ancient earth, and some form of age-day or gap-theory creationism.[165] The discontinuity between fundamentalism and the modern young-earth creationism is, unfortunately, disguised not only by the young-earth creationists themselves, but by secular writers such as Eileen Barker.[166] An excellent article, however, is that of M B Roberts: 'The Roots of Creationism'.[167]

One learns to be suspicious of 'turning-points', but if there was one for young-earth creationism, it was the publication in 1961 of *The Genesis Flood*. One author was the Lutheran theologian J C Whitcomb. The other was a man who says of George McCready Price: 'His tremendous breadth of knowledge in science and Scripture, his careful logic, and his beautiful writing style made a profound impression on me when I first began studying these great themes, back in the early 1940s.'[168] That man was, of course, Henry M Morris, an engineer who had, like Price, no training in either theology or geology. Morris admits that in 1959 'almost all Christian colleges and seminaries' were going along with the evolutionary creationism of the Christian American Scientific Affiliation, and 'the few who still rejected theistic evolution were either teaching progressive creation or ignoring the issue via the gap theory'. The book, he says, catalysed 'a significant revival of creationism'.[169] The effect of the book was certainly marked, though it was really a birth rather than a 'revival' of what Morris means by 'creationism'. It introduced both a view of geology and a view of the relationship of science and Scripture which had never been that of the mainstream of Bible-believing Christians. Not all, however, may have been aware of its novelty — for example, the Evolution Protest Movement slid, almost without noticing it, from the older creationism of Fleming and Dewar into the new young-earth creation-ism,[170] eventually in 1980 changing its name to the Creation Science Movement. The subsequent rise of young-earth creationism, its takeover of much of the fundamentalist movement, and its various legal challenges in America are all now well known.

Any movement with anything worth saying has its cranks and bigots, but we can in general terms discern several phases in the development of evangelicalism and fundamentalism. Mid-nineteenth-century evangelicals were committed to a Baconian 'two books' approach and accepted mainstream geology. Age-day and gap-theory creationism (with tinges of framework theory) prevailed and literalism existed, if at all, in liberal caricatures of evangelicals!

After Darwin's 1859 book attitudes varied. The predominant evangelical view, however, between 1859 and 1915 was that evolution by natural selection was compatible with Christian faith, as long as it did not deify chance. As Baconians, however, evangelicals saw its truth as to be established by scientific observation not Scripture, and differed about how far observational evidence supported it. The Bible was, they asserted in response to theological liberalism, accurate on matters of history and science, though was not a scientific source-book.

A rising tide of secularism and perceived social and political threats had led by 1925 to more pure anti-evolutionism. There was, then, considerable grass-roots support for Bryan's stance in the famous Tennessee Monkey Trial in 1925, in which he tried to prosecute school-teacher Scopes for teaching evolution. Bryan himself (though confused) mostly accepted mainstream geology, and his supporters retained the Baconian approach. Marsden's study, however, states that it would be difficult to overestimate the impact of the trial in transforming American fundamentalism.[171] The public mind forgot the witness of the distinguished scholars whose simple faith was combined with a true intellectualism, and thought of fundamentalism in terms of the muddled ignorance of Bryan. Some moderate evangelical scholars felt compelled to distance themselves from this image, which may have helped to polarise evangelicalism. In the period between, say, 1925 and 1961, then, evangelicalism became divided between those who accepted evolution as compatible with the Bible, and those who did not. Neither group adopted young-earth schema. In theory they all accepted a Baconian 'two books' approach, though in practice many of the more popular anti-evolutionary works may have seemed to derive scientific ideas from Scripture.

It may be that this prepared the way for the final post-1961 phase: young-earth creationism. The classic evangelical commitment to the reliability of Scripture now became identified with its primacy as a source of science. A commitment to the inspiration of its words became identified with the simple translation of those words into modern scientific terms and concepts never in the minds of its writers. In short, the Baconianism which had formed the foundation of the whole evangelicalism and early fundamentalism was finally abandoned.

We suspect, however, that many of those who have espoused young-earth creationism are unaware that, in doing so, they have cut themselves off from their own roots. We fear that many of its critics will throw out the baby of biblical Christianity with the bath water of a young-earth creationism. Finally, on a personal note, we hope that those in the young-earth movement will not cut themselves off from fellowship with those of us who share their evangelical experience, their spiritual aspirations, and their belief in biblical inspiration — but who uphold the older evangelical approach to science.

## Conclusion

The objectives of this chapter have been to show the following:

1. The idea that biblical Christianity and science have throughout history been locked in conflict is a myth. Many of the very greatest scientific geniuses have been deeply religious, and the supposed examples of conflict are largely folklore, not history.

2. In general the mainstream of the church has *never* taken it that the language of Scripture was precise enough to be a basis on which to reject scientific ideas like the moving earth, the ancient earth, or evolution. Where such ideas have been opposed, it is more usually on a basis of reason or observation.

3. Though espoused by many sincere Christians, modern young-earth creationism is rooted not in mainstream evangelicalism or even early fundamentalist history, but in a combination of Adventist theology and some sixteenth-century interpretations made when there was very little empirical evidence available at all.

These assertions, which we believe the evidence in this chapter has substantiated, are relevant both to the Christian and to the sceptic in assessing the relationship between science and Christianity.

## Notes

1. T H Huxley, *Collected Essays* (1894) Vol II p 52.
2. See J V Jenson, 'The X-Club', *British Journal for the History of Science*, vol 5 (1970): pp 63–72.
3. See C A Russell, *Science and Social Change 1700–1900* (1983), p 239, etc and *Cross-Currents* (1985), p 192.
4. J R Moore, *The Post Darwinian Controversies* (1979), p 84.
5. See *The Conflict Thesis and Cosmology* (OU Unit), p 30, which also gives a useful analysis of White, Simpson and Dijksterhuis.
6. See, for example, H Butterfield, *The Whig Interpretation of History* (1931).
7. *The Conflict Thesis and Cosmology* illustrates this with works of Simpson (1925) and Dijksterhuis (1961).

8. See, for example, the entry on Clerk Maxwell in *Encyclopaedia Britannica* (1987), vol 23, p 725.

9. H M Morris, *Men of Science, Men of God* (1982).

10. R Hooykaas, *Religion and the Rise of Modern Science*.

11. See, for example, A E Bell, *Christian Huygens* (1947), p 202; Huygens had a Protestant belief in a Creator. Also see L Koenigsberger, *Herman Von Helmholtz* (first published, 1906; this edition, 1965), p 234.

12. In *Let Newton Be* (J Faurel et al, 1988) John Brooke has recently argued persuasively that writers who have suspected Newton of some species of deism were mistaken. See also the earlier F E Manuel, *The Religion of Isaac Newton* (1974).

13. A Koestler, *The Sleepwalkers* p 451. Of the numerous introductions to cosmological history, we still prefer *The Sleepwalkers*, which is accurate enough for most general purposes and certainly the most readable.

14. D McKie, *Antoine Lavoisier* (first published, 1952; this edition, 1962), p 306.

15. See *Encyclopaedia Britannica* (1987), vol 7, p 593.

16. Eg E W Heaton, *Everyday Life in Old Testament Times* (1956), pp 185–6.

17. J W Draper, *History of the Conflict Between Religion and Science* (1875), p 63.

18. A D White, *A History of the Warfare of Science with Theology in Christendom* (1896), p 102.

19. Lactantius, *The Divine Institutes*, III, 3 (*Ant Nic Fath*, vii, 71).

20. *Ibid*, III, 24 (*Ant Nic Fath*, vii, 94); Lactantius, *Epitome of the Divine Institutes*, 39 (*Ant Nic Fath*, vii, 237).

21. Augustine, *The City of God*, XVI, 9 (*Nic & Pos Nic Fath*, 1, ii, 315).

22. E J Dijksterhuis, *The Mechanisation of the World Picture* (1961), p 93.

23. *Encyclopaedia Britannica* (1987), vol 3, p 600.

24. N Oresme, *Le Livre du Ciel* (1377).

25. *Ibid*.

26. See Koestler, *The Sleepwalkers*, for all these details.

27. White, *op cit*, vol 1, p 126.

28. See C Russell, *Cross-currents*, p 42.

29. See R Hooykaas, *Religion and the Rise of Modern Science* p 154 n 27.

30. See Koestler, *The Sleepwalkers*.

31. *Discovery*. Published by Marshall Cavendish 1987, p 118.

32. See Stillman Drake, *Galileo At Work* (1978), p 348, or *Galileo* (1980), p 78.

33. Drake, *Galileo At Work*, p 351.

34. *Ibid*, p 239.
35. John Wesley, *Works* (third edition, 1872; this printing, 1986), vol II, p 454; see also pp 388–89 and 441.
36. See J H Brooke, 'Natural Theology and the Plurality of Worlds', *Annals of Science*, vol 34 (1977): pp 221–86.
37. Sedgwick's own annotated copy of his friend Whewell's book is in the Cambridge Geological Museum.
38. M B Roberts, 'The Roots of Creationism', *Faith and Thought*, vol 112:1 (1986): pp 21–36.
39. W Irving, *Apes, Angels and Victorians* (1956) and G Himmelfarb, *Darwin and the Darwinian Revolution* (1959).
40. See, for example, R Porter, *The Making of Geology* (1977), p 129.
41. See Mary Midgely, *Evolution as a Religion* (1985).
42. Paul Marston tried this in a paper to the RSCF/ASA 1984 Oxford Conference.
43. R J Berry does this in *God and Evolution* (1988).
44. M W Poole and G J Wenham do this in *Creation or Evolution — A False Antithesis?* (1987).
45. Berry and Poole and Wenham in their books try this.
46. B Ramm, *The Christian View of Science and Scripture* (1954); Alan Hayward, *Creation and Evolution* (1985).
47. Morris, *The Biblical Basis for Modern Science*, pp 107, 114.
48. *Ibid*, p 107.
49. J W Clark and T M Hughes, *The Life and Letters of Adam Sedgwick* (1890), vol i, p 369.
50. R Hooykaas, *Natural Law and Divine Miracle* (1963), p 32.
51. Morris, *The Biblical Basis for Modern Science*, p 305, says Gould 'was one of the first to distinguish' between these two meanings of uniformitarianism — but actually Sedgwick made a similar distinction in the 1830s.
52. Porter, *The Making of Geology*, p 10.
53. *Ibid*, p 56.
54. Davis A Young, *Christianity and the Age of the Earth* (1982), p 28.
55. Porter, *The Making of Geology*, p 166.
56. *Ibid*, p 64.
57. *Ibid*, p 70.
58. *Ibid*, p 23.
59. J Woodward, *Essay Toward a Natural History of the Earth* (1695), cited in J M Levine, *Dr Woodward's Shield* (1977), p 34.
60. Baker to Woodward on 15th April 1700 (Camb MS no 35); John Edwards to Woodward on 4th February 1697; Ray to Lhwyd on 8th June 1696.
61. See Yushi Ito, 'Hooke's Cyclic Theory of the Earth in the Context

of Seventeenth Century England', *British Journal for the History of Science*, vol 21 (1988): pp 295–314. Like later writers, Hooke's belief in an ancient earth was based on strata thickness. Ellen T Drake, 'The Hooke Imprint on the Huttonian Theory', *American Journal of Science*, vol 281 (1981): pp 963–73 suggests Hutton was aware of Hooke's writings.

62. Porter, *The Making of Geology*, p 24.

63. D Young, *Christianity and the Age of the Earth*, p 30.

64. Bowden, *The Rise of the Evolution Fraud* (1982), p 10; Morris, *Men of Science, Men of God*, pp 40, 49.

65. J Ray, *Reflections on the Study of Nature* (translated by Smith, 1786).

66. R Rhappaport, 'Geology and Orthodoxy', *British Journal for the History of Science*, vol xi:1 (1978): p 8.

67. M Neve and R Porter, 'Alexander Catcott', *British Journal for the History of Science*, vol x:1 (1977): pp 37–60.

68. Morris and Whitcomb, *The Genesis Flood*, p 95; Morris, *A History of Modern Creationism*, p 34.

69. Bowden, *op cit*, p 19.

70. S Baker, *Bone of Contention* (1976), p 3.

71. See V Paul Marston, *Science, Methodology and Religion in the Work of Adam Sedgwick*, Open University PhD thesis (1984), p 385, for an analysis of this.

72. Bowden, *op cit*, p 219; Morris, *The Biblical Basis for Modern Science*, pp 463–4.

73. W Buckland, *Reliquiae Diluvianae* (1823).

74. See V Paul Marston, *Science, Methodology and Religion*, p 396.

75. *Ibid*, section 2.3; the letter quoted by evangelical Carus in *The Churchman* of February 1889 contains Sedgwick's reference to Simeon.

76. W Buckland, *Geology and Mineralogy Considered with Reference to Natural Theology* (1836).

77. See M Rudwick, 'Lyell's Chronological Model', *ISIS*, vol 243 (1977): pp 440–3.

78. M Bartholomew, 'The Singularity of Lyell', *History of Science* (1980): pp 276–93. Also: M Rudwick, *The Meaning of Fossils* (1972); A Hallam, *Great Geological Controversies* (1983), p 54; Peter J Bowler, *Fossils and Progress* (1976), p 5.

79. R Porter, 'Charles Lyell and the Principles of the History of Geology', *British Journal for the History of Science*, vol ix (1976): pp 91–103.

80. Morris and Whitcomb, *The Genesis Flood*, p 113 (see also p 91).

81. *Ibid*, p 93.

82. Bowden, *op cit*, p 23.

83. V Paul Marston, *Science, Methodology and Religion*, p 356, etc. R Laudan, *From Mineralogy to Geology: The Foundation of a Science 1650–1830* (1987).

84. Morris, *The Biblical Basis for Modern Science*, p 302.

85. See, for example, C A Russell, *Science and Social Change, 1700–1900*.

86. M Rudwick has analysed this in 'Charles Darwin in London: The Integration of Public and Private Science', *ISIS*, vol 73 (1982): p 190.

87. Morris and Whitcomb, *The Genesis Flood*, p 95.

88. Morris, *A History of Modern Creationism*, p 34.

89. See Hallam, *op cit*, p 46.

90. Fleming's letter to Sedgwick of 15th November 1831 is in the Cambridge Sedgwick collection.

91. See V Paul Marston, *Science, Methodology and Religion*, section 7.3, especially p 415.

92. R Van De Fliert, 'Fundamentalism and the Fundamentals of Geology', *ASA Journal*, 'Origins and Change' (1978).

93. Bowden, *op cit*, p 94.

94. See M Rudwick, 'Charles Lyell and His London Lectures on Geology', *Royal Society Notes and Records*, vol 29 (1974): pp 231–63.

95. See V Paul Marston, *Science, Methodology and Religion*, p 290, etc.

96. See P Toon, *Evangelical Theology 1833–1856* (1979), p 4.

97. Bowden, *op cit*, p 97.

98. *Ibid*, p 40.

99. See, for example, P Bowler, *Fossils and Progress*, p 76.

100. M Bartholomew, 'Lyell and Evolution', *British Journal for the History of Science*, vol 6:23 (1973): p 266.

101. E O Gordon (ed), *The Life and Correspondence of William Buckland, DD, FRS* (1894), p 111.

102. Morris and Whitcomb, *The Genesis Flood*, p 132.

103. *Ibid*, p 134.

104. There is presently a dearth of good material on the geological method of William Smith, but a paper and field trip given in Bristol and Bath in September 1988 by Hugh Torrens (a geologist and geological historian with a special interest in Smith) was invaluable in preparing this section. See also, Hugh Torrens, 'Hawking History — a Vital Future for Geology's Past', *Modern Geology*, vol 13 (1988): pp 83–93.

105. V Paul Marston, *Science, Methodology and Religion*, p 449 analyses this.

106. *Ibid*, section 6.2.

107. In particular the PhD refers to A Thackray and F Morrell's

*Gentlemen of Science* (1981), which exaggerates the broad-church influence and is misleading over the evangelical one, which was actually high on science of the period. It also contains some criticism of Milhauser's classic article 'The Scriptural Geologists' (*OSIRIS*, vol 11, pp 65–86).

108.  See G R Balleine, *A History of the Evangelical Party in the Church of England* (1908), p 163.

109.  F K Brown, *Fathers of the Victorians* (1961), p 129; A Ashwell, *Life of Samuel Wilberforce* (1880–2), vol 2, p 219; E Stock, *The History of the Church Missionary Society* (1899–1916), vol 4, p 60.

110.  J D Yule, *The Impact of British Religious Thought in the Second Quarter of the Nineteenth Century* (PhD thesis, Cambridge, 1976), p 328.

111.  B Ramm, *op cit*, p 172.

112.  See V Paul Marston, *Science, Methodology and Religion*, p 529, etc. Davis Young summarises such attempts at concord in *Christianity and the Age of the Earth* (p 55, etc) and in his article 'Scripture in the Hands of the Geologists', *Westminster Theological Journal*, vol 49 (1987): pp 257–304.

113.  See B G Gale, *Evolution Without Evidence* (1982).

114.  Charles Darwin, *Origin of Species* (1859), chap 9.

115.  Jenkin's brilliant 1860 review is in D Hull, *Darwin and His Critics* (1973), though Hull's comments, for example, on Sedgwick and Owen are misleading.

116.  See R J Berry, *Neo-Darwinism* (1982).

117.  Eg S J Gould and N Eldredge, 'Punctuated Equilibria: The Tempo and Mode of Evolution Reconsidered', *Paleobiology*, vol 3 (1977): pp 115–51.

118.  Richard Dawkins, *The Selfish Gene* (1986).

119.  Eg Mae-Wan Ho, Peter Saunders and Sidney Fox, 'A New Paradigm for Evolution', *New Scientist*, 27th February 1986.

120.  F Darwin (ed), *The Life and Letters of Charles Darwin* (1887), vol iii, p 324.

121.  See R J Lucas, 'Wilberforce and Huxley: A Legendary Encounter', *The Historical Journal*, vol 22 (1979): pp 313–30; D N Livingstone, *Darwin's Forgotten Defenders* (1987). Bowden's account of the incident is also accurate. The best recent account is J V Jensen, 'Return to the Wilberforce–Huxley Debate', *British Journal for the History of Science*, vol 21 (1988): pp 161–80.

122.  J R Moore, *The Post Darwinian Controversies* (1979) and David N Livingstone, *op cit*. The present treatment is also based on contact with these and other writers and on reading of primary material.

123.  H Morris, *The Genesis Record*, p 54.

124. H Morris, *Science and the Bible* (1988), pp 37–8.

125. See, for example, Brooke's 'Darwin's Science and His Religion' in J Durant (ed), *Darwinism and Divinity* (1985), which gives further references and speaks from a viewpoint sympathetic to evangelicalism. The present treatment is also based on personal discussion with the author.

126. A Desmond, *Archetypes and Ancestors* (1982), p 17.

127. *Ibid*, pp 52–3.

128. *Ibid*, p 134.

129. *Ibid*, p 137.

130. See Moore, *op cit*, p 117.

131. *Encyclopaedia Britannica* (1987), vol 5, p 437.

132. Livingstone, *op cit*, p 61.

133. Moore, *op cit*, p 271.

134. Livingstone, *op cit*, p 58.

135. Morris, *The Biblical Basis for Modern Science*, p 463 and *A History of Modern Creationism*, p 45, etc.

136. Moore, *op cit*, pp 280–2, 295–6; Livingstone *op cit*, pp 65–70.

137. Moore, *op cit*, p 42.

138. Morris, *op cit*.

139. Livingstone, *op cit*, p 75; also in Moore, *op cit*.

140. *Encyclopaedia Britannica* (1987), vol 3, p 870.

141. Cited in Livingstone, *op cit*, p 93.

142. *Ibid*, p 87.

143. Morris, *A History of Modern Creationism*, p 39.

144. Livingstone, *op cit*, p 82.

145. Quoted in Livingstone, *op cit*, p 84, from J W Dawson, *Modern Ideas of Evolution* (reprint 1977), p 227.

146. Morris, *A History of Modern Creationism*, p 37.

147. *Ibid*, p 38.

148. C A Russell, *Cross-Currents*, pp 170–4.

149. See Charles Hodge, *What Is Darwinism?* (1874), p 48, etc. Hodge is totally explicit on these things.

150. *Ibid*. References to Darwin and Wallace are widespread in the book.

151. G M Marsden, *Fundamentalism and American Culture: The Shaping of Twentieth Century Evangelicalism, 1870–1925* (1980), pp 19–20.

152. *Ibid*.

153. Moore, *op cit*, pp 203–4, 211–12; Livingstone, *op cit*, pp 102–5. The present treatment again reflects some personal discussion with the authors.

154. R A Torrey, *Difficulties in the Bible* (1907), chap 4.

155. Morris, *A History of Modern Creationism*, p 58.

156.  R A Torrey, ed *The Fundamentals*, 1988 reprint of the 1917 four-volume edition, vol 1, p 340.

157.  *Ibid*, vol 1, p 345.

158.  *Ibid*, vol 4, chap 6.

159.  Though many would describe the Adventists as a cult, it cannot be denied that they share many orthodox beliefs, and that Christians are found among them.

160.  Morris, *A History of Modern Creationism*, p 60.

161.  *Ibid*, p 105.

162.  *Ibid*, p 66, issues like the Scopes trial are given in the attractively produced volume titled *Evolution The Great Debate* by Vernon Blackmore and Andrew Page (1989).

163.  *Ibid*, p 107.

164.  *Ibid*.

165.  See also G M Marsden, 'Creation Versus Evolution', *Nature*, vol 305 (1983): pp 571–4; and 'Understanding Fundamentalist Views of Science' in A Montagu (ed), *Science and Creationism* (1984), chap 95 (though it may be noted that there is material in this volume with which we do not agree).

166.  See V Paul Marston's review in the *RSCF Newsletter*, no 6 (June 1986).

167.  M B Roberts, *op cit*.

168.  Morris, *A History of Modern Creationism*, p 80.

169.  *Ibid*, p 145.

170.  This can be dated to the EPM review of *The Genesis Flood*, October 1961.

171.  Marsden, *Fundamentalism and American Culture*, p 184. Some further interesting historical comment on twentieth-century developments is given in R J Berry, *God and Evolution* (1988), chap 7, or given by J R Cole in chap 3 of *Scientists Confront Creationism* (ed L R Godfrey, 1983). It must, however, be said that some of this last book seems to us a muddled liberalism (eg in Cole's sympathy with 'cultural relativism').

# 14
# THEOLOGICAL QUESTIONS ON GENESIS 1–3

## Introduction and the options today

AS EVANGELICALS COMMITTED TO A belief in the inspiration of the Bible, we must face a number of questions
raised by scientific thinking: the timescale of events, the
mode of creation, the individuality of 'Adam', and the date
and nature of the Flood. The main options for modern
evangelicals have already been identified historically, but we
will summarise them schematically here:

| TIME SPAN OF THE 7 'DAYS' | CHRONOLOGY AND NATURE OF THE 'DAYS' | CREATIVE MODE |
|---|---|---|
| Long span (very old earth) | Gap theory 'Days' of Revelation Intermittent fiat days Age-day theory Framework theory | Instantaneous appearance or evolutionary creation for each chronology |
| Young earth (6–10,000 years) | All 'days' literal 5 'days' literal 3 'days' literal | Usually linked with instantaneous appearance |

We cannot agree with young-earth creationists that any physical theories can be derived from Scripture, for we hold the classical Baconian view on this. We can still ask, however, whether or not their physical systems are consistent with Scripture. The present chapter aims to do this, both for the youth-earth systems and for others listed in the table. We shall begin, therefore, by recapping on the physical implications of each theory, and considering how well they harmonise with biblical theology. In doing so we must, of course, recognise that in any schema (scientific, philosophical or theological) we should expect to find some puzzles or mysteries, because our view is partial. This should not, however, stop us from making as rational an assessment of any such system as we are able.

## Young-earth creationism: recap and theology

The young-earth creationism we shall consider is mainly that of the founding figure H M Morris, though we recognise there are variations. Usually, it implies that the earth is only a few thousand years old, and was completed in 144 hours (though some young-earthers may take only three or five of the 'days' literally). Physical death of both man and animals is believed to have started only after the sin of the first man and woman, which occurred at least twenty-four hours after the creation of birds and sea creatures. There were, therefore, no animal predators in the original creation, and all of them were vegetarian throughout the first day or so of their existence. At the first human sin (or the Fall) it is believed that substantial changes occurred both in biology and physics. Though some young-earthers deny it, Morris also emphasises that the second law of thermodynamics began only at that time. The strata and all the fossils in them are to be attributed to a flood of a few months which occurred even more recently.

All this implies, then, that the animal world as we now see

it has undergone very substantial modification in some way since the six-day creation. Morris and other young-earthers read a great deal into Genesis 3:17–18: 'Cursed is the ground because of you; through painful toil you will eat of it all the days of your life. It will produce thorns and thistles for you, and you will eat the plants of the field.' Most commentators seem to have taken the phrase 'for you' to imply that a changed relationship with mankind was what God meant. Morris takes it to mean a fundamental change not only in the thistles themselves, but in the all physical laws and the relationship of God to those laws:

> It seems unlikely that God actually either created or 'made' thorns and thistles at this time. He did not 'create' death in the direct sense, but rather withdrew that extension of his power which had maintained a 'steady state' of life and order, thus allowing all things gradually to disintegrate toward disorder and death ... God merely 'allowed' certain plant structures which previously were beneficent to deteriorate into malevolent characteristics ... In terms of modern genetic knowledge, such changes probably were in the form of mutations, or random changes in the molecular structure of the genetic systems of the different kinds of organisms ... If deteriorative mutational changes occurred in plants, it seems reasonable and even probable that they would also occur in animals. As smoothly rounded structures deteriorated to thorns in plants, so perhaps teeth and nails designed for a herbivorous diet mutated to fangs and claws which, in combination with a progressively increasing dietary deficiency of proteins and other essentials, gradually created carnivorous appetites in certain animals ... Parasites and viral systems may also have developed in some such way.[1]

Let us be clear here how novel is this suggestion. He is saying that as originally created, all animals were vegetarian, and there was no animal death. Then at the moment of that Fall of Adam, God 'withdrew' his power in some way, leaving the physical world to a new system of physics which operated in some sense independently of God. Animal life evolved very rapidly (within a few thousand years between Adam and Noah) to transform the originally vegetarian structures of the Genesis 'kinds' into carnivores with claws and teeth, into parasites, etc. The mode by which these changes occurred was random mutations: not God-directed in any way, but, as Morris seems to imply, by natural selection. When, therefore, we look today, for example, at a member of the feline kind (ie a cat), we see a structure which is unrecognisable as the original vegetarian creature God made, having 'degenerated' into the lissome, efficient hunter with claws and teeth we know so well.

It is a supreme irony that Morris seems to have a greater belief than any other writer we know in the efficacy of a purely godless system of mutation and natural selection to produce intricate and amazing new structures within a very short time span. The scientific problems with this will be considered later, but here we need to think about its theological novelty and how far it may be reconciled with the Bible.

Of the Genesis passages themselves, it is a far from obvious interpretation. Morris emphasises that when God in Genesis 1:25 pronounces the animal creation 'good', that this must imply a pain-free world. The biblical usage does not support this. God's promise in Deuteronomy 8:7 to bring the Israelites into a 'good land' does not suppose it to be without struggles. The word may mean 'fitting' or 'beautiful' among a wide range of meanings. That most unfanciful of early commentators, Ambrose of Milan, took God's pronouncement that the sea was 'good' (Gen 1:10) to imply its beauty (which he took as the same for us to appreciate today) and added:

> Notwithstanding all this, I am of the opinion that the beauty of such a creation is not to be estimated by the standard of our own eyes, but is to be gauged in the design of the work as a whole by its conformity and agreement with the intention of its Creator.[2]

There is no hint here, or anywhere we know in early commentators, of an inconceivably different world which is now virtually above all knowledge. There is no indication that 'good' might mean a world free from predation and pain. Chrysostom, likewise, took God's pronouncement of 'good' to apply to the created world as we now see it.[3]

Morris, moreover, has to ignore the overtones of conquest which he admits are there in the Genesis 1:28 phrase 'subdue the earth'.[4]

Morris' second main novelty of interpretation is not only to take the promised death in Genesis 2:17 as referring to physical death, but also as introducing death not just for humans but for all animal-kind. Now it actually promises Adam that 'in the day you eat of it [the fruit] you will surely die'. Taken literally, of course, Genesis 5:4 implies that Adam lived at least 800 years after he ate the fruit, he certainly did not die physically on the day he ate it. In fact, however, the New Testament indication seems to be that spiritual rather than physical death is the primary issue. As we have seen, Paul speaks in Romans 5 of the death which Adam's sin brought, and continues throughout the ensuing passage to develop the theme. In Romans 7:9 he speaks of how his own individual experience mirrored that of Adam: when first he felt the binding nature of a moral law, 'sin sprang to life and I died'. Clearly, the reference is to spiritual, not physical death. Even if it were physical death, there is not the slightest indication here or anywhere else in the Bible that it introduced death for animals. Indeed, if physical death had not been familiar to Adam, then it is hard to see what meaning at all God's warning could have had to him. We understand the concept of the second or spiritual death *only* by analogy to the physical one with which we are familiar.

Turning now to Genesis 3:17, we have found no reason to follow Morris in taking it to imply much more than it says. Henceforth, Adam will find himself in a different relationship to his task in the world.

Does the New Testament give any support to Morris' ideas? Romans 8:19–23 says:

> The creation waits in eager expectation for the sons of God to be revealed. For the creation was subjected to frustration, not by its own choice, but by the will of the one who subjected it, in hope that the creation itself will be liberated from its bondage to decay and brought into the glorious freedom of the children of God. We know that the whole creation has been groaning as in the pains of childbirth right up to the present time. Not only so, but we ourselves, who have the first-fruits of the Spirit, groan inwardly as we wait eagerly for our adoption as sons, the redemption of our bodies.

The word 'frustration' means powerless, ineffectual or aimless.[5] The word 'decay' means destruction or corruption.[6] In Paul's writings (Rom 8:21; 1 Cor 15:42, 50; Gal 6:8; Col 2:22) it seems to take the meaning of mortality. Paul does not say in Romans 8:21 at what time God subjected the creation to a servitude to mortality, which he pictures as a state of ineffectuality. It is far from clear that it was the Fall and involves moral evil. This could be one possible interpretation, but it is also possible that it was at creation, and that mankind's task was to transform and give it purpose by the introduction of eternity.

The coming kingdom is pictured in Revelation 21:4 as a place with 'no more death or mourning or crying or pain'. The context, however, is clearly one of human experience. Isaiah 11:6 gives a picture of the wolf lying down with the lamb, the goat with the leopard and the calf with the lion. Does he mean this literally? Well, in Isaiah 35:9 he says that there will not *be* any lions there at all, so presumably not! Whether or not there will, in fact, be a new order of animal-kind is hard to tell from the hints we are given about the new heaven and new earth. It is not even possible to say whether or not we are intended to be vegetarian — if, indeed, such categories have any meaning for those who are to be 'like the angels' (Mt 22:30). Jesus, in his resurrected state, ate a piece of fish (Lk 24:43), so to say the least this must be in question.

The simple fact is that there is much too slender a base of evidence to support Morris' new ideas. There are, moreover, formidable theological problems with them. His picture of God withdrawing and letting some other principle take over is almost a deistic one. The classic Christian view (including Christians in the early church, scholasticism, Reformation, Counter-Reformation, evangelical revival and early fundamentalism) is that God is immanent in present natural processes — and in their benificient effects in supporting the possibility of organic life.

If we consider the world of nature, the Bible surely takes it that this world is God's created world. Psalm 104, for example, pictures God in verses 5–9 as making the earth. It then passes smoothly into God's continuing activity in making springs bring waters to present animals (104:10–12), in growing grass (104:14), etc. There is not the slightest hint here to support the novel young-earther idea that God somehow withdrew and let the second law of thermodynamics take over. The lions (104:21) seek their food from God — not from the effects of altered physiology (claws, teeth, etc) in a struggle for survival introduced by God's withdrawal from nature after the first human sin (as Morris seems to suggest). Psalm 104:25 speaks of the sea teeming with living things, implying that these are the ones mentioned in the previous verse: 'In wisdom you made them all; the earth is full of your creatures.' Then verse 26 mentions the frolicking leviathan 'which you formed', going on in verse 27 to speak of all those sea creatures also looking to God to feed them.[7]

Classically, the church has always taken it that it is this world which is God's created world — not one which effectively perished at the instant of humankind's first sin. Only early Gnosticism took it that the actual present world was not the work of the one true God, but of some kind of inferior deity.

Consider, for example, our own wonderfully made bodies, with all the mechanisms of white blood corpuscles, immune systems, etc. None of this should have been necessary before the Fall introduced the possibility of disease, so presumably Morris believes it all to be the product of blind chance mutations and natural selection in a nature from which God had withdrawn. Is such a view really compatible with the Bible, where David sings praise to God in Psalm 139:13–14 for forming him in the womb, and because he is 'fearfully and wonderfully made'?

Surely the Christian view is that the wisdom and power of God is seen in this world, not in a world where physics, biology and ecology were totally different and which degenerated into this one when God supposedly withdrew in some way from nature at the time of the first human sin. The hints of Gnosticism, semi-deism, and various other historical heresies in this side of young-earth science should give much cause for concern, as its advocates clearly think of themselves as orthodox.

On the Flood, the young-earth-creationist package of ideas (which includes Flood geology) faces biblical problems which may be less serious, but still need to be answered. There is, of course, the age-old objection that the details of rivers, etc, mentioned before the Flood in Genesis 2:10–14, match those after the Flood. This might be a problem for a truly literal interpretation, although personally we have no theological objection to Morris' suggestion that it be taken allegorically. The language of Genesis 6–9 itself certainly could be reinterpreted to imply a global universality. There may, however, be more problems with Morris' idea of a water-vapour canopy which disappeared with the Flood and so caused a more extreme climate. The idea of a perpetual warm climate before the Flood is not, of course, explicitly denied in Scripture (though, ironically, it is explicitly denied by Lactantius, so cannot be early orthodoxy!).[8] It would, however, seem rather strange for God to go to the trouble (as Morris seems to suppose) of saving two of each kind of dinosaur, etc, in the ark, knowing full well that the change in climate would kill them off immediately afterwards. Furthermore, if the mechanism of change were a water-vapour canopy, then Morris is forced to take a very strange interpretation of Psalm 148:4, which speaks *in the present tense* of the 'waters above the skies'. It seems more likely that this is a poetic reference to clouds rather than a literal reference to a water-vapour canopy which disappeared with the Noachic Flood.

In summary, then, as a scientific system, young-earth creationism has to face considerable problems to harmonise itself with Scripture. If, as is often claimed, there really is independent scientific evidence for the young-earth physical theories, then evangelical theologians committed to scriptural authority will have to face some thorny issues of reinterpretation of the Bible. Whether or not there is such scientific evidence will be considered in our next chapter.

### Long-span theories: recap and theology

Certain groups of different long-span theories share two particular problems. Firstly, all share questions about animal suffering and death, and, secondly, those which take the 'days' as chronological share the problem that the sun is 'made' (Gen 1:16) two days after day and night begin. We need also to consider particular linguistic questions about each, though the present authors must disclaim any personal expertise on this, and simply represent the conclusions of good scholars.

All the long-span theories accept that animal suffering and death predated the time of the first human sin, and that the physics and biology of the present world are broadly as originally designed. We believe that *this* is God's created world. Yet this does involve paradox. We enjoy the beauty of hawthorn hedges and fields of buttercups — even though we regard buttercups in the flower-beds as weeds! We enjoy the singing of the birds — even though they are 'really' territorial challenges. One of us has a family cat, a Siamese, who is affectionate, gentle, and curious about everything the family does — but who, viewed biologically (or from the point of view of a greenfinch, for example), is an efficient hunting and killing machine. There is paradox in all this. It is not the darker side of nature which we perceive as beauty, yet often it is something which in our present world is inseparable from it. We are aware that not all is as God would want it in his world, yet none the less it is his world. It is God we praise for, say, the white blood corpuscles and immune systems in our bodies, not (as Morris' view implies) a kind of godless natural selection from random mutation; but the beauty of their mechanisms is only apparent because there is a need for them.

Death and animal suffering was in the world even when God pronounced it fitting for his purpose in Genesis 1. Yet Paul does put a particular perspective on this in Romans 8:18–25. All that suffering should be regarded as a kind of birth pangs. God intended that Adam would choose the tree of life, and presumably become 'revealed' or 'adopted' (ie placed as a son) for world redemption, as Romans 8:19 and 23 say. Those birth pangs should then have released the creation from its servitude to a kind of aimless or impotent state. It would have introduced a God-directed volition into physical beings, and a dimension of eternity into the mortal to give it meaning. The failure of our ancestors has meant that those birth pangs have extended even until now.

Why, then, did God choose to do things in this way? We must point out that this exact same question could be asked no less of young-earth than long-span schema. Young-earthers believe all animal suffering dates from the first human sin. Yet there is no obvious reason as to why God should have felt compelled to change, say, the ecology of deep-sea fishes as a result of one human sin. The changed human relationship to nature signified by the thistles in Genesis 3 does relate directly to the human sin. But why should God decide to make deep-sea fish eat each other when before they had, supposedly, been vegetarian? If Morris objects to pre-Fall animal suffering because it would make God an 'ogre', then surely it would be even more the work of an ogre to introduce such habits among fish as a result of human sin, when previously none had apparently been necessary. What object could it serve?

Like most of our contemporaries, we find abhorrent those human actions which cause unnecessary suffering of animals (especially those which seem conscious of pain in ways analogous to human experience). But it may perhaps lessen the moral objection to the death of animals in nature if it is actually cosmically necessary as a part of the birth pangs of producing the new kingdom order of things. We admit that it is difficult for us to tell why, for the data on which we can base such a judgement is very limited. Is a world of mortality necessary to permit righteousness to triumph into a realm of immortality? We really know so little about questions of free-will and choice, the relationship of love and freedom, and so on. If animal suffering and death is really a necessary route to the coming kingdom, then we may also wish to ask whether or not this price were too high. Would we (and both atheists and Christians may consider this) have preferred that there had been nothing? The mother usually feels after the birth that the pangs have been worth it, but how could one possibly weigh the gains and losses of millions of years of animal death against the eternity of the kingdom?

The question, indeed, has been with us throughout human history: it is not new to a scientific age. It has always been, as it remains, the most profound problem to face Christians making sense of their faith. The idea that God created the best of all possible worlds was trivialised and mocked by the eighteenth-century deist Voltaire. Yet it did represent a serious attempt by Christian philosophers to think through these kind of issues. The ultimate question facing mankind is whether the universe is meaningful or not — and we will see it in these terms in our last chapter. The point here is that the long-span creationists give the same kind of answer to these basic questions about suffering as Christians have always done.

## Long-span chronological theories

Any long-span theory which takes the 'days' to be describing events chronologically, faces the problem that the sun seems not to be made until the fourth day, some days after the creation of day and night. This is not, of course, new, for it was a question with which the early church was also familiar. Suggestions have been made that it really means 'made to appear' or 'newly appointed' instead of 'made', but Hebrew scholars seem to have ruled this out.[9] It seems equally artificial to suggest that it really means 'reformed' or 'remade' rather than 'made'. It is, of course, possible that the light of day was created in some other way than from the sun, or that the sun only appeared to be there before the fourth day. Augustine, for example, recognised this possibility, though seems to think the passage more likely to be allegorical.[10] There is no logical way to refute this, since from the earth's point of view exactly the same effects would result if the sun were really there or not (on this basis it might not be really there now for all we know!). It all seems, however, rather artificial. In practice, many chronological approaches introduce an element of the framework theory at this point to make a more plausible system.

How far do the different long-span schema fit the actual text of Genesis 1–3? We have tried to make our own assessment of this independently, though we have found that there is much to agree with in the way in which the issues were summarised by Ramm for the 1950s[11] and Blocher in the 1980s.[12] Further references may be found in both these books, among others.

There are several theories which are long-span, but find a way to take the 'days' literally. In our view there is no particular reason to favour literality on this point, and there are various exegetical difficulties in so approaching it.

Let us begin by considering the ideas of P H Gosse.[13] His apparent-age theory argued that any type-ii miracle (as we have called them) involves creation of an apparent history. If God created a full-grown oak-tree, for example, it would presumably have rings indicating years of growth which had not in fact happened. Gosse suggested that all the geological ages are really part of that apparent history (which he termed 'ideal time' as distinct from real time).

Philosophically, this is unassailable. We would, indeed, have no way of telling whether, for example, fossils are actually the remains of once living animals or merely cleverly made to look as if they were. Equally clearly, however, when God does do a type-ii miracle, he does not adjust *all* the evidence of apparent history. If a person is miraculously cured of cancer, for example, we do not find that the X-ray photographs in the hospital (which are, after all, a part of the history of that cancerous growth) miraculously disappear, with appropriate alterations in the hospital records and memories of the doctors. If God always totally adjusted for apparent history, then no one would actually be conscious of any type-ii miracle at all. It is precisely the apparent contradiction between the historical records and the present state which provides us with evidence that such a type-ii miracle has occurred! Clearly, once we accept that we are in a universe whose Creator allows us knowledge that type-ii events occur, we must accept that there is a degree of arbitrariness about the extent to which he creates apparent history in doing them. We must presume that in making such decisions God chooses to view objects, for example, like oak-trees or patients as entities which need a certain apparent history to be built into their own structure, but which do not need other connected phenomena to be adjusted. Thus the type-ii miracle event introduces not only a historical discontinuity, but a continuing inconsistency in the material world viewed as a total system (eg between hospital records and cancer-free patients). This, indeed, is how we know it has occurred.

The reconstruction of an elaborate fossil ancestry does not seem to us to be a part of such adjustment. We cannot, however, prove that a consistent Gossism is wrong. We can only argue that it does not 'feel right' as being of a pattern with other type-ii miracle events.

A second suggestion which can take the 'days' literally is the gap theory. In essence, this assumes that the word 'was' in Genesis 1:2 should be rendered 'became', and that somewhere in Genesis 1:1–2 occurred a vast geological age, leaving the world 'formless and empty' ('*tohu*' and '*bohu*', Gen 1:2). The six 'days' (taken literally or allegorically), then, describe the remaking of the world. The view has sometimes assumed that there was a pre-Adamic form of man, of which we are not told in the Bible because it is irrelevant to us. It has been advocated by a number of leading scholars — biblical and scientific.

Various linguistic objections to the gap theory have been made.[14] There is much doubt as to whether or not the Hebrew words could have this meaning, and it would, to say the least, be a poor way to express it. In this instance it is not a question like that, for example, of whether or not the Flood was global. The latter question raises concepts not in the mind of the Genesis writer, and asks questions which would not have occurred to him. Whether the six 'days' were a creation or remaking would have been an issue easily understood. There are also problems about the remaking of the sun and moon on the 'fourth day', leaving aside for the moment the scientific difficulties. Our own view is that the gap theory is possible, but highly unlikely as an interpretation of Genesis.

Alan Hayward in a fairly recent book has argued that the 'days' are days of 'divine fiat'.[15] God actually made his decrees about what would happen in six consecutive twenty-four hour periods, but the coming into being of what he decreed took millennia. Hayward then suggests that the description of actual events are parentheses, these events taking place in millennia after the six 'days' of divine decree. What is not clear, however, is how the six 'days' can be literal if they all occur before the earth or sun have been formed. What possible meaning could be given to 'the evening and the morning were the first day' (1:5 AV) if neither earth nor sun existed? Hayward does not tell us. If, of course, he means the 'days' in some metaphoric (or perhaps angelic?) sense, then his view seems little different from an Augustinian form of framework theory.

P J Wiseman took the 'days' literally, but as days of revelation to Moses,[16] in a theory which resembles in some ways the nineteenth-century work of Kurtz, which portrayed them as days of vision.[17] His suggestion, however, received immediate criticism from F F Bruce, who reasserted that the Hebrew clearly means 'God made' and cannot mean 'God shewed'.[18] It is, of course, quite open to us to take the six 'days' as representing six sets of visions — as long as we do not try to take the actual language of Genesis as implying it. To do so, however, would make the view little removed from the framework theory.

None, therefore, of the interpretations which take the 'days' literally, seem to us theologically likely.

The age-day schema departs from this. If taken strictly, it implies that each 'day' was a long period of time. It seems clear to us, for reasons given, that the word 'day' could be used thus, and that to take it thus would be in harmony with the very earliest Christian use of language. This is not, of course, to say that the early church had an age-day theory, for it raises questions they had no reason to ask about geological epochs. The main difficulty with it seems to be the order of the 'days'. The problem of the making of the sun has already been mentioned. It does also seem a little strange that the flying creatures are on the 'fourth day', but the land creatures on the 'fifth day'. If the age-day theory is to be plausible, it generally requires elements of framework theory in the sense of recognising two sets, each of three days. Modern versions of it, such as those of Filby or Kidner, have generally done this.[19] The argument for this (given at length by Filby) is that the Hebrew language used has a fairly complex pattern of words. Though this may be taken too far, it is clear that Genesis 1 is not simply prose, and there may be something in the argument. The version of age-day theory which recognises two triads of days is plausible as an interpretation of Genesis 1, though it is not entirely clear what advantages it has over a more pure form of framework theory.

## The framework theory

In our own view the most plausible interpretation of Genesis 1 is what is called the framework theory or a 'literary interpretation' or by some other terms. It has the most ancient foundations in both Greek (Origen) and Latin (Augustine) early leaders. Blocher also mentions advocates in the Middle Ages and in the nineteenth century.[20] Other nineteenth-century figures also introduced elements of it into 'days of vision' or age-day schema, as we have seen. In modern times Blocher chooses to mention A Noordtzij, N H Ridderbos, B Ramm, M G Kline, D F Payne, and J A Thompson. We may feel that some of these writers go too far (eg in over-emphasising the nature of the passage as a supposed prologue to a covenant), but this does indicate a respectable weight of Bible-believing Hebrew scholarship. Blocher himself identifies with it, and gives good reasons to accept it as most likely.[21] In a scholarly recent commentary, another conservative writer, Gordon Wenham, writes:

> Properly understood, Genesis justifies the scientific experience of unity and order in nature. The six-day schema is but one of the several means employed in this chapter to stress the system and order that has been built into creation. Other devices include the use of repeating formulae and the tendency to group words and phrases into tens and sevens, literary techniques such as chiasm and inclusio, the arrangement of creative acts into matching groups, and so on. If these hints were not sufficient to indicate the schematisation of the six-day creation story, the very content of the narrative points in the same direction. In particular, evening and morning appear three days before the sun and moon, which are explicitly stated to be for 'days and years'.[22]

The framework theory takes Genesis 1, just as most commentators regard Genesis 2, as not necessarily intended to be chronological. The chapter is a polemic work, designed to reassert the truth of God's supremacy and creatorship against the claims of worshippers of chaos, sun, stars or other created things. The effect on sun-worshipping neighbours of leaving the creation of the sun until the 'fourth day' can easily be imagined.[23] The events described do follow a logical order (the most casual observer would surely put creation of plants before creation of animals to eat them), which in some instances happens to follow the geological order. This is, in many ways, coincidental, and was not part either of the writer's purpose nor, necessarily, of the guiding Holy Spirit's purpose. The chapter was not intended to be a framework for science but for theology.

This does not, of course, mean that the account of the creation is not historical. As we have seen, some of Jesus' own words described historical events in metaphorical ways. The Gospels are historical, but from the beginning Christians recognised, for example, that Mark 'the interpreter of Peter, wrote down accurately, though not indeed in order, whatsoever he remembered of the things said or done by Christ'.[24] They were historical, but not wholly chronological. Mark did not consider that the order of the events was of any significance, and arranged them for continuity of theme rather than chronology.

Likewise, in Genesis 1–3 the events did occur, but from the second century, thinking Christians recognised that its writer never intended them to be taken as chronological. In the two accounts of Genesis 1 and Genesis 2–3 the writer arranged incidents to bring out particular theological points. Chapter 1 deals with God's pre-eminence and relationship to all creation. In it chaos is denied divinity and shown as a stage in creation from which God was never absent. The celestial bodies arrive in the 'third day', given not a divine role but a subordinate one in the affairs of mankind. In Genesis 2 the same events are arranged in a different order to bring out the relationships of man, woman and God. In our Chapter 11 we have already looked at Paul's reference in 1 Timothy 2:13 to Genesis 2. Paul refers to the order of events, but if, of course, he were really arguing on a literal chronological basis, then he would have to accept that the animals (formed even before Adam) stood to Adam as Adam to Eve — and Paul's whole argument would fail. Paul's argument holds only if we take the Genesis writer to be rearranging events to bring out a theological point in dealing specifically with mankind's human relationships.

To try to use Genesis 1–3 to derive either a chronological order of events or technical scientific detail, would be to misuse the passage to acquire information from it which it was not intended to give.

What we would emphasise is that we are not saying that Genesis 1 is 'only' a literary framework. The passage describes real events in an amazingly powerful way, majesterial in its vision of God, and the word 'only' is wholly inappropriate. The framework approach may come as a disappointment to those brought up on the kind of statement: 'Isn't it amazing that God put into his word all the correct orders revealed by modern science.' But this kind of statement was trying to make it do something it was never intended to do. God's word does not need that kind of support. Its majesty stands on its own merits, and we consider it totally fitting that it was actually read on man's first trip to the moon. Its teaching is timeless, and no less relevant today than to those in the ancient world who first heard it. God is the Creator, he creates and acts in space-time, but his design is in eternity.

## Evolution

Suppose someone argued as follows:

> A large percentage of atheists believe that the earth is very small compared with the size of the universe. These small-earthers have now taken over the media, and many Christians have compromised their faith in accepting the ideas. We large-earthers know that God's word clearly states in Matthew 24:29 that the stars will one day fall from heaven, so we know that the stars cannot really be so much larger than the earth, as the small-earther astronomers claim. Small-earthism was an ancient god-less philosophy introduced by the Greeks, and wonderfully combated by the great early scientific naturalist Cosmas — though unfortunately re-established by later figures. Small-earthers are responsible for all kinds of atheism and torture, for small-earthism implies the insignificance of mankind and the freedom of men to dominate others because of that insignificance.

We would regard this as absurd. Jesus' prophecy in Matthew 24:29 was not meant to teach us about the size of stars, but is seen by scholars as speaking in a graphical Hebrew way of the portents of titanic events. To take Jesus thus (rather than as scientifically literal) is not to deny the Bible, but to take it as it was intended. The smallness of the earth is a purely physical issue. It would be absurd to use it to build a system of ethics or metaphysics, and it implies nothing either way about God's involvement in creation.

The theory of evolution is likewise a purely physical theory. Atheists of various kinds — Marxist, humanist or materialist — may well have accepted it, but it in no way logically implies any of their religious or metaphysical theories. Various prominent non-Christian biologists have shown a naïve tendency in last-chapter speculations on the future to equate evolutionary biological change with progress.[25] It is, of course, invalid to do so. As a physical theory, evolution concerns adaptive change; it contains no moral overtones of progress. Darwin recognised this, though sometimes forgot it in the rhetoric of the moment! Christians need to remind such biologists that no physical fact could dictate moral values; we should not be confirming them in the mistaken belief that it could do so! A pure physical theory of evolution by natural selection would imply neither a metaphysics of progress nor one of chance as an alternative agent to God. It was only evolutionary schema with these kind of connotations which evangelicals in the late nineteenth century rejected.

A further point concerns the so called 'social Gospel' of the late nineteenth century. Based largely on the evolutionary ideas of Herbert Spencer (which, of course, predated Darwin), this was an extraordinary mixture of liberal optimism and a belief in divinely ordained progress. What is interesting, however, is to note that T H Huxley himself wrote in 1892 that he thought the old Calvinist notions of 'predestination; of original sin; of the innate depravity of man and the evil fate of the great part of the race; of the primacy of Satan in this world', etc, to be 'vastly nearer the truth' than the 'liberal' popular illusion that the ethical ideal is reachable and 'everything will come right (according to our notions) at last'.[26] Perhaps this lends some support to Moore's assertion that the more liberal theologians were the less orthodox in their Darwinism. In any event, the scientific theory of evolution implies nothing about the future progress of human society.

Sometimes objections have been made to evolution on grounds of animal suffering. In actual fact, however, this issue is common to any schema which portrays (as does the Bible) a God who operates through a nature in which predation is present. Evolutionary creationism offers, perhaps, a better reason for it as a part of the creative process itself. We will reconsider this in our last chapter.

Perhaps the key theological question about evolutionary creationism concerns the meaning of the words 'made' and 'created'. Some Hebrew experts would assert of the word *bara* (create) that: 'There is no evidence in the entire Old Testament that the verb itself ever expresses the idea of creation out of nothing.'[27] Other uses of the word (though few) also indicate that it neither implies a type-ii miracle, nor something instantaneous (Is 54:16; Amos 4:13). To the true Christian theist (unlike a deist, who may see matter as independent of God), God is just as operative through natural processes as in type-ii miracles. God could, of course, have used instantaneous type-ii miracles to create new species — but did he?

This question is, of course, a modern one, and probably was of little interest to the writer of Genesis, whose language is not designed to answer it. Genesis 1:11 actually says, 'Let the land produce vegetation.' An early church figure like Ambrose of Milan, for example, seems to have taken this to imply a spontaneous generation, which he saw as a continuing process.[28] A leading early evangelical like John Wesley, for example, saw the question of whether or not life is spontaneously generated as a purely scientific one.[29] If the first beginning of life occurred through spontaneous generation, it would simply imply that God worked through what we call natural processes rather than by a type-ii miracle; it would in no way contradict any full belief in the authority of the Bible. Evolution of plant and animal life we see similarly as a purely scientific question. The Genesis account leaves open the question of whether God created all plant and animal life at the same instant (as Augustine thought), or in separate acts of type-ii miracle over millions of years (as many age-day theorists thought), or through the natural processes of evolution. There is no inherent problem in seeing God working through the evolutionary processes, just as we see him working through other secondary causes to create the winds, feed the birds, and so on.

The evolution of mankind has always been regarded — even by most evolutionary creationists — as a different issue. As we saw in Chapter 11, Adam and Eve may have represented Everyman, but the most obvious interpretation of some of the New Testament passages would see them as two actual individuals. There may, then, be a difficulty if mankind is imagined to have slowly evolved. Genesis seems to imply that there is an actual moment of consciousness of sin, just as Paul implies in Romans 7:9 that such a conscious-ness came for him personally at a moment of time in his own life. Whether or not that could come gradually is hard to say, though it would seem not. One of the problems is that consciousness is not, in a sense, a scientific concept at all — and this relates back to the body-mind problems in our Chapter 10. We will return to consider this in our next chapter, but at present note that the whole issue relates to these much larger problems.

### Notes

1. Morris, *The Genesis Record* (1976), p 125; he later calls mutations 'random disruptions in their highly ordered genetic structures'. See also *Many Infallible Proofs* (1974), p 238.
2. Ambrose, *Hexameron* in *The Fathers of the Church* (translated by J J Savage, 1961), vol 42, p 83.
3. Chrysostom, *Homilies on Genesis*, in *The Fathers of the Church*, vol 74.
4. *The Genesis Record*, p 76.

5.  *Mataiotes*: see Colin Brown, *The New International Dictionary*, vol i, pp 549–51.

6.  *Phthoras*: see *ibid*, vol i, pp 467–71; see also G Kittel, *Theological Dictionary of the New Testament* (1964–74), vol iv, p 104.

7.  The fearsome leviathan (if it is the same creature) is described in Job 41.

8.  Lactantius, *The Divine Institutes*, II, 13 (*Ant Nic Fath*, vii, 60).

9.  H Blocher, *op cit*, p 45.

10.  Augustine, *City of God*, XI, 7 (*Nic & Pos Nic Fath*, 1, ii, 208).

11.  B Ramm, *op cit*.

12.  Blocher, *op cit*.

13.  P H Gosse, *Omphalos* (1857).

14.  See, for example, Ramm, *op cit*, p 137, or Blocher, *op cit*, p 41, both of which also give references to proponents of the theory.

15.  A Hayward, *Creation and Evolution* (1985), p 287. The intermittent-day ideas in R C Newman and H Eckelman, *Genesis One and the Origin of the Earth* (1977), offer no advantage over the framework theory.

16.  P J Wiseman, *Creation Revealed in Six Days* (1949).

17.  J H Kurtz, *Bible and Astronomy* (1842).

18.  F F Bruce in *The Evangelical Quarterly*, vol 20 (October 1948): p 302.

19.  F Filby, *Creation Revealed* (1963); D Kidner, *Genesis* (1967).

20.  Blocher, *op cit*, p 50.

21.  *Ibid*, p 49, etc.

22.  J Gordon Wenham, *Genesis 1–15* (1987), p 39.

23.  This deliberately polemical aspect of Genesis is emphasised by several modern scholars, eg Von Rad, *Commentary on Genesis* (1961), p 55, Wenham, *Genesis 1–15*, p 21, or the readable account given in Howard J Van Till, *op cit*.

24.  Eusebius *Ecclesiastical History*, III, 39 (*Nic & Pos Nic Fath*, 2, i, 172), citing very early sources.

25.  See M Midgley, *op cit*. Midgley tended to exclude Darwin, but at a conference in 1986 where she gave a paper, John C Greene presented good evidence that Darwin and Huxley were also metaphysical — see Greene, 'The History of Ideas Revisited', *Revue De Synthese* (1986), pp 201–27.

26.  Cited by J R Moore, *op cit*, p 349.

27.  See, for example, A Heidel, *The Babylonian Genesis*, p 89 (though Von Rad seems to dissent from this).

28.  Ambrose, *op cit*, p 101.

29.  J Wesley, *Journals*, Friday 21st June 1758.

# 15
# GENESIS AND MODERN SCIENCE

## Scientific evidence: the age and nature of strata

TWO INITIAL POINTS NEED TO be made. Firstly, our own tendency to accept the framework theory of interpretation of Genesis is based on commitment to consistent biblical interpretation and the historical approach to it of the Bible-believing church. It is not based on any particular scientific ideas. It does, however, leave open the question of whether the earth is ancient or recent, and whether evolution or an instantaneous type-ii miracle was the means of creating new species. We believe such questions are answered by science, not theology.

We feel it only right here to give our own personal assessment of the state of the scientific evidence on these various points. In doing so, however, we must emphasise that we are not experts in the particular relevant fields, and can give only amateur views on the issues in the light of available evidence.

On geology there are two basic issues for Christians. The first is whether the existing strata (which no one denies exist) were laid down over long periods of time (mainstream geology) or all within a period of a few weeks during one short flood a few thousand years ago (Flood geology). The second is whether or not it is possible actually to date the time periods concerned in the millions of years commonly claimed.

Flood geology is supported by a very small minority of scientists, all committed to the young-earth creationist viewpoint. In our own view there are both good historical and good contemporary reasons to believe that geological strata were laid down over long periods of time. The historical reasons are as follows:

1. The mainstream theory developed over a period of many decades of solid empirical study.
2. Any alternative Flood-geology theory was consistently found to be at variance with observation by scientific specialists, many of whom were committed Bible-believing Christians.
3. A large volume of consistent and detailed study has been based on the theory.

Sometimes, of course, accepted scientific theories are later rejected, but not in these kinds of circumstances.

What, then, of the contemporary evidence concerning the geological strata? Before turning to this, we must briefly mention Morris' insistence that any part of science which concerns a reconstruction of the past is a model rather than part of hard science.

Now experimental science concerns laws of the type: 'IF ... , THEN ...', for example, 'IF zinc is added to sulphuric acid, THEN zinc sulphate will result.' These cannot be absolutely verified, for they refer to all such future events, and we obviously cannot observe them all. What we can do is to test their consistency with other scientific beliefs by setting out to observe some instances of them. Science, however, cannot be restricted to only such statements. There are also statements which say, 'NOW ... BECAUSE ...' One example might be: 'NOW we have zinc sulphate BECAUSE zinc was added to sulphuric acid.' In a strict sense, of course, no one can test this statement. No one can go back and observe it, since it took place in the past. But the principle in science is that the past is like the present and future, and 'IF ..., THEN ...' statements are projected back to serve as explanations of what now is.

It would, of course, be absurd to try to regard one but not the other kind of statement as a part of rigorous science. If we disallow 'NOW ... BECAUSE ...' type statements, we can never test any 'IF ..., THEN ...' ones, since the only tests which we can know to have been applied are, by definition, now past events! The belief that an 'IF ..., THEN ...' type law has passed a test depends on existing human memory and records of the past, together with observation of the present resulting state of the test. If, in the present, we make our judgement, we have to reconstruct logically what the past must have been like through present records and memory. Scientific laws are, therefore, as much a means to reconstruct logically the past as to predict the future — you can't have one without the other.

A logical reconstruction of the past may be complex and cannot be guaranteed correct. But, equally, the set of laws upon which, say, the success of a particular new drug depends may be complex — and even if the particular prediction is correct, we might well be mistaken about the mechanism. If it is wished to call complex systems of laws 'models', then this is unusual but linguistically acceptable. But it would emasculate science to try to imply that these are somehow less scientific when used to explain the present by reconstructing the past, than when used to predict the future from the present. Testing is a logical and deductive process, whether we are deducing the future from the present or the present from the past.

Nor should it be supposed that past reconstructions do not enable actual prediction of future observations. In February 1987, a particularly spectacular type-II supernova (1987a) caused a flurry of observation as scientists rushed to test theoretical predictions based on their models of the life-cycles of stars.[1] This shows the way in which experimental physics, historical astrophysics, theoretical stellar dynamics, etc, all form part of one continuous scientific whole. The end object is to make sense of the universe in terms of physical cause-effect laws.

Christian geologist Arthur Fraser uses a past reconstruction model in a very similar way in point 6 which follows. It makes sense of features now observed and enables predictions to be made of what will be found. Such predictions go back early in nineteenth-century geology — one remembers the geologist Dr William Buckland insisting that no coal would be found in a particular area and offering that, if it were, then he would use it to cook his hat and eat it!

We will now, therefore, briefly compare how well the two models of mainstream and Flood geology explain present observation and enable prediction of future ones. It must, of course, be clear that neither of us are geologists, and can make only a lay judgement on these matters, relying particularly on work of Christian geologists like Davis Young and Arthur Fraser. Let us first consider some of the main points today which seem to indicate the truth of the mainstream view of long time spans:

1. *Cosmological data* Astronomers estimate the universe to be millions of light-years across, and have a good idea of the life-cycle of stars over millions of years. Morris once claimed that 'as long as man has been observing the sky, the stars have stayed absolutely the same'.[2] This statement revealed an amazing ignorance of some of the key events in the history of astronomy, eg the nova of 1572 (carefully recorded by Tycho in his *De Stella Nova* (1573)) and the supernova of 1604 (carefully recorded by Kepler in his *De Stella Nova in Pede Serpentarii* (1606)). Presumably, this was pointed out to Morris, who maintained the same approach but toned down the actual claim in later books. Study of stellar evolution is, however, an

integral part of astrophysics, and it seems quite extraordinary for a hydraulics engineer to continue to write off huge areas of physics in this way. Christian astronomer Howard Van Till describes in *The Fourth Day* the methods of study of stellar evolution.[3] On the size of the universe the astronomers might, of course, be in error, but to suppose that they are in error by factors of millions seems far-fetched.

2. *Radiometric dating* It must be pointed out that all such methods were developed well after Christian geologists of the eighteenth and nineteenth centuries concluded that the earth was very ancient, and the actual timescale now often placed at the side of the geological column was developed many years after the column itself. The arguments about the accuracy of such methods are highly technical, and it has to be remembered that there are various different methods and some may be more reliable than others. Christian geologists like Young and Fraser seem to place more emphasis on the rubidium-strontium isochrone method.[4]

3. *Heat flow from crystallising magma* Davis Young asserts that there are rocks for which the cooling time may be calculated in tens or hundreds of thousands or even a million years.[5]

4. *Plate tectonics* Current evidence is greatly in favour of the idea that continents are parts of plates which move across the surface of the globe. There is simply no room for this on the Flood-geology model, as plate tectonics necessitates great periods of time after many of the strata have been laid down.[6]

5. *Coral-reefs* Particularly large coral-reefs (such as one in Wisconsin) would have required a very long time to grow. The fact that the coral remains are all the right way up rules out the possibility that it somehow piled up during one big flood.[7]

6. *Palaegeographic reconstructions* Sometimes young-earth creationists have thrown out the challenge that fossil-bearing rocks are not being formed today. This is simply untrue: geologists can cite examples today of most situations which are deemed to have given rise to structures in the strata. Arthur Fraser gives one such detailed example relating to the Torridonian sediments.[8] There is clear evidence of raised shore-lines, river-basins, etc — all within thousands of feet of rock (and all according to the young-earth model laid down in a one-year flood!). Often predictions can be made and tested based on such reconstructions.

7. *Thickness* Volumes of fossil-carrying rock are immense.[9] The total amount of water on the globe today simply could not carry this volume of material as sediment — a problem recognised by the eighteenth-century Christian naturalists and confirmed over and again.

8. *Layering* Different rock types are laid under different conditions. Metamorphic are originally laid down under water, then changed by heat. Conglomerates are mixtures of consolidated gravel and pebbles, laid down under conditions of shallow water and vigorous currents possible under flooding. Fine grained sedimentary rock can be laid down as sediment (eg sand), which settles out of water and is consolidated — or in desert conditions. The point is that such types of rock, laid down under different conditions, are found in layers — often up to a thousand in number — with sharp lines of demarcation between them. This indicates long periods of deposition followed by consolidation.[10]

9. *Fossil volume* The sheer volume of fossils in some rocks is difficult to explain other than as a result of long periods of deposition.[11]

10. *Fossil layering* There is a clear zoning of fossils in the rocks, irrespective of whether these zonings are time-based or invariant. In general these zones follow a clear deposition order. Where they do not, there are often clear signs of folding, either in the inversion of specimens or in tracing along to actual folds. Mainstream geology explains this as a time-sequence.

What about the young-earth model? On the cosmological issues, two approaches are generally taken. One is to relapse into Gossism and assert that God created stars with light beams (including blips for nova) already in position — so the apparent history of the universe since the big bang is illusory. Philosophically unassailable, it leaves one wondering why one should not go the whole way with Gosse, who was at least consistent.

One alternative might seem to be the suggestion of Barry Setterfield that the velocity of light had decreased considerably since the creation a few thousand years ago. His work, however, is marred by such poor statistical method, and so many problems of physics, that even young-earth creationists cannot support it. Writing in the young-earth journal *Creation Research Quarterly*, G E Aardsma and D R Humphreys state that the decay in the speed of light hypothesis 'is not warranted by the data upon which the hypothesis rests', and cite various fundamental problems and unintelligibilities within it. [12]

On radiometric dating, young-earthers advance various technical reasons to doubt the methods for longer periods. As noted, however, such dating is in no way important to the development of mainstream geology. On the other points in 3–10, they have all kinds of problems. On the 'volume' kinds of argument, even simple calculations indicate the impossibility of laying down so much rock and fossil in one year — without a hefty dose of apparently pointless miracles. On the 'structures' types of argument, in a quarter of a century of the theory young-earthers have produced no detailed explanations of how various structural features of the strata could conceivably have been produced by rushing flood waters. On the layering of rocks, for example, an area containing 30,000 such layers would require about eighty distinct strata to be laid each day during a one-year flood — often under contrasting conditions.[13] On the correlation of fossils they have various ideas, of which the only one with any plausibility is that of ecological zoning. If animals, they say, were overwhelmed in their natural habitat, then similar animals would be found in similar rocks. This sounds plausible, yet in all levels of strata, creatures of varying habitats are found. What distinguishes, say, Eocene from Carboniferous is not the habitat but the particular organisms. In any detail their model simply does not fit. Why, for example, do coal seams not contain modern plants?

Young-earth creationists often cite lists of supposed difficulties for mainstream geology, but many of these are actually perfectly explicable on mainstream principles. Others are supposed problems based on early conjectures long since disproven or absorbed by specialists in the field. All too frequently, too, young-earth creationists copy the citations from one to another — with the certainty of expression increasing with each re-quotation![14] Here are some favourite ones:

1. *Fossil graveyards* These are frequently cited as a problem, but in fact it has long been recognised that they are caused by local catastrophes and no problem at all for mainstream geology.[15]

2. *Polystrate trees* These are fossilised trees which stand upright in the strata. The argument goes that they could not do this if strata formed slowly over millions of years. In fact, of course, no geologist says that all strata were laid down slowly, and most such trees present no particular problem. Some young-earth creationists so

misunderstand their theme as to cite it as a 'problem' that the 'same plant and insect forms which are found at the top of the seam are found at the bottom'.[16] Actually, it would be a far greater problem if they didn't, for then the tree would span geological ages. The need to further explore exact conditions of fossilisation for such trees is a very minor problem compared with the massive problems in Flood geology.[17]

3. *The shrinking sun*  Howard J Van Till has presented details of the way in which some early suggestions (1979) about variations in the sun's size — soon abandoned by the scientific community — were taken up by a young-earth creationist in 1980. He took the results as definite, projected them back indefinitely and concluded that if this sun were really very ancient, then it would have been big enough to fry the earth.[18]

4. *The moon dust*  In a 1960 article in *Scientific American*, H Petterson conjectured about the amount of cosmic dust which might have settled on the moon, assuming it to be as old as astronomers said. The moon landing-craft was prepared for dust, but in fact no thick layer of dust was found. This was taken by young-earth creationists as proof that the moon (and therefore earth) was young. By the late 1970s, however, actual measurements of amounts of the dust in space had been made, and these showed that the layers which had accumulated on the moon were well in accord with the age usually ascribed to it. Young-earth creationists, however, ignore this later work, and continue citing earlier conjecture as though it were relevant.[19]

5. *Magnetic field*  Few young-earth books on age fail to quote Dr Thomas Barnes' work in 1973 which took the 150 years of data on changes in the earth's magnetic field, extrapolated it back exponentially for 20,000 years, and proclaime that this gave an impossible figure, so the earth must be young! Actually, there is

now clear evidence that the earth's field fluctuates; it is not getting less. Yet, later papers by Barnes and others continue to cite early sources (even including Jacobs' key 1962 book, which was totally changed in later editions).[20]

6. *Footprints*  Young-earth creationists have repeatedly claimed that human footprints found in Paluxy rock beds alongside dinosaur tracks are a problem for conventional geology. Yet, in 1986, one of their main experts on this, John D Morris, showed great integrity by admitting that they had been mistaken. There was, in fact, no scientific evidence for such tracks.[21] Their film, *Footprints in Stone*, was to be withdrawn.

7. *Human remains*  A number of human skeletons have been claimed to have been found in early strata. Alan Hayward looks at these, showing the clear evidence that each one is no such thing.[22]

8. *Surtsey*  Professor Andrews and others make much of the development of landscape on the volcanic island of Surtsey, formed in the late 1960s. Actually, all Andrews cites is geologists' 'first impressions as they wandered about'. As Christian geologist Arthur Fraser points out, conventional geology has no difficulty in explaining Surtsey, and the conditions which resulted in some superficial features of age could not explain more structural features found in genuinely old rocks.[23]

Alan Hayward follows various other problems which young-earth creationists raise about mainstream geology, finding similar features in each one. What is, perhaps, most sad is that often such supposed problems continue to be quoted and re-quoted long after they have been conclusively refuted in mainstream Christian literature.

It is not worth following all this further. We see no reason at all to doubt that the basic theories of modern geology are correct, though doubtless they will continue to be amended and improved. The contemporary evidence continues to confirm the work of those early Christian geologists who developed the ideas of strata laid down over very long periods. We may remain sceptical about the precision of some of the radioactive dating methods, but the bulk of church leaders have been right in believing for the last couple of centuries that the age of the earth is greatly in excess of 10,000 years.

### Scientific evidence: evolution

Few if any would believe that no evolution at all has taken place. The Galapagos are comparatively recent volcanic islands — and no one believes that God created separately each species of finch and placed them there at that time. All the species evolved from one original type (or 'kind' as some prefer to call it). Micro-evolution, involving a mutated change in genetic coding, is a fact — and is seen in domestic species no less than in Darwin's Galapagos finches.

But what of more major changes? A range of possibilities exists:

1. *Neo-Darwinism* All modern species evolved from one or a few original life forms by the main mechanism of natural selection operating on small genetic mutations. Classically, this view is represented by Julian Huxley and John Maynard-Smith, and has been developed on a gene level by Richard Dawkins. Within its broad field there are figures like Stephen Jay Gould and Niles Eldredge, who suggest that evolution has proceeded in a series of 'lurches' rather than smoothly. There are also those who have suggested that genetic drift, or an in-built chemical programming, may be as important as natural selection. Whilst sometimes these may describe themselves as 'giving an alternative paradigm', we must realise that they are all variations within a theme.[24]

2. *Progressive creation* Major changes in living forms arose by a process of creation of which we now know nothing, but which God did at various times throughout geological history. A majority view in the mid-nineteenth century, this has its modern adherents, eg Alan Hayward.

3. *Young-earth evolutionism* Over a period of four days, about 10,000 years ago, God used a series of type-ii miracles to create basic kinds — none predatory — by processes nowhere now seen. After the Fall (and before the Flood) a very rapid process of major evolutionary change (based on mutation and natural selection) took place, to develop within a couple of thousand years a set of complex systems of immunity, attack and defence, claws, fangs, antibodies, poison sacs, and life styles. This is the view of Morris, Gish, and their school.

It must be said that the vast majority of practising biological scientists, including many evangelicals, come under 1. Sometimes various divergent ideas such as Gould's are quoted (to his justifiable annoyance) in an attempt to show that evolution is in disarray. This is misleading. In any developing science there are divergences of opinion, and the debates between Smith, Dawkins, Gould, and others are interesting. But they no more indicate any fundamental disarray than divergences between, say, Feynman, Hawking, and Davies show such a thing in physics.

But what is the evidence for and against the three alternative theories cited above? We must admit that 3 seems to us quite incredible, even did geology not already make it so. We have called it here 'young-earth evolutionism' to bring out the impossible dilemma of its advocates. On the one hand, Henry Morris argues that complex organs could not possibly evolve through evolution, that mutations are practically all harmful, that random genetic change has 'only an infinitesimal chance of improving the functioning of the system', etc.[25] On the other hand, he is forced to conclude (as we saw in Chapter 14) that a non-divinely directed process of evolution by random mutation and natural selection, over just a few thousand years, has produced all the elaborate mechanisms of attack and defence in living creatures which would have been unnecessary before the Fall. Morris may call this process 'degeneration' rather than evolution, but this is a moral judgement not a comment on the newness and complexity of the structures involved. Few of us who watch any television nature programmes can fail to be aware of the great number of very elaborate specialist structures for defence, attack and predation. In some cases it is hard to imagine how some vegetarian version of the creature could meaningfully be called the same 'kind' — and even harder to believe one could have evolved into the other in just a few thousand years.

We appreciate the motives which have led Morris and his associates into such a self-contradictory situation, and share his earnest desire that God should be glorified. But he is in the strange position of being, at one and the same time, one of the most extreme evolutionists and one of the most anti-evolutionists we know. We simply cannot make coherent sense of it.

Any final proof between 1 and 2 seems to us presently impossible. What kind of arguments could actually be used to show that macro-evolution (ie 1) was the more probable? These fall into four basic categories:[26]

(a) *Arguments from micro-evolution* Arguments by analogy to domestic breeding (eg of dog variety) or laboratory breeding of invertebrates.

(b) *Arguments from resemblance* Arguments centred around the similarities of bone structure, embryo, behaviour and biochemistry of divergent species and genera.

(c) *Arguments from palaeontology* Arguments from the

development found in fossil forms towards present-day species.

(d) *Arguments from genetic mechanism*   Arguments that look in detail at genetic processes and deduce from this the effects of genetic mutation within a wider model of natural selection.

The arguments from micro-evolution are unconvincing. Generally the results remain interfertile, and do not change basic structures. Micro-evolution results are compatible with a view based on gene pools which sees selective breeding as able to push a species only to a limit on a particular characteristic, at which point further change becomes infinitely slow. The argument gives, as Darwin himself used it, a powerful analogy but nothing more.

The arguments from resemblance do not provide any proof. It would be quite possible to believe that God used variations on a theme — much as Bach in his music — in a creative process not involving direct descent. What, perhaps, constitutes a rather stronger line of argument is that, looking, for example, at the forelimbs of various mammals, in the words of Stephen Jay Gould: 'An engineer, starting from scratch, could design better limbs in each case.'[27] The adaptation of a common pattern is less efficient in engineering terms than a purpose-built model. Conceivably, of course, the Creator may have valued symbolic unity of all the divergent living creatures more than he valued engineering efficiency, but it does seem to offer some argument for genetic descent.

The arguments from fossils have always been controversial. In general terms the fossil record does show development: invertebrates began in the Cambrian period, fish in the Silurian, amphibians in the Devonian, reptiles in the Permian, and mammals not until the Cretaceous. What, however, we do not find is a slow gradation of fossil forms. In Darwin's day the incompleteness of the fossil record was used to explain this, though many geologists found this argument unconvincing. More recently, Gould and Eldredge's theory of 'punctuated equilibria' has suggested that evolution proceeds in a series of 'lurches'.[28] New species evolve rapidly in thousands or tens of thousands of years, and may then last for ten million almost without change. This would then explain the sudden origin of new species in the fossil record, and failure to change thereafter. It must, of course, be noted that Gould is not saying that there are no transitional forms, nor that change was instantaneous (though, to his justifiable annoyance, he is sometimes quoted as though he were). But the implication of the theory, if true, is that the fossil record never is likely to tell us whether new species appeared literally instantaneously or, as Gould supposes, in a rapid evolutionary 'lurch'. Missing links may be found, but missing chains are likely to stay missing.

Finally, what of arguments from genetical processes? Christian Professor of Genetics R J Berry points out that, whilst Darwin knew nothing of such processes, it is incorrect to assume that nothing is known today.[29] He claims that it is now possible to reconstruct the speciation process in the laboratory. This obviously increases the circumstantial evidence for macro-evolution as a past event.

Our own view is that there is good circumstantial, though not conclusive, evidence that macro-evolution occurred. It must be added that several of the popular arguments against evolution are invalid, eg:

1. *The second law of thermodynamics* This states that entropy in any closed system must increase. It actually relates to a set of equations regarding energy levels. Henry Morris, however, has done three things with it. Firstly, he has elevated it into a kind of sanctified and privileged principle, which is not open to any amendment. Secondly, he has chosen to describe it in non-technical

terms: 'The amount of usefulness and availability that the energy possesses is always decreased.'[30] Thirdly, he has extended it on this popular level to concepts of 'degeneration' to which it does not apply and for which no actual calculations of entropy (in the true technical sense) have been made.

Now, speaking on a popular level, a tiny sugar-cane plant can convert unusable elements hydrogen, carbon and oxygen into usable sugar energy. On a scientific level, however, the equations show that entropy has increased. Morris cites as a supposed 'unnatural' process the 'temporary increase of order in specific open systems' as when 'the seed develops into a tree'.[31] But actually in such processes the overall entropy equations will always show an increase; they are not an exception to anything. Similarly, on a popular level, a theory of evolution implies an increase in organisation — but no one has ever presented scientifically calculated entropy levels to show that it implies a decrease rather than an increase. Entropy is relevant to the question of whether the universe as a whole is eternal, but not to the question of organic evolution.

2. *Pure chance* Sometimes anti-evolutionists ridicule the idea that complex organisms could evolve by accident — using analogies such as the chances of an explosion in an aircraft factory producing a jet. Such arguments are as misguided as the common-sense 'proofs' that the earth does not move. The theory of evolution by natural selection does not either say or amount to saying that complete animal structures arose instantaneously by pure chance. It proposes a mechanism by which small random changes can be locked on to a progressively developing structure.

There have been various specialists, usually though not always Christians, who have presented problems for evolutionary theory at a more technical level. Though we can say that any history of science in them is often inaccurate, we are not competent to judge on their more specialist technical scientific details, and can only refer the reader to them.[32] We see no need to pursue this any further, since, although the question of macro-evolution is a very interesting and important scientific one, it seems relatively unimportant to theology. Evolutionary creationism faces no more problems than any other long-span theory, with the possible exception of issues of human evolution noted in our next section.

From a historical perspective, there is an analogy between the seventeenth-century theory that the earth moved and the twentieth-century theory of macro-evolution. In both instances there have been Christians who thought the new theories posed a threat, whilst the mainstream of the Bible-believing church have not thought so. In both instances there has been no conclusive proof for the new theory, but it has offered a kind of unification of apparently hitherto disconnected physical facts and laws. This analogy does not prove, of course, that evolution is true, but it is worth bearing in mind.

Since we cannot see any real theological difference between (a) and (b) (with the possible exception of human evolution), the remainder of this chapter will consider the interaction of an evolutionary view with a biblical view of the world.

## Human evolution

Of especial interest to us is the subject of human evolution. What is presently known scientifically about human origins?

There is today general agreement that 'all modern human populations are placed in a single subspecies *Homo sapiens sapiens*'.[33] We all descend from this 'true man' (sometimes called Cro-Magnon after one location of early finds) who reached the American continent across the Bering Straits some time after 50,000 BC.[34] One study puts it thus: 'A new breed of *Homo sapiens* appeared on the scene 35,000 to 40,000 years ago and with it major changes representing the first steps of a worldwide cultural revolution.'[35] The 1989 *Encyclopaedia Britannica Yearbook of Science and the Future* states of this period: 'The Upper Palaeolithic or late Ice Age (from 35,000 to 12,000 years ago) witnessed the remarkable accomplishments of the first anatomically and culturally modern humans in Europe. . . . This revolutionary period of human achievement contrasts sharply with the preceding period.'[36] By 30,000 years ago Cro-Magnon had spread throughout the world, so what do we know about them?

1. *Physique*   Relatively tall, Cro-Magnon had an average cranial capacity larger than modern averages.

2. *Social/aesthetic skills*   Richard Leakey in 1981 stated that with them came 'a distinct leap in manipulative and organisational abilities. . . . Accompanying this was a sudden rich effervescence of art: cave painting, carving and engraving became an important and integral part of human life.'[37] This is art which 'does not represent a first artistic attempt but artistic work that reaches the level of the masterpiece'.[38] Modern views see this not merely as done for magical purposes but as genuinely aesthetic.

3. *Religion*   Cro-Magnon buried their dead, though the earlier Neanderthalers also seemed to do this. The magical properties of their cave paintings were once emphasised, but more recently this has been called into question and we are now left with little idea of their religion in general.

4. *Social nature*   Cro-Magnon lived settled lives in caves and in carefully built huts. They wore sewn mammoth-skin clothes in colder areas (the Ice Age finished about 8,000 BC). At one time there were conjectures that they had savage practices and that many skulls showed

evidence of violent death. This now seems highly doubtful.[39]

5. *Modern relatives* Whether chimpanzee, gorilla or orang-utan is our closest modern relative depends on which particular physiological structures are seen as primary. Most probable is either the omnivorous, promiscuous chimp or the gentle vegetarian gorilla, though the orang-utan has his supporters![40] In any case, all three are clearly pongid not hominid, and the indecision about which is closest leaves no evidence from their behaviour about early hominid behaviour.

Perhaps the question most important is that of descent. John Reader provides an interesting account of the finding and subsequent changes in assessment of fossil ape/human bones up to the 1980s.[41] This amply illustrates both the problems of drawing conclusions from very fragmentary remains, and the pressure to do so in spectacular ways for purposes of reputation and funding. The 'missing link' or 'oldest man' headlines have appeared again and again, only later to disappear quietly under more sober reassessment. The predisposition to bend the evidence (accompanied by occasional intentional fraud) does not inspire confidence, and when we learn that radiometric dating produced results varying from 0.29–19.5 million years (after an initial result of 221 million), our confidence is not increased![42] Reader concludes:

> For the time being, the ambiguous nature of fossil evidence obliges palaeonthropologists to pursue the truth mainly by hypothesis and speculation. And in a science powered by individual ambitions and so susceptible to preconceived beliefs, interpretations are bound to differ whenever the evidence is sufficiently ambiguous.[43]

Anthropologists seem to differ as much today as they ever did in their preferred lines of descent for modern man, though now there may be a little more tendency to acknowledge that dogmatism is misplaced. The British Museum (Natural History Museum), at the time of writing, has a display which portrays none of the early hominids as ancestral to us, and its publications assert the improbability of ever being able to find direct ancestors. The 1987 *Britannica* more cautiously asserts: 'The question of the relation of Cro-Magnon man to earlier forms of *Homo sapiens* is still unclear.'[44]

It does seem clear that a series of skulls can be formed, with later ones showing more advanced hominid (human) characteristics. The problem comes in deciding what is distinctively human. Is it upright gait, toolmaking, brain size, language, or religion? Upright gait is interesting, but scarcely crucial. There are animals today which use tools of a sort. Brain size may be indicative, but does not necessarily show what went on in it! Language is important, and there is today increasing doubt that the experiments once thought to show chimpanzees capable of 'true language' do anything of the kind.[45] The difficulty is to have any way of knowing what kind of language early hominids used. Similarly, it is difficult to know what kind (if any) of religion they had. It does not, therefore, seem particularly intelligible to proclaim that all the earlier skulls were 'definitely human' — what could that mean?

There does seem fairly good evidence that Neanderthal man inhabited Europe around 100,000–40,000 BC, and Cro-Magnon had replaced him by 30,000 BC. There is no present actual evidence for an overlap, nor any that they interbred, nor on whether Neanderthal was wiped out by Cro-Magnon, succumbed to changes in climate, or perished in some natural disaster.

On the actual origins of Cro-Magnon there is no evidence, but two schools of thought. One school favours the view that his evolution was slow and on a wide front, the other (sometimes called the Garden of Eden theory, for obvious reasons) that in the words of Richard Leakey: 'Important steps in human evolution took place in restricted locations rather than on a worldwide scale.'[46] There continues to be disagreement on this.[47]

Modern microbiologists have identified 'mitochondria' within cells, which typically are minute sausage-shaped particles (around $0.7 \times 7$ microns). Mitochondria have a degree of autonomy which makes them unlike other cell components. They contain DNA in the form of a chromosome, carrying genes for some enzymes; thus the mitochondrion can synthesise some of its own proteins, and reproduce itself — almost like an organism independent of the cell of which it is a part. The mitochondria, therefore, have their own evolutionary development — not obviously connected with the major physiological developments shown in the animal carrying them. These can be used to trace family trees for the mitochondria, which are, of course, also the family trees for the animals. This technique has, in recent years, been applied to human fossils. The human *male* sperm does not have room to package mitochondria, and they are contributed to the organism only through the *female* ovum. The technique, then, might enable biologists to trace back through the female line to (presumably) a single original source — a mitochondrial Eve! So what have such techniques shown? Biologists — who may be used to working in geological time spans of millions of years — have been surprised by the results which apparently show that all modern humans descend from a relatively recent 'bottle-neck'. Leading figure Allan Wilson of the University of California writes:

Our tentative interpretation ... fits with one view of the fossil record: that the transformation of archaic to anatomically modern forms of *Homo sapiens* occurred first in Africa, about 100,000 to 140,000 years ago and that all present-day humans are descendants of that African population.[48]

It must, however, be emphasised that there are divergences of opinion both about the accuracy and the interpretation of the mitochondrial results.

What we can conclude from all this, however, is that it would be entirely scientifically plausible at the present time to suggest that modern mankind (Cro-Magnon) originated from a very small population group at around 35–40,000 years ago, without any interbreeding with older hominid groups.

## Adam and anthropology

It should by now be clear that we will make no claims to any final synthesis of the truth on these issues, but only that we may be able to present what seems at the present state of knowledge the most likely hypothesis.

The following are possible interpretations of Genesis 1–3:

1. *No Adam and Eve*: the view that they are figurative representatives of humankind and the account is not meant to refer to literal individuals.
2. *Federal head*: the view that Adam was a literal individual, but not the physical ancestor of all modern humans. Rather he was the federal head, the first to experience sin, which later spread to all mankind because all people were deemed to have sinned under one federal head.
3. *Literal progenitors*: the view that all modern humans descend from one original pair.

Suggestion 1 has found little acceptance among evangelicals and the biblical evidence would point to 2 or 3. In either case we must seek to identify the actual period of Eden in one of the following ways:

(a)  *Adam and Eve first Cro-Magnons*   This could imply an Eden of around 35,000 years ago, after which human population spread worldwide.

(b)  *Adam and Eve first Neolithics*   The New Stone Age (Neolithic) culture began around 12,000 years ago, being defined by the first farming settlements. In this case either Adam and Eve must be taken as federal heads, or else a second wave of migration supposed around 11,000 years ago, with modern mankind descended from these early Neolithics.

Any of these interpretations take Adam and Eve as literal individuals, but also suggest some kind of pre-Adamic mankind existed. This was accepted by influential evangelical G H Pember, by founding fundamentalist R A Torrey, and later by the early President of the Evolution Protest Movement, Ambrose Fleming.[49] It is, therefore, hardly novel. The reason, presumably, that the Bible does not enlarge upon them is that it is not written to satisfy our idle curiosity, and the information would be no practical use to us.

The federal headship idea is espoused by evangelical Douglas Spanner. A former London University Professor of Plant Biophysics, now an Anglican minister, he writes: 'Adam was the head of the human race not in the sense that all men have physically descended from him but in the sense that, before God, he represented them all.'[50] Spanner suggests an evolution of a species physiologically and genetically identical to ours. But, he argues, being truly human also implies a 'culture', a perspective not physiological but learned. The species may have 'had a rudimentary language, some power of conceptualisation, musical and artistic sense, toolmaking ability, the power to plan ahead, a recognition of and an elementary response to death. But the members were still not truly human.'[51] Adam was selected by God, instructed in agriculture and in knowledge of right and wrong (perhaps also a different use of language, though Spanner does not say this), and intended to return in due course as a kind of missionary to the species. After his moral failure, the culture he brought them was actually inclusive of the guilt of sin, and their experience became that of Paul in Romans 7:9–10. When the commandment came — perceived as a moral commandment divinely revealed — the breaking of it brought knowledge of sin and through it a new perception of death. Early teaching followed Paul in believing that: 'Wrong does not exist except when the mind and conscience are implicated and bound up with the guilt.'[52]

Views (a) or (b) could leave room for a literal single pair of ancestors to modern mankind. The latter, (b), is the particular idea of the evangelical Canon E K Victor Pearce, who has a degree in anthropology. Pearce argues that the 'mankind' of Genesis 1 is a 'hunter gatherer' of the Old Stone Age. We are not told that any particular moral prohibition is given him, he is simply commanded to fill and subdue the earth — which was done. Pearce argues that Genesis 2 refers to an agriculturalist Adam, a man of the New Stone Age (or Neolithic) period beginning about 12,000 years ago. He then suggests that we may all be descended from this Neolithic founder:

> The archaeological break (*hiatus*) between the Mesolithic or Natufian seems widely general in cave stratigraphy. This would indicate that the Adamic race was a fresh start 11,000 years ago. Thus to all parts of the world the new revolutionary mode of subsistence was diffused.[53]

Pearce suggests that all modern men (including aborigines) descend from this one Neolithic stock. He does also recognise, of course, that there could have been intermarriage with the older stock, but sees Eve as the 'mother of all living' as a problem to this.[54] Spanner, in contrast, argues that this title indicates the hopeful state of Adam's mind, and is not necessarily the comment of the inspired narrator. In itself, therefore, it does not seem particularly conclusive.

Pearce also gives a fair amount of detail correlating the subsequent chapters of Genesis with the results of scientific findings on the Iron Age, etc. He presents evidence to show that the biblical genealogies and the associated age calculations fall well within the ranges of years needed to fit within present margins of scientific accuracy on dating.

Suppose that one of these schema is adopted. How are we actually to imagine Adam and Eve to have appeared? What would have been observed at the time? We can think of three possible suggestions:

1. Bodies came together in a pure type-ii miracle, fully formed adults coming straight from raw earth, complete with a new genetic code.
2. Adam and Eve were born into previous hominid families with a small mutation of genetic code, causing significant physical differences, associated also with a new cultural relationship with God.
3. Adam and Eve were born without significant physiological difference from their parents, but experienced through divine action a new cultural relationship with God.

As already argued at length, no one takes Genesis 1–3 totally literally, and we certainly see no reason from its language to take it that the forming of Adam and Eve was necessarily any more miraculous than the forming of Jeremiah in the womb, referred to in Jeremiah 1:5. Our own personal assessment of the probabilities might rank these in order 2, 1, 3, but it is possible at the present time for scientific evangelicals to hold any one of them.

The Fall of Adam was a historic event, heralding a new relationship of mankind to work, the physical world, sin and death. Whilst no certainty is presently possible concerning its exact place in the space-time scale of archaeology and anthropology, there do not seem to be any insuperable difficulties of harmony either.

## The Flood

We turn, finally, to consider current evidence from science and the Bible regarding the Flood. It will by now be clear that we regard as extremely improbable the theories of the Flood geology which claim that most of the strata were laid down in one recent flood. So what did happen?

We have seen in Chapter 11 that the Genesis writer wrote that the whole land was submerged, but did not intend his language to answer modern questions about whether or not this meant the whole globe. To conclude either that it was or that it was not global would equally be a reinterpretation of what he actually said. The New Testament and early church were generally interested in the significance of the Flood rather than its scientific details. During the last three centuries, however, there has been discussion of it, and we have seen that Christians took the account to mean: a global all-covering flood, or a worldwide but not all-covering flood, or a localised one. Flood geology (ie the idea that all the strata were laid down during the Flood) never became Christian orthodoxy at any time.

By the mid-nineteenth century, evangelical geologists and leaders had generally concluded that the Flood was local. Leading Scottish evangelical geologist Hugh Miller argues this at length in his 1857 work *Testimony of the Rocks*. Standing in the mainstream of evangelical Bible-believing scientists, he did not believe the Bible designed to give scientific information, and did not believe that the Genesis language implied a global flood. His scientific reasons for concluding that it was localised are still valid today. What kind of reasons are they?

Firstly, there are evidences of local floods in various

locations, but no evidence for a single global flood at one time.

Secondly, there is insufficient water to cover existing mountains unless they are much flattened, and there is no geological evidence that this happened globally in the recent past.

Thirdly, the problems of gathering all the world's animals pale into insignificance compared with the task of redistribution facing eight people. Even supposing that before the Flood the land masses were joined, clearly they were not joined after it. How did creatures like the South American sloth (mentioned by Miller) get home again afterwards? What about the thousands of distinct small species, all needing to be re-transported home? Why did all the marsupials converge on Australia? What about areas where a delicate balance between predator and prey exists? Could a pair (or seven pairs) of each form a basis for restarting the balance — assuming that Noah took notes about which went with what? Unless a massive quantity of miracle is involved, a worldwide totally destructive flood would have left totally insurmountable problems for eight people.

Could such problems be overcome by suggesting miracles? Christians have long recognised that some element of the miraculous must have aided Noah. Thus Bede (c673–735) suggested in his *Hexameron* that the animals were put to sleep or hibernated during the voyage, which seems sensible enough. Others, however, have tried to save improbable theories with wild degrees of miracles which go far beyond the text, such as the suspension of physical law to enable all the strata to become sediment, or the miraculous angelic re-transportation of animals throughout the globe. In the main, however, the Bible-believing mainstreams of Christians seem to have rejected this kind of extravagance.

Miller never doubted that the Flood was historical, but believed it to be a local event. He suggested that the subsidence of a 'trench-like strip of country that communicated between the Caspian and the Gulf of Finland' would have laid under water 'an extensive and populous region'.[55] American evangelical geologists Dawson and Wright followed Miller in suggesting mechanisms of subsidence and local flooding.[56] Dawson's treatment emphasised that the Deluge was universal in terms of the area of observation and information of the narrator extended — this was not necessarily universal even as far as mankind were concerned.

Our own view is that the evidence is strong that the Flood was localised, though exactly how it happened and how widespread it was are still questions of debate. Few actual suggested scientific/theological syntheses for this have been offered in recent years. In 1987, Christian geologist Davis A Young cites F Filby's *The Flood Reconsidered* as 'perhaps the most extensive'.[57] Filby presented a variety of Flood accounts in different cultures, and geological evidence to indicate a widespread, though not necessarily global, flood. It is difficult for non-geologists to judge the competence of this work. Davis Young himself is non-committal, and a Christian professional geologist in England whom we asked about it was similarly non-committal. The book does seem at times to rely on rather dated sources. Thus Filby asserts: 'Beds of sand and gravel with RECENT shells can be found on Moel Tryfan at a height of 1,350 feet, showing that N Wales was plunged beneath the sea at no great time past and has risen again.'[58] The book cited on this is Geikie's 1882 textbook. The HMSO Geological Survey work on this area when Filby wrote would have told him that there is clear evidence that during the recent Ice Age, movements of glaciers forced the Irish Sea ice up and across the land and 'the great force of its movement may be gauged by the occurrence of patches of such ice-dredged marine sand at heights of nearly 1,400 feet on Moel Tryfaen'.[59] Any recent subsidence of the mountains to the degree needed for a covering flood seems highly unlikely.

This is not to say that the various other Flood evidences

which he cites are invalid, but that no proper theory linking them has yet been shown.

In 1977 Davis Young was writing that:

> There is also the very strong possibility that a great flood could have produced rather ephemeral kinds of geological deposits. One might expect the development of widespread silt and gravel deposits and piles of debris that could well be eroded away quickly. It is entirely possible that the Genesis Flood may have in some fashion covered much of the globe's surface and produced a great redistribution of materials. Since that time, much of the physical evidence for such a flood could easily have been destroyed or rendered difficult to decipher. Remnants of flood deposits scattered around the world would be extremely difficult to correlate stratigraphically or geochronologically.[60]

Perhaps Young has now moved from this viewpoint, but it is interesting that he could hold it. It is reminiscent of the tranquil-flood theories of John Fleming in the early nineteenth century. Obviously, however, if the Flood was a worldwide marine incursion, then one would expect to find recent marine shells scattered far and wide — and this does not seem to be the case. On the other hand, it is more plausible to suggest that a more localised event might well leave indistinct traces in this way.

Another attempt to reconstruct the Flood (also mentioned by Young) is that of the anthropologist, Canon E K Victor Pearce.[61] Pearce detects a widespread archaeological break in cultures between the Copper-Stone Age and the Bronze Age, which he dates in the fourth millennium BC. In Mesopotamia in particular (though also elsewhere) Pearce identifies flooding as the cause of this break. He suggests, however, that the effects of the Flood were restricted to the Old World, ie that 'the land' in Genesis did not extend to the Americas or S E Pacific.[62]

At the present time there is no available complete synthesis of scientific and theological knowledge regarding the Flood. What may be needed is a team including a competent recent geologist, an anthropologist, and an expert on Bible languages and culture to work out a modern synthesis. The present lack of such a synthesis does not, however, worry us unduly. It has been a feature of the history both of scientific and archaeological development that from time to time anomalies or problems have been thrown up to which existing paradigms and theories have no immediate answer. It would be foolish on this basis to conclude that the whole framework of the theory is wrong, at least until some higher order synthesis becomes available.

## Notes

1. See, for example: R Talcott, 'A Burst of Discovery: The First Days of Supernova 1987a', *Astronomy* (June 1987): p 90; N Henbest, 'Brightest Supernova for Four Centuries', *J Brit Astron Assoc*, vol 97:3 (April 1987): pp 130–2; and numerous articles in *Astronomy and Astrophysics*, etc. It is also chronicled in the *Encyclopaedia Britannica 1989 Yearbook of Science and the Future*, pp 52–65.

2. Morris, *Many Infallible Proofs*, p 234.

3. Howard J Van Till, *op cit*, chaps 6–7.

4. Davis A Young, *Creation and the Flood* (1977), p 185; A Fraser, 'Radiometric Dating', *Christian Graduate*, vol 30:4 (1977): p 120.

5. Young, *Ibid*, p 184.

6. *Ibid*, p 200.

7. Young, *Christianity and the Age of the Earth*, p 85.

8. In *Creation and Evolution* (ed D Burke, 1985), p 19.

9. A Hayward, *op cit*, p 122 gives figures, though we have no way to check these.

10. See Davis Young, *Creation and the Flood*, p 197 on metamorphics, and Alan Hayward, *op cit*, p 121 on conglomerates, etc.

11. Hayward, *op cit*, p 125, etc.

12. B Setterfield, *The Atomic Constants, Light and Time* (1987), issued by Stanford Research Institute International. G E Aardsma and D R Humphreys, 'Has the Speed of Light Decayed Recently?', *Creation Research Society Quarterly*, vol 25 (1988): pp 36–45. Our own conclusions are also based on a reworking of the statistics and some comment from a Professor of Astrophysics.

13. Hayward, *op cit*, p 124.

14. See, for example, M W Poole and J Gordon Wenham, *op cit*, p 44, for examples. P Kitcher, *Abusing Science: The Case Against Creationism* (1982) also highlights inadequacies of young-earth creationist citation, though we dislike the tone of his book.
15. Young, *Christianity and the Age of the Earth*, pp 71–80.
16. Eg Roger Price, *The Age of the Earth* (1979), p 49.
17. Young, *Christianity and the Age of the Earth*, p 83.
18. See Howard J Van Till, 'The Legend of the Shrinking Sun', *ASA Journal*, vol 38(3) (1986): pp 123–32.
19. On this see Hayward, *op cit*, p 142, etc. A fuller treatment is by K Miller in *Science and Creationism* (ed: A Montagu), chap 6.
20. See: Hayward, *op cit*, p 137; Poole and Wenham, *op cit*, p 39; Young, *Christianity and the Age of the Earth*, p 123, etc.
21. *Impact* 151, 1, 1986 (published by the Institute for Creation Research).
22. Hayward, *op cit*, p 146, etc.
23. See Andrews and Fraser in *Creation and Evolution* (ed Burke).
24. Eg see Mae-Wan Ho, Peter Saunders and Sidney Fox, *op cit*.
25. Morris, *Evolution and the Modern Christian*, p 28.
26. See, for example, *Encyclopaedia Britannica* (1987), vol 18, p 981, etc.
27. In A Montagu (ed), *op cit*, p 122.
28. Gould and Eldredge, *op cit*.
29. R J Berry, *God and Evolution*, p 114.
30. Morris, *Science and the Bible*, p 18.
31. Morris, *The Biblical Basis for Modern Science*, p 207.
32. Some less aligned ones are M Ridley, *The Problems of Evolution* (1985) and G Rattray-Taylor, *The Great Evolution Mystery* (1983). M Denton, *Evolution: A Theory in Crisis* (1985), is less clear on where he does stand, and the inaccuracy of some of his historical comment does not inspire confidence — though in his own field of molecular biology he may raise some valid points. Books in more popular style, such as M Pitman's *Adam and Evolution* (1984), may be of interest but are coloured more by young-earth influences.
33. B A Wood, *Human Evolution* (1978), p 9.
34. *Ibid*, p 75.
35. J E Pfeiffer, *The Emergence of Man* (third edition 1978), p 178.
36. *Encyclopaedia Britannica Yearbook of Science and the Future*, p 32.
37. R Leakey, *The Making of Mankind* (1981), p 159.
38. *Encyclopaedia Britannica* (1987), vol 18, p 967.
39. Leakey, *op cit*, pp 223–5.
40. See J H Schwatz, *The Red Ape* (1987).
41. J Reader, *Missing Links* (1981).
42. *Ibid*, p 206.

43. *Ibid*, p 226.
44. *Encyclopaedia Britannica*, 1987, vol 18, p 967.
45. Leakey, *op cit*, p 130.
46. *Ibid*, p 156.
47. See also *Science* (1987), vol 237, 11th September, p 1292.
48. *Science* (1987), vol 238, 2nd October, p 26. See also the original article: R L Cann et al, 'Mitochondrial DNA and Human Evolution', *Nature*, vol 325, 1st January 1987, pp 31–33.
49. G H Pember, *Earth's Earliest Ages* (1876), p 73; R A Torrey, *op cit*, chap 5.
50. D Spanner, *op cit*, p 79. See also D Kidner, *Genesis*, p 29.
51. D Spanner, *op cit*, p 111.
52. Ambrose of Milan, *Hexameron*, in *The Fathers of the Church*, vol 42, p 36.
53. E K Victor Pearce, *Who Was Adam?* (1987 edition), p 63.
54. *Ibid*.
55. H Miller, *The Testimony of the Rocks* (1857 edition), p 356.
56. J W Dawson, *The Meeting Place of Geology and History* (1894), p 151, etc, *The Origin of the World According to Revelation and Science*, p 256; G F Wright, *Scientific Confirmations of Old Testament History*, p 206.
57. Davis A Young, 'Scripture in the Hands of the Geologists', *Westminster Theological Journal*, *op cit*.
58. F Filby, *The Flood Reconsidered*, p 5.
59. *British Regional Geology: North Wales* (HMSO, third edition 1961), p 84.
60. Young, *Creation and the Flood*, p 174.
61. Mentioned in Pearce, *Who Was Adam?*, chap ix and also in 'The Flood and Archaeology', *Faith and Thought*, vol 101 (1974): pp 228–41.
62. *Faith and Thought*, vol 102 (1975): pp 18–21.

# 16
# GOD, CHANCE AND DESIGN

## Chance and design

WE NEED FIRST TO ESTABLISH what are the meanings of 'design' and 'chance'. In our understanding of it, the word 'design' implies the presence of a personal agent, in the mind of whom there is an intention prior to something happening. As dualistic-interactionists (in the sense of Chapter 10), we believe that the human mind is an agent of such design: as Christian dualistic-interactionists, we believe that God (in whose image we are made) is a similar agent.

To spell this out further, consider how a person could say, 'I made the watch,' or 'My hands made the watch.' Both are causal, but at different levels. The 'I' is at the metaphysical or personal level, whilst the 'hands' are at the purely physical level. Whether or not both are meaningful depends on the view taken of the mind-body issue as we saw in Chapter 10. As dualistic-interactionists, we believe that both are meaningful. But what would we make of the statement that: 'No one made the watch'? In this sense 'no one' is clearly not a causative agent at either level, but rather a way of saying that at the personal or metaphysical level there is no causative agent (even if there is one at the physical level).

The word 'chance' is used in three very different senses, and within each of these takes a number of different shades of meaning. These three main senses are as follows:

1. *Chance$_1$* This is the sense used in the theory of probability. Actually there are three different basic definitions of probability. The range theory defines probability as the ratio of 'favourable' cases to 'all cases possible', assuming 'all cases equally likely' (eg two sides of a coin are equally likely, so the chance of a head is 1:2).[1] The limiting-relative-frequency concept defines probability as the ratio of 'favourable cases' to the total number of trials in an indefinite sequence of trials (eg that the long-run ratio of heads to tosses is 1:2).[2] The subjective theory of probability sees it as nothing more than betting odds which follow the probability formulae (eg a person might be prepared to bet evens on a head coming up).[3]

   There are variations on these, but all see probability as essentially a feature of human ignorance — none deny the essential determinism of events.

2. *Chance$_2$* This is the sense used in Heisenberg's Principle of Uncertainty, established in 1928. There are various readable summaries of this.[4] The mainstream interpretation of it is that 'particles' such as electrons cannot be seen wholly as particles, but as waves of 'potentia' (Heisenberg[5]) or 'probability waves' (Max Born[6]). The position of an electron can be determined at the instant of its observation, but its path between two successive observations is not only unknown but undefined. It can be ascribed either a velocity or a position, but not both at once. After an impact with another particle, its position when next observed cannot in principle be predicted. This is not just because there are hidden variables which we don't know, but it is an essential part of the system itself. Particle paths after impact are unpredictable in principle.

3. *Chance$_3$* This is in a sense of lack of design. 'John met Mary by chance' implies that there was no design on either part. In this sense the word must imply

the absence of any personal agent (whether human, demonic or divine) who has an intention that something should happen.

Some further points may be useful. Firstly, another sense of chance is sometimes presented as 'the interaction of two totally independent chains of events', eg 'John met Ann by chance', where the chain of events which led to John being there was quite 'independent' of the chain which led to Ann's presence.[7] It is not really clear what this means, however, since 'chains of events' are abstractions we pick out from a world in which cause-effect is simply one continuum. Unless this is $chance_3$ in our sense of there being no design or intention for it to happen, it has no meaning at all.

The second point is that sometimes the applicability of one particular sense of chance tells us nothing about the others. If, for example, we have the statistical details of Ann's habits, we can say, 'There is a 60% $chance_1$ that Ann will go out tomorrow.' Yet this does not imply that there is no design on Ann's part, for whether or not she goes out is determined by volition, not by $chance_3$. Finally, it may well be that within Ann's brain, were we able to see micro-scopically, we would observe the physical results of her volition reflected in the magnified effects of a particle reaction which was unpredictable in principle, since it was subject to the $chance_2$ processes of the uncertainty principle.

It must be noted that $chance_1$ and $chance_2$ are both descriptive terms of the physical world. Both concern unpredictability: $chance_1$ in practice and $chance_2$ in principle. The third, $chance_3$, does not concern the physical world alone, but in relation to the realm of persons and volition. In this sense $chance_3$ is a purely negative term: it asserts the non-presence of a personal causal agent. Thus 'The watch arose by $chance_3$' would mean the same as 'No one made the watch', as given earlier.

The non-existence of a personal agent is a hard thing of

which to be sure. Thus we might, for example, say, 'John met Mary by chance,' in the sincere belief that there was no personal causal agent — when, in fact, Ann had been planning for weeks to contrive this 'chance meeting'. In 1 Kings 22:34 a soldier 'drew his bow at random', and shot the disguised King Ahab. The soldier had no design to shoot the king, but perhaps a providential God had contrived it. 'It happened by chance$_3$' is really a statement that something (ie an intention) does not exist. It should be noted that, whilst positive evidence for something's *existence* may be presented, it is hard to present positive evidence for something's *non-existence* — and so hard actually to present any evidence that chance$_3$ applies to a particular set of events.

Now the processes of mutation, which (according to the neo-Darwinian synthesis) cause the differences on which natural selection works, could be said to be 'chance'. But this must simply be chance$_1$, or possibly (if the mutation processes turn out to be triggered by particle reactions subject to the uncertainty principle) a process of chance$_2$. In itself it says nothing about chance$_3$, ie whether or not there is a personal design behind it. As we have seen, a number of leading early Darwinians such as Asa Gray believed that there was.

Sceptics, however, frequently confuse the different meanings of 'chance'. Thus, for example, in 1970 Jacques Monod published a quite extraordinary book, *Chance and Necessity*. Defining 'design' much as we have, the book discusses various ways in which designed structures might be recognised. Then it asserts that recent genetical research

has, in particular, made it possible to analyse the different types of discrete accidental alterations a DNA sequence may suffer. Various mutations have been identified as due to: ... [physical descriptions follow]

We say that these events are accidental, due to chance. And since they constitute the *only* possible source of modifications in the genetic text, itself the *sole* repository of the organism's hereditary structures, it necessarily follows that chance *alone* is at the source of every innovation, of all creation in the biosphere. Pure chance, absolutely free but blind, at the very root of the stupendous edifice of evolution: this central concept of modern biology is no longer one among other possible or even conceivable hypotheses. It is today the *sole* conceivable hypothesis.[8]

For so influential a book, this is astonishingly confused. He has been quite happily describing the sequences of biological physical cause-effect phenomena which constitute genetic change, and which involve processes to which chance$_1$ descriptions apply. But then Monod suddenly announces, 'We say that these events are accidental, owing to chance' (ie chance$_3$). Presumably, a Christian geneticist could equally suddenly announce, 'We say that these events are designed, owing to God.' Neither would relate immediately to any part of the physical observation: both are purely metaphysical statements. For Monod to go on to say that his particular metaphysics is the 'sole conceivable' one is absurd.

Monod's switch to using 'chance' as a causative agent rather than a process description has often been noted.[9] More significantly, however, Monod seems to go on to confuse unpredictability with lack of design. Yet, ironically, if events were totally predictable, then presumably sceptics could argue that there were no room left for any purpose or design to operate! If everything is law-like, then sceptics argue that there is no room for God to exercise volition, but if it isn't, then it must be chance and not God!

Richard Dawkins seems to exhibit a similar confusion in statements like: 'The "watchmaker", that is cumulative natural selection, is blind to the future and has no long-term goal.'[10] Natural selection is the term used to describe a physical process — of course, it can have 'no long-term aim'. The question, however, of whether or not there is any volition behind that process is a quite different one, a metaphysical question which Dawkins seems to assume he has answered, but never actually addresses. Most of his book *The Blind Watchmaker* attempts nothing beyond a demonstration that, given the existence of chemical and physical laws, no type-ii miracle is necessary to explain organic life. But let us suppose ourselves convinced by his arguments that Darwin and Wallace more or less correctly described the physical processes by which organic or even human life developed. It is extraordinary for him to claim simply on this basis that they 'solved' the 'greatest of all mysteries' which is, he says, the mystery of 'our own existence'.

One final point is to note that Christians, too, may confuse the senses of 'chance'. One author, for example, writes off the association of human volition and the uncertainty principle because 'to the physicist, the outcome among quantum probabilities is strictly a matter of chance. The electron's behaviour shows randomness, not freedom ... Within physics the only alternatives are determinate cause and indeterminate chance, and freedom cannot be equated with either.'[11] But physicists *as* physicists are simply asserting *in principle* unpredictability, ie chance$_2$. To go on to assert that behind this unpredictability is either a lack of design, ie chance$_3$, or an unpredictable human volition, is to talk metaphysics not physics. Presumably some physicists may deny that human volition could be associated with this unpredictability just as others (like Eddington in 1928) asserted its possibility. But in either case it is a synthesis of physical and metaphysical statements, and must be judged on this as to whether or not it makes sense of our experience.

## Chance, free-will and providence

How, then, may we best synthesise from the book of the Bible and the book of nature a Christian view of the relationship between God's will, human volition, and chance?

'In the beginning, God . . .' The universe was created by a personal God who is the only necessarily existing entity. God, whom we picture in the three Persons of Father, eternal Word or 'self-expression', and Holy Spirit, has a self-sufficiency of love relationship independently of the created sphere of space-time.[12] In what relationship to time stands the dimension of eternity, in which the Triune God exists? Theologians since Augustine have recognised space-time as itself a part of creation, and have debated the relationship of time and eternity.[13] Twentieth-century physics, whilst confirming the rationality of the concept of time as created, has left its nature more mysterious even than before. The problem is that our normal human conceptualisation is in terms of space-time, and all our language (even the idea of a different dimension) can only reflect this. The problem reflects the classic Kantian difficulty of conceiving 'things-in-themselves', when all we can know is things as we experience them. The one thing, however, which twentieth-century physics has taught us is that we may not always be able to picture reality, and our inability to do so need not prevent us from making various statements about it. If eternity is unimaginable and almost inconceivable, this need not negate its reality.

The physical universe, then, began its existence and continues to exist through the creating and sustaining power of God. What was asserted in Chapter 9 must be reiterated, God is *the* cause$_2$ of the universe, and not merely *a* cause$_1$ operating within it.

Does this dependence of the universe imply that everything which happens in it is the will of God? The Bible says not. The Old Testament declared it not to be God's desire that any should perish (Ezek 18:23), and yet they do. The New Testament teaches that neither the will nor the plan of God are always done by men and women.[14] The early church teachers in every tradition explained these clear biblical teachings by reference to a concept of human free-will. This may be seen in Justin Martyr,[15] Irenaeus,[16] Athenagoras,[17] Tatian,[18] Clement of Alexandria,[19] Tertullian,[20] Novatian,[21] Origen,[22] Methodius,[23] Archelaus,[24] Arnobius,[25] Chrysostom,[26] Cyril of Jerusalem,[27] Gregory of Nyssa,[28] and Jerome.[29] Augustine, when first converted, accepted this universal Christian belief, but later introduced ideas of absolute providence new to the church, previously found only in the kind of Manichaen systems to which he had given allegiance before his conversion. Some later schools of theology have held that human free-will was lost at the Fall of Adam. If this were accepted, then it would raise both scientific questions of how the relationship between mind and brain changed at the Fall, and theological difficulties of interpreting the verses cited earlier. The present authors therefore stand by the early church understanding of Scripture, and see free-will as a concept descriptive of the present condition of men and women. The early church saw nothing inconsistent in an omnipotent God creating and sustaining human free-wills, which enabled human choices to be made between following or rejecting the will of God.

In modern terms, as shown in Chapter 10, since the very inception of the uncertainty principle in 1928, there have been those (physicists and theologians) who have seen the unpredictability-in-principle of subatomic physics as associated in some instances with the freedom of human choice.

### God as constructor-participant

In a critique of D J Bartholomew's *God of Chance*, Donald MacKay asserts: 'The God of trinitarian theism is not merely a "constructor-participant" of and in our space-time; he is also its *Author*.'[30] With this, we agree (and so, as we understand him, would Bartholomew), but to be the author of space-time is not necessarily to be the author of every event within it. MacKay is fond of the analogy of God being like the author of a book, with us as the characters in it.

Whilst this analogy may have its uses, it can also be misleading. The author of a book cannot meaningfully enter into personal relationships with characters in it, and certainly none of them can do anything against the author's will. To have a personal relationship implies a mutual interaction. If God were really determining all we say or do (or if, equivalently, we had somehow been preprogrammed by him to do exactly what he wanted), then how could he enter a relationship with us? The wonder of Judeo-Christian theology is that God *has* chosen to construct a universe in which he enters as a participant.

This is pictured graphically in Jeremiah 18:1–10. God says that if a people concerning whom he has promised good do evil, then he 'will repent of the good' (18:10 RSV) he intended and break them down (and vice versa). The principle is seen in operation in Jonah 3:9–10. Though the Hebrew verb can sometimes mean 'have compassion', in Jeremiah it is used of God's changing his mind both of doing good and of doing harm, and can only mean a change of mind. The Septuagint renders it by using *metanoeo*, which means 'in retrospect one thinks differently about a matter'.[31] *God changes his mind*. Actually, the Old Testament is full of such incidents (Gen 6:7; 1 Sam 15:11).[32] The very fact that both Old and New Testaments say, 'The Lord has sworn and will not change his mind' (Ps 110:4 cited in Heb 7:21), implies that on other issues he may do so.

Now it might be said that all of this is just anthropomorphism. This, however, is misleading. When the Bible speaks, for example, of Moses meeting God 'face to face' (Num 12:8, literally 'mouth to mouth'), we recognise that God has no literal 'face', but that it has some clearly identifiable meaning of a direct and open personal encounter. But what metaphorical meaning can we attach to 'God repented him of the harm' or 'I will change my mind about the promised good'?

The Hebrew concept of God as time-participant is well

illustrated by the account of Jonah. Was there ever a time when God really did intend to overthrow Nineveh? Suppose that God had intended only to threaten, but knew all along that they would repent and so had no real intention of destroying the city. In this case he might have sent a message: '*Unless* you repent, I will destroy Nineveh.' But the actual message given through Jonah was a simple statement of intention: 'Forty more days and Nineveh will be over-turned' (3:4). If God really had no intention of doing this, then he was deceiving them. The text, however, specifies that the Ninevites 'believed' this message: they recognised that it really was God's intention (3:5). Yet both the Ninevite king (3:9) and Jonah (4:2) recognised that God was the kind of God who might well change his mind if they repented. This, of course, was what made Jonah angry — he thought that God's change of mind on an unconditional statement of intent left Jonah himself looking rather foolish — and his knowledge that God was the kind of God who could change his mind on such issues had made Jonah reluctant to carry the message in the first place. We note, moreover, that all this concerns God the Father as a time-participant who can change his mind in mutual interaction with other personal agents; it is not only the Son who so acts.

No theology can be biblical if it magnifies the eternal nature of God at the expense of his time-participant nature. We have discussed this at length, because we are fully aware of theological traditions for which the thought of God changing his mind in reaction to human choice is abhorrent. We have heard such comments as 'Wasn't it all rather risky if God's plan depended on human volition?' and 'Was the death of Jesus just a contingency plan?' Well, in one sense Jesus was 'the Lamb that was slain from the creation of the world' (Rev 13:8). The 'slain lamb' redemptive nature of God must be fundamental. But the particular outworking of it was determined as God interacted with his creatures. Was it risky? Could God's plan have failed? God does not plan that any human being should perish in the eternal sense (Ezek 18:23; 2 Pet 3:9), but there are individuals who 'rejected God's purpose for themselves' (Lk 7:30). They will not stop the coming of the new heaven and new earth, but personally opt out of it. Now an analogy can be drawn between this and certain types of chaotic physical system. In these, it becomes impossible to predict the path of any individual particle, yet the overall pattern which will emerge can be predicted with certainty. There will certainly be a new heaven and a new earth, but God does not determine which individuals will enter it, for he wants freely committed children not automata.

How does God's participation in his world reflect at the physical level? We would suggest a number of ways. The first is that the fundamental physical laws of the universe are his design, and the operations of physical nature are therefore working these out moment by moment. In this sense it is the unfolding of a preprogrammed set of relationships. Secondly, moreover, the whole continues to exist only because God sustains it. Thirdly, there may occasionally be type-ii miracles, in which God alters the usual pattern of physical law. Finally, we see no reason why the volition of God should not be operating within the unpredictability-in-principle of the uncertainty relationship, just as we have suggested for the volition of humans who are made in God's image. If we take this view, of course, we have then to ask whether this applies to all uncertainty reactions not affected by human free-will, or simply to some of them. Personally, we do not believe that we can know this, and we are open to either. There is, however, certainly a possibility that in some instances pure chance$_3$ operates, ie there is no personal agent, either human or divine. If this is true, then both free-will and chance$_3$ are entities created and sustained by God, but producing results which he does not directly will.

Criticisms which some conservative writers have made of these kinds of concept seem either to misrepresent them or else discount them without real consideration. Thus one author implies that God could not create and sustain an agent making decisions not willed by him, because this would be 'almost deistical'. Another refers to it as implying a 'hole-and-corner deity, fiddling around at the rickety roots of the cosmos'. The phrase 'God of the gaps', which has become almost a modern shibboleth, is airily waved by several. Of course, if volition operating under the unpredictability-in-principle was portrayed as the only involvement of God, then some of these criticisms might be true. But our belief that God may act in the phenomena continually found at the roots of all physical reactions, can surely not be said to constrict God or make him small.

## God and evolutionary creation

Let us, for the present, suppose that something like the neo-Darwinian version of evolution is a true picture of the physical processes by which organic life developed. How, then, should the Christian interpret these processes in terms of theology? Are the creatures the result of chance$_3$ or not? Several different answers have been suggested:

1. *Theological Determinism* D M MacKay, in *Science, Chance and Providence* (1978), takes this view. The corner-stone of his approach is a universal extension of Proverbs 16:33: 'The lot is cast into the lap, but its every decision is from the Lord.'[33] This, says MacKay, shows that God is the author not only of space-time but of all the events in it.

On a level of consistency with evolutionary processes this is unassailable. Chance, on this basis, is a property in human relationships; it does not apply to God's authorship of the events in the world which are strictly directed and willed. We have already looked at theological problems of this, but note here MacKay's particular application of it to the concept of pure chance or chance₃.

One has firstly to note that it is dangerous to use the Book of Proverbs to derive this kind of universal. Of this verse Derek Kidner wisely remarks:

> The Old Testament use of the word 'lot' shows that this proverb (and 18:18) is not about God's control of all random occurrences, but about his settling of matters properly referred to him. Land was 'allotted' (Josh 14:1, 2), likewise temple service (1 Chron 25:8).[34]

It seems extraordinary to conclude from God's control of lots during matters specifically and prayerfully referred to him, that he determines all details of all events. It is made the more so as MacKay himself asserts that the 'doctrine of divine sovereignty over "chance" events . . . says nothing to warrant the idea that all or indeed any such events are intended to offer divine guidance to men.'[35] MacKay universalises the control, but not the guidance. In reality, of course, his view of chance depends on his view of God who, he claims, is 'one who ordains all events according to his determinate counsel and foreknowledge'.[36] As we reject this theology, we must also reject his objections to chance₃.

Some movement from this strict determinism is found in W G Pollard's earlier *Chance and Providence* (1958). Pollard takes it that if God acts in free-will, then (by definition) the results will be unpredictable. Whilst not denying that God is the sustainer of all phenomena, he then takes it that this unpredictability is reflected in the subatomic world, where particles have just this property. Pollard actually seems to think God decides all such events, however, which is a theological determinism we cannot share because of human free-will, as already indicated.

2. *Deterministic Chance* A different approach was adopted by Arthur Peacocke. Writing from a non-evangelical position but as an emphatic Christian theist, Peacocke gives chance a positive role. Implicit in the initial conditions set by God, was a vast range of potential universes — the random sorting of possibilities is the means for potential to become actual:

> The full gamut of the potentialities of living matter could be explored only through the agency of the rapid and frequent randomisation which is possible at the molecular level of the DNA ... potentialities are written into creation by the Creator himself and they are unveiled by chance exploring their gamut. 'Gamut' is a musical term which has come to mean 'the whole scale, range or compass of a thing' ... God ... is more like a composer who, beginning with an arrangement of notes in an apparently simple tune, elaborates and expands it into a fugue.[37]

Actually, it is difficult to see exactly what kind of phenomenon chance is according to Peacocke. He seems to disregard the freedom found at the subatomic level, and sees evolutionary events as an unfolding of the 'fugue' God intends. His system is taken, for example, by Bartholomew to be as deterministic as MacKay's.[38]

3. *Creative Chance* As we have made clear, we do not believe that on such issues of the interaction of science and theology it is possible to achieve certainty of knowledge. We are, however, prepared to make our own suggestions about the best way at the present state of science to synthesise existing knowledge in the two areas. This synthesis owes something to the works of MacKay, Pollard and Bartholomew, and also to P Geach's *Providence and Evil* (1977). At the level of everyday macro-events, of course, the uncertainty at the subatomic level does not prevent predictions being made with virtual certainty. At the subatomic level, however,

events are predictable only within probabilistic boundaries. At the present time it seems entirely possible that
the mutation of DNA (which is the raw material of neo-
Darwinian evolution), and at least some of the human
brain processes, may be at so subatomic a level as to
have elements of unpredictability. It must, however, be
emphasised that such unpredictability (whilst it may
leave us open to apply probability theory) does not
necessarily imply chance$_3$ as an 'explanation' (or rather
as a lack of explanation, since, as we have seen, chance
in this sense is the assertion that there is no personal
agent). Within this unpredictability-in-principle there is
no reason why human volition *and* divine volition *and*
chance$_3$ (ie no volition at all) should not all play a part.

The first obvious feature of this picture is its complexity. This is, however, no reason to disbelieve it, for the
physical world provides analogies in the complexity of its
picture.

Secondly, this system places the human observer in a
privileged position. Again, however, analogy is found in
physical theory where some physicists hold it to be
decided only at the point of observation which of several
alternative universes actually comes into being — and in
one theory nothing in the strict sense exists at all unless
there is an observer![39] All these issues remain, of
course, controversial, but the debate about observer-
role is significant. It must make much more plausible any
suggestion that the human consciousness or 'person'
plays a causally interactive role with physical reality.

Thirdly, some people may accuse us of a 'God of the
gaps' mentality. We would deny this, however, for we
are not saying that God operates only in the 'gaps' of the
uncertainty relationships of subatomic particles; nor are
we saying that their existence somehow proves that
there is a God. In the past people have sometimes
suggested 'gaps' which turned out to be illusory, which

might make us wary of dogmatism; but it does not necessarily imply that the present 'gaps' will also turn out to be illusion. The 'gaps' in uncertainty are, in a sense, different from some other kinds of gap. They are not just occasional phenomena, but are at the heart of the whole continuous existence of matter itself.

Bartholomew objects that to get a sequence which appeared random would place a lot of restriction on God.[40] We do not understand this comment, even allowing the paradoxical 'test for randomness' to be valid. For one thing, it begins from the wrong end. Surely no one is suggesting that God faced an a-priori requirement that his series of choices must look random? Rather, we are looking after the event at a series of choices which do, in fact, look random, and asking whether or not they are consistent with a hypothesis that divine volition was involved. Certainly, if a sequence were actually caused by interacting voli-tions, there is no reason why it should not look random. Suicide statistics are random, but each is the result of an act of volition.

What does this say about evolution? Interestingly, atheist Richard Dawkins, gives us a wonderful extended analogy in *The Blind Watchmaker* (1986).[41] Dawkins set up a computer to produce what he called 'biomorphs': patterns generated by step-by-step branch-ing procedures. He then compared the process to genetic mutation and natural selection. From this he argues (in a deliberate reference to Paley) that 'natural selection is blind to the future and has no long-term goal'. As we have already pointed out, 'natural selec-tion' is a process description not a personal agent and, of course, has no goals. But how could it be known whether or not there were some personal agency (ie God) behind it all? Dawkins could programme his computer to use chance and natural selection so that a particular kind of end-product would be reached, even though details of the pattern would be undetermined. Similarly, it is entirely possible to believe that a personal God set up the physical laws of his universe so that a general end pattern was assured, but details were left to creative chance₃.

Dawkins' extended example, then well illustrates how divine volition and design could enter the system in two ways. Firstly, in setting up the initial conditions for DNA-based life, God could have created chance as a means of ensuring the development of richly varying life forms and the eventual emergence of personal consciousness. The system itself would have ensured that all the ecological niches (sea-dwelling, air-dwelling and land-dwelling) would be occupied, and in this sense ordained broad groups of animals. But it would have left details to chance₃, as part of the creative process. The second kind of involvement of divine volition could be in an interaction of immediate divine volition with chance, by direct involvement within the uncertainty relationship. At one level, of course, the universe, chance₃, and human minds and beings would continue to exist only because of the sustaining power of God. We are not deists, and have no belief that anything exists independently of God. But, at another level, God as Constructor-participant enters into space-time to relate as a player on his own stage. Dawkins' experiment illustrates both levels of involvement of divine volition. The programmer would be involved in setting up the system, and laying down the rules of the game. But he could also intervene in his own system to determine by choice at particular points some of the directions in which the biomorphs would develop. Finally, on occasions (though, for obvious reasons, not very often or it would effectively change the rules altogether), the programmer could perform a miracle by jumping the picture from one particular biomorph to a quite different one, not reachable strictly within the rules of chance at all.

On this suggested approach, then, chance$_3$ or chaos (ie a lack of personal volition behind events) could actually be a creation of God, to be used as part of the creative process. Genesis 1:1–2 states majestically: 'In the beginning God created the heavens and the earth, and the earth was chaos (*tohu*) and empty (*bohu*) ... and God's Spirit was brooding over the face of the waters.' If we wanted to reinterpret all this for today, we might say that the starting-point in creation was an 'emptiness' (ie a kind of empty stage waiting to be filled), a creative interaction between chance$_3$ (itself a creation of God), and the spirit of God acting in volition as participant in the world. Not for one moment are we suggesting that the Genesis writer pictured it in this way, but that some of the concepts (in whatever culturally based versions) are set deep in human consciousness. Chaos is not a divinity, an enemy to be defeated by a god in a struggle to produce an ordered world, nor a pre-existing material from which a world could be made, but something created by God to be used as part of the creative process in the world.[42] Chance is not an alternative to design, but a creative part of it.

Why should God have chosen to create in this way? We must in considering this remember the great limitation on human understanding. The use of chance$_3$ may have been the best means to produce the strange, beautiful world in which we find ourselves — experiencing beauty and an aesthetic sense even though it is a world of predation. The tensions and opportunities such a world presented may have been the best theatre in which to see the final overthrow of moral evil, and the establishment of a kingdom in which the human allegiance was freely pledged. At present the human capacity to conceptualise is too limited to enable penetration much beyond these kinds of glimpses of God's ultimate strategy.

## The design argument: structure and history

The Christian believes that all nature is a product of divine design. How far, though, does this present itself as objectively the most probable explanation?

In this context the study of nature could have three possible purposes:

1.   To make us aware of the possibility that the world can be regarded as an artefact, and therefore make the concept of 'Creator' meaningful to us
2.   To show that specifically considered alternatives to a biblical creation (eg that it just happened) are less plausible
3.   As an alternative (perhaps better) way to know of God than through the revelations of Christ and the Bible.

The last of these was in past ages explicitly suggested by some deists, and is implied in some schema of liberal theology, but is of little relevance to us here. We will, therefore, consider the other two.

The role for the study of nature suggested in 1 must certainly be true. In order for the words 'God' and 'Creator' as used in Scripture to mean anything at all to a person, that person must have conceived the possibility that the physical world is an object which has been made. Even atheists must recognise this: as 'a-theists', they assert the non-existence of a concept (God), the meaning of which can be understood only through a natural theology, ie through considering nature as a possible product of divine design.

The second level of function may be either an unconscious or a conscious weighing of the 'God hypothesis' against alternatives. To some it may simply seem obvious that nature requires a Creator. To others, it is part of a rational process of argument. Given that the universe is as it is, God is recognised as the most rational explanation of it.

The Hebrews firmly believed that God had spoken directly to their nation through the Lawgiver, Moses, and the prophets, and proved himself a living God by past acts. Passages like Psalm 19 picture the created world as joining in a praise of God, but there is little in the Bible directed to the Jews which resembles a conscious argument from design.

To Gentiles, however, we find Paul directing the following speech:

> We are bringing you good news, telling you to turn from these worthless things to the living God, who made heaven and earth and sea and everything in them. In the past, he let all nations go their own way. Yet he has not left himself without testimony: he has shown kindness by giving you rain from heaven and crops in their seasons (Acts 14:15–17).

This is not so much a deductive argument from design. Rather it is an appeal to the created order, in illustration of who is the God of whom Paul speaks; it is nearer 1 than 2.

Elsewhere Paul gets nearer to a design argument:

> The wrath of God is being revealed from heaven against all the godlessness and wickedness of men who suppress the truth by their wickedness, since what may be known about God is plain to them, because God has made it plain to them. For since the creation of the world God's invisible qualities — his eternal power and divine nature — have been clearly seen, being understood from what has been made, so that men are without excuse (Rom 1:18–20).

Paul is here contrasting the 'righteous who live by faith' with the 'men who suppress the truth'. Through the created order and through conscience (Rom 2), people can recognise both that there is a Creator and that he is a God concerned with morality. The attitude which should be taken is repentance and faith, and through this seeking for 'glory, honour and immortality' (2:7). Primarily here, of course, he speaks of faith in God, the specifically Christian faith comes later in the book. The alternative reaction is to deify some part of the created order. In this sense, Romans 1 applies just as much today. Claiming wisdom in suppressing their in-built awareness that there must be a Creator, they actually become foolish by deifying something less (1:21–3). What do people deify today? Some deify mankind, speaking of onward and upward progress. Some deify nature, speaking of human responsibility and the need (never quite specifying *why* it is so important) to reserve variety of species on the planet. To Paul, deifying anything less than the Creator appeared as foolishness.

The early church developed Paul's approach in dealing with their own gentile world. They developed, however, much more of a conscious argument from design (ie 2), following the style of pagan theists reflected in the writings of Cicero.[43] Thus, around AD 140 the Christian Athenian philosopher Aristides wrote his *Apology*, an exposition and defence of the faith addressed to the emperor. From the nature and 'orderly disposition' of the world, Aristides deduced that it must be controlled by a being who was eternal, perfect, good beyond comprehension, immortal, all-knowing, the Father of all mankind, and self-sufficient. He concluded that the 'Mover of all the world' was 'God of all, who made all for the sake of man'.[44] Aristides also believed this God to be the one incarnate in Christ who died for sin, but did not begin from this point in addressing pagans. Like Paul, he recognised that before the good news of the Incarnation can be declared, there is a need for people to understand what the term 'God' means, and how nature points to his character and existence.

Most of the early Fathers accepted the design argument.

One of the most complete forms of it comes in the Latin Father Minucius Felix. Around AD 210, he wrote his *Octavius*, a dialogue between the Christian lawyer Octavius and a pagan. The pagan argues that the world is a chaos of unpurposeful spontaneous generation of forms, with capriciously occurring catastrophes. Octavius responds:

> I feel the more convinced that people who hold this universe of consummate artistic beauty to be not the work of divine planning, but a conglomeration of some kind of fragments linking together by chance, are themselves devoid of reason and perception — even of the very power of seeing. For what is so manifest, so acknowledged and so evident, when you lift your eyes to heaven and examine all the things which are below and around you, than that there exists some divine Being of unequalled mental power by whom all nature is inspired, moved, nourished and governed?[45]

Octavius goes on to give instances of design in the sky, day and night, the stars, the seasons, the sea, animal design and environment, and human design and function of limbs. We note his contrasting of design with chance$_3$, ie a lack of design.

This is the basic design argument. It relates to the body-mind issue already much discussed. It begins with an experience of a unity of consciousness, of something which each of us calls 'I'. This 'I' has purpose, which is translated into actions which affect the material world in some way. In humans, the 'I' operates through a body which exhibits purposive action. Our belief that there are other minds or centres of personal consciousness, stems from observation that other bodies — resembling our own — are exhibiting apparently similar purposive action.

A similar line of reasoning can be applied to artefacts. A watch is designed if it exists first in the mind of its creator, and afterwards in actuality as a result of purposive action. We understand this relationship, of course, from our own experience of mind. But the problem comes if we try to tell whether or not an object was designed, ie is in its present form as a result of purpose, just from its structure.

Suppose that we are strolling across a heath on a new planet, and we see something which resembles a watch. We would look at it, note its resemblance to artefacts produced by our own mind, and conclude that somebody designed it. But supposing that it was a neat pile of stones we found? It might have been put there by human design, but it might not. It could either be design or chance$_3$, ie a lack of design. To help decide, we might hypothesise a purposive use for which it might have been intended, and then consider whether or not it seems well arranged to fulfil that use. We could also ask (if experience is available) how often similar patterns might have been expected when no one had any purpose in mind. But we could never be sure as long as we were inferring design from its structure alone.

To Christians, many structures observed in the world look like structures which have been designed. Their conclusion is that the world has a designer. Others (like Octavius' opponent) look at the world, argue that events appear capricious, without any obvious end in mind, and conclude that they are chance$_3$, ie have no designer. The choice between these two basic alternatives is the same now as it ever was.

Later thinkers extended the design arguments in various ways, seeing up to five variations.[46] Two are still of some relevance. The cosmological argument Kant summarised: 'If there exists anything, there must also exist an absolutely necessary Being.'[47] Essentially, it asks not about particular features of what exists, but why there is anything rather than nothing in existence. Surely it cannot just be there? The teleological argument is the more classic argument from particular features of the universe, ie that the pattern exhibited looks as if it were purposefully designed.

The rise of modern science saw the continuation of that

idea. Robert Boyle, and a stream of writers afterwards, used the same basic arguments from design. At the beginning of the nineteenth century two writers, William Paley and Baptist Robert Hall, wrote influential books on the subject.[48] Both argued similarly. The structures in the world around us, such as the human eye, are clearly contrived for a purpose (to enable organic beings, and in particular us, to live effectively). This being so they indicate design.

Paley used the analogy of finding a watch. A watch, he said, would imply a designer even if we had never seen one made, if it sometimes went wrong, or we could not always understand its working. He also added that even if someone could imagine 'the watch before us to have been produced by another watch, and that by a former, and so on indefinitely ..., contrivance is still unaccounted for. We still want a contriver.'[49]

Now although Paley argued thus, it would obviously give strength to the argument if it could be shown that the watch had begun existence at some point in time where no watches had previously existed. When Paley wrote, however, the geological school of Hutton held that there was no physical evidence for a beginning to the world as we know it. By the 1830s (as we have seen) this had been refuted, and virtually all geologists accepted that in the earliest strata there were no animal remains at all, and that species came into being as time progressed. This they saw as a powerful new dimension to the argument from design.[50] The series of discontinuities in natural law at each moment of new species creation proved, they thought, that God was still operating in his world.

Now Darwin's theory brought changes to this situation — but what exactly were they? Firstly, it effectively nullified the additional arguments brought by geologists during the previous few decades. This had, really, been an argument not so much about design structure as about the miraculous discontinuities in natural law. Ironically, Francis Bacon had faced an outcry from some seventeenth-century Christians who objected to scientists finding secondary causes (ie natural explanations) for phenomena. He responded:

> If they mean that the ignorance of a second cause doth make men more devoutly to depend upon the providence of God, as supposing the defects to come immediately from his hand, I demand of them, as Job demanded of his friends, 'Will you lie for God as man will for man?'[51]

But all this concerns an argument from miracles rather than from design. The effect of Darwin on the actual argument from design was to remove the series of individual questions as Paley had put them (ie the question about each individual organic structure), and leave the one grand question about why the universe was structured so as to enable organic life to emerge. Even Darwin's fiercest advocate, T H Huxley wrote: 'There is a wider teleology which is not touched by the doctrine of evolution.'[52]

This question still remains, and will always remain unless it can somehow be shown one day that, on some purely logical basis, existence cannot be any other way. If ever that time arrives, it would effectively mean that philosophical rationalism would finally be acknowledged as a surer way to knowledge than empiricism. In principle it should then be possible to deduce the whole history of the universe from pure logic alone, and without making any observations at all! At present this does not seem very likely!

In the present time, therefore, we can still ask the cosmological and teleological questions. Why is there anything rather than nothing, and why is it structured to enable the emergence of organic life and consciousness? Actually, one of the most extraordinary statements made by Richard Dawkins is: 'Biology is the study of complicated things that give the appearance of having been designed for a purpose. Physics is the study of simple things that do not tempt us to invoke design.'[53] Not only (as illustrated in Chapter 13) have most important discoverers of key ideas in the structure of matter been profoundly affected by the idea of divine design, but the force of the design argument in the increasing complexity of modern physics is felt with even a cursory reading of the current literature.

There are also some further questions relating to the probability of us being here, which we now consider.

## The improbable us

At the present time there remain several interesting problems and questions about probability and design. Firstly, there is the question of the probability of life beginning by chance, given the conditions on the primeval earth. On the assumption, that is, that there was no divine design behind the beginning of life, in how many similar planets would one expect the atomic structure necessary to start independent life forms to have happened to come together. There is very serious disagreement over this. M Eigen and others conclude that the chance was near 100%, based on the assumption that, in a sense, the build-up to life could itself have been evolutionary, ie each stage could have been 'locked on' before the next.[54] Eigen (and Richard Dawkins, who makes a similar point) is, of course, right to assert that a model in which the successive stages in the formation of the first organic life are 'locked on' is not the same as supposing that all the elements came together like components spontaneously forming a jet plane by an explosion in the spares shop. Yet it cannot be said that such a model has, in fact, been constructed, and there are others including some famous agnostics, who have argued that the chance would be very low. Hoyle and Wickramasinghe, in a famous book, argued that it was near zero.[55] More significant, Francis Crick, who earned the Nobel Prize for discovery of DNA, believes life so complex that it could not have evolved here by chance.[56] Both, however (not being willing to admit a God), suggest what seem wildly unlikely theories about earth being seeded with life by a god or superbeing somewhere out in space. Though we must insist that we see no particular problems for theology if an Eigen-type model were constructed to explain life's origin, it does appear that hopes for this have receded rather than advanced in recent years.[57]

A second issue concerns the second law of thermodynamics. According to this law, entropy (or disorder) is constantly increasing in the universe. Professor Stephen Hawking of Cambridge, one of the most profound thinkers on this subject, notes in a 1987 article three time clocks: (i) thermodynamic (increase in entropy), (ii) psychological (we feel time passing), and (iii) cosmological (the universe is expanding).[58] The universe is believed to have set out from a 'singularity': all space and time is 'curved up with an infinitely small radius'. The 'big bang' threw out the present expanding universe, which will eventually, says Hawking, begin to recontract. He now believes, however, that when it does so, entropy will continue to increase. He compares this with travelling from North to South Pole. One is all the time travelling south, but there is an expanding and then contracting stage.

From an atheist viewpoint this is a puzzle, because it puts us in a privileged position. We just happen to be at an inhabitable stage of the universe on a one-way trip to total entropy at a point of no return. There is not, in the strict sense, any beginning or end to the process, but it appears not to cycle, since the entropy only increases.

Further puzzles are contained in his book *A Brief History of Time* (1988). He writes:

The laws of science as we know them at present contain many fundamental numbers, like the size of the electric charge of the electron and the ratio of the masses of the proton and electron

... The remarkable fact is that the values of these numbers seem to have been very finely adjusted to make possible the development of life ... Most sets of numbers would give rise to universes that, although they might have been very beautiful, would contain no one able to wonder at the beauty ... The initial rate of expansion would have had to be chosen very precisely for the rate of expansion still to be so close to the critical rate needed to avoid recollapse ... It would be very difficult to explain why the universe should have begun in just this way, except as the act of a God who intended to create beings like us.[59]

Paul Davies is another British physicist who has talked in similar terms: 'If the primeval material was churned about at random, it would have been overwhelmingly more probable to have created black holes than stars.'[60]

But in black holes no life could apparently exist. The odds, then, Davies gives against an inhabitable starry cosmos 'become mind-boggling: one followed by a thousand, billion, billion, billion zeros at least'.[61]

So how, apart from design, can we explain the 'mind-boggling' improbability of an inhabitable universe?

Davies uses the anthropic principle. This argues that, only in a universe in which life was indeed possible would there be anyone to wonder about it. Since we are here to wonder about it, we can conclude that out of the infinite plurality of universes (actually seriously suggested by some physicists) it is no surprise to learn that we are in one which is inhabitable. This may sound plausible but, as Bartholomew shows, it involves a misuse of probabilities.[62] Going on from Bartholomew, we would assert that the only correct form of statistical analysis one could use in this kind of situation is the one known as Bayes theorem.[63] Supposing that an agnostic would agree that, without any knowledge about the particular nature of the universe but knowing that one did exist, there might be, say, a one in a million chance that there was a personal God who had created it. Suppose that our agnostic friend further agreed that if such a God existed, then the chance of that God creating an inhabitable universe might be again, say, one in a million. Both these figures are, obviously, fairly conservative! Now supposing that we add to this the figure given by Davies, who is not a Christian, that the probability of the universe being inhabitable if no God existed would be one in a number 'one followed by a thousand, billion, billion, billion zeros at least'. The application of Bayes theorem would be as follows:

1.  Prior probability: Pr [God exists] = 0.000001
    Prior probability: Pr [no God] = 0.999999
2.  Prob [universe inhabitable if God exists] = 0.000001
    Prob [universe inhabitable if no God] = [0.00 (one billion, billion, billion zeros) 1]

THEN: Prob [God exists given universe is inhabitable]

$$= \frac{\text{Prob [universe inhabitable if God exists]} \times \text{Prob [God exists]}}{\left[\begin{array}{c}\text{Prob [universe inhabitable if God exists]} \times \text{Prob [God exists]} \\ + \text{Prob [Universe inhabitable if no God]} \times \text{Prob [no God]}\end{array}\right]}$$

$$= \frac{0.000001 \times 0.000001}{\left[\begin{array}{c}(0.000001) \times (0.000001) \\ + (0.999999) \times (0.00 \text{ (a billion, billion, billion zeros) 1})\end{array}\right]}$$

This is so near to 1 (or 100% certain) as to make no odds. Taking, then, Davies' figure, even very low views of the a-priori probability of God's existence, and the probability that if he did exist, he would create an inhabitable universe, the fact that the universe is inhabitable makes the probability that God exists virtually 1. Once we accept the meaningfulness of a concept like 'the probability that there is a God', the correct application of statistical theory would be reflected not in the anthropic principle (into which so many modern non-Christian physicists seem to retreat), but in a Bayesian analysis which would make God's existence a virtual certainty. It is, of course, possible that physicists in the future might revise the probability figures given by men like Davies and Hawking. At present, however, it is true to say that atheistic physicists face massive problems of inconsistency.

## Conclusion: God or chance?

The most basic question facing human beings is the same now as it has been throughout the centuries. Is the world in which we find ourselves something designed by a personal God, or is it something which has not been designed by any personal being (ie it is a result of chance$_3$)?

This is more than just a vaguely interesting academic question. The meaningfulness of human personhood, right, wrong, and all human values, may be in question if we are *no more than* by-products of a blind chance$_3$ in a one-way dance of atoms towards a state of total entropy, which is little removed in practical terms from absolute nothingness.

What we have tried to show in this book is that a belief in the Christian God of creation makes sense of our human situation, in a way that a hypothesis of total lack of design in the universe does not. There are still puzzles and anomalies, for we 'know in part' (1 Cor 13:12), and some of the synthesis we have suggested may well look as unlikely in future generations as Newtonian dynamics seems now in the age of Einstein. Nevertheless, in view of what is at stake, we believe that the development of such a synthesis for our generation is crucial.

God, however, does not want to be left as a conclusion at the end of a book on astronomy and the big bang. He is a participant, wanting us each individually to enter a personal relationship with him. This is what biblical Christianity, the Christianity of Jesus Christ, has always preached — and it makes sense of our human situation as much now as ever it did.

# Notes

1. Classically expressed by Laplace in *Analytic Theory of Probability* (1812) and *A Philosophical Essay on Probability* (1814). Laplace was a determinist and believed probability expressed only human ignorance.

2. This can either be seen as an observed feature of empirical sequences as R Von Mises, *Probability, Statistics and Truth* (1939; revised edition, 1957), or as a mathematical theory conjectured to apply to an actual sequence as K Popper, *The Logic of Scientific Discovery*.

3. Eg J M Keynes, *A Treatise on Probability* (1921), or L J Savage, *Foundations of Statistics* (1954).

4. For a readable account see, for example, P Davies, *God and the New Physics* (1983), chap 11, or *Other Worlds* (1980), or J Polkinghorne, *The Quantum World* (1984), or J Power, *Philosophy and the New Physics* (1982), chap 4. Some of the philosophical differences are summarised in Ian G Barbour's *Issues in Science and Religion*, chap 10, iii.

5. W Heisenberg, *Physics and Philosophy* (1971).

6. M Born, *The Natural Philosophy of Cause and Chance* (1949).

7. Jacques Monod, *Chance and Necessity* (translated by Knopf, 1970; this edition, 1971), p 111; also A Peacocke, *Creation and the World of Science* (1979), p 91 and D J Bartholomew, *God of Chance* (1984), p 131.

8. J Monod, *op cit*, p 110.

9. Eg MacKay, Peacocke and Bartholomew all take him thus.

10. R Dawkins, *The Blind Watchmaker*, p 21. In *The Selfish Gene* he equally airily remarks: 'There is, of course, no "architect". The DNA instructions have been assembled by natural selection' (p 24). Elsewhere, however, he balks at the idea that biology can itself imply metaphysics, asserting: 'I am not advocating a morality based on evolution' (p 3) and proceeding to irrationally advise us to try to act totally against the supposed preprogramming of our accidentally evolved natures. The altruistic behaviour he seems to advocate for humans, he sees in animals as no more than a 'misfiring of a built-in rule' (p 109), though it is a mystery why he should call it a 'misfiring', since he claims it has no design or purpose. Like other crusaders against Christianity, his metaphysics seems written more in passion than in reason.

11. Ian G Barbour, in *Issues in Science and Religion*, p 309.

12. The use of male-gender language (like 'Father' and 'he') for God can, of course, be seen only as a model, but it is the preponderant model God has chosen to use in Scripture and we will keep to it.

13. The thinking on this of theologians from Augustine to Barth and beyond is discussed by Jurgen Moltmann in his 1984–5 Gifford Lectures, *God in Creation: An Ecological Doctrine of Creation*, chap v.

14. For 'will' (Greek root: *thelo*), see Matthew 7:21, 12:50, 23:37; Mark 3:35; Luke 13:34; John 7:17; 1 John 2:17. For 'plan' (Greek: *boule*), see Luke 7:30; 2 Peter 3:9. See also chap 6 of our *God's Strategy in Human History*.

15. Justin, *Dialogue with Trypho*, vol cxli (*Ant Nic Fath*, i, 269).

16. Irenaeus, *Against Heresies*, vol xxxvii (*Ant Nic Fath*, i, 518).

17. Athenagoras, *A Plea for the Christians*, vol xxiv (*Ant Nic Fath*, ii, 142).

18. Tatian, *Address to the Greeks*, vol xi (*Ant Nic Fath*, ii, 69).

19. Clement, *Miscellanies*, ii, 4 (*Ant Nic Fath*, ii, 349).

20. Tertullian, *Against Marcion*, bk 2 chap vi (*Ant Nic Fath*, iii, 301).

21. Novatian, *On the Trinity*, vol i (*Ant Nic Fath*, v, 612).

22. Origen, *On First Principles*, preface, (*Ant Nic Fath*, iv, 240).

23. Methodius, *Banquet of the Ten Virgins*, vol xvi (*Ant Nic Fath*, vi, 342).

24. Archelaus, *Disputation with Manes* (*Ant Nic Fath*, vi, 204).

25. Arnobius, *Against the Heathen* (*Ant Nic Fath*, vi, 458).

26. Chrysostom, *Homily on Hebrews*, vol xii (*Nic & Pos Nic Fath*, 1, xiv, 425).

27. Cyril, *Catechetical Lectures*, vol iv of the soul (*Nic & Pos Nic Fath*, 2, vii, 23).

28. Gregory of Nyssa, *On Virginity*, vol xii (*Nic & Pos Nic Fath*, 2, v, 357). Gregory, among others, specifically linked human free-will with the image of God in mankind.

29. Jerome, *Letter*, vol cxxxiii (*Nic & Pos Nic Fath*, 2, vi, 278).

30. D MacKay, review of Bartholomew's book in *Religious Studies*, vol 21 (1986): pp 622–4. Also reprinted in Spanner, *Biblical Creation and the Theory of Evolution*, pp 155–158.

31. Colin Brown (ed), *The New International Dictionary*, vol i, p 356.

32. See also Exodus 32:12–14; Judges 2:18; 1 Chronicles 21:15, Jonah 3:9–10; Jeremiah 18:8–10, 26:3; Joel 2:14; Amos 7:3.

33. See also MacKay, *The Clockwork Image* (1974), chap 5, and his review of Bartholomew's book in *Religious Studies*, *op cit*.

34. D Kidner, *Proverbs* (1964), p 122.

35. See MacKay, review *op cit*, p 624.

36. *Ibid*, p 623.

37. Peacocke, *Creation and the World of Science*, p 105.

38. Bartholomew, *God of Chance*, p 136.

39. P Davies, *Other Worlds*, chap 7.

40. Bartholomew, *God of Chance*, p 128.

41. Openly anti-Christian, the book is in several ways strangely naïve. In particular we note in this chapter Dawkins' confusion over whether or not biology implies a metaphysics (see note 10), and over the lack of argument from design which he asserts of physics.

42. The Babylonian myths are discussed in A Heidel, *The Babylonian Genesis*; also G Westermann, *Genesis 1–11* (1984), pp 25–33, discusses chaos in detail. The Greek Hesiod presents chaos as the first thing in existence.

43. See Cicero's *The Nature of the Gods* (c 45 BC), where the Stoic arguments for the existence of God were given. We are indebted to Dr Norma Emerton for pointing out to us the extent of debt of the Christian fathers to Cicero.

44. Aristides, *Apology*.

45. Minucius Felix, *Octavius* (*Ant Nic Fath*, iv, 182).

46. Aquinas in *Summa Theologiae*, I q 2 a 3, suggested five

47. Kant analysed Aquinas' five into three in *Critique of Pure Reason*, vol 3, pp 1–6.

48. R Hall, *Modern Infidelity Considered* (1804) (in O Gregory (ed), *Works of Robert Hall*, 1832); W Paley, *Natural Theology* (1802).

49. Paley, *ibid*, p 13.

50. See, for example, W Buckland, *Vindiciae Geologicae* (1829), p 18.

51. Bacon, *Valerius Terminus*, in *Philosophical Works of Francis Bacon* (ed, J Robertson, 1905), p 187.

52. T H Huxley, 'On the Reception of the Origin of Species' in *The Life and Letters of Charles Darwin* (ed, Francis Darwin, 1887), vol 2, p 479.

53. Dawkins, *The Blind Watchmaker*, p 1.

54. See Bartholomew, *God of Chance*, for some details.

55. F Hoyle and C Wickramasinghe, *Evolution from Space* (1981).

56. F Crick, *Life Itself* (1981).

57. Some of the problems are explained by biologist L R Croft, *How Life Began* (1988), and Jim Brooks, *Origins of Life* (1985).

58. S Hawking, 'The Direction of Time', *New Scientist* (9 July 1987), pp 46–9.

59. S Hawking, *A Brief History of Time* (1988).

60. P Davies, *Other Worlds*, p 168.

61. *Ibid*.

62. Bartholomew, *God of Chance*, p 64.

63. Bayesian statistics was one specialist area of study in Paul Marston's first degree in the LSE.

# APPENDIX I
# THE RESURRECTION OF JESUS

## People involved

THE IDENTITIES OF THOSE INVOLVED in the Resurrection appearances are analysed in John Wenham's book *Easter Enigma*. Most of them have been adopted in our own treatment in Chapter 6, for reasons we shall very briefly outline here.

Firstly, Matthew 27:56, Mark 15:40 and John 19:25 all mention three women watching the crucifixion. These were:

1. The mother of the sons of Zebedee, James and John (Mt),
   the sister of Jesus' mother (Jn),
   Salome (Mk)
2. Mary the mother of James and Joses (Mt),
   Mary the mother of James the Younger and Joses (Mk),
   Mary the wife of Clopas (Jn)
3. Mary Magdalene (Mt, Mk and Jn).

The most logical course is to equate the three accounts. This means that Salome was Jesus' aunt, and her sons James and John were his cousins. This may explain why John calls himself the 'beloved disciple' (Jn 19:26) and why his mother was so ambitious for her sons (Mt 20:21).

James the Younger, son of the second woman mentioned,

433

is generally taken as the one listed among the disciples as 'James son of Alphaeus' (Mt 10:3, Acts 1:13), because 'Alphaeus' and 'Clopas' can (surprisingly) be different pronunciations of the same Hebrew name.[1] According to Eusebius, the second-century historian Hegesippus calls Clopas the Lord's uncle[2] and Eusebius takes this to mean that Clopas was Joseph's brother.[3] The Latin and Syriac versions identified Clopas with Cleopas, and it would have been natural for Luke to Graecise the name in this way in Luke 24.

An extant fragment of a medieval dictionary states the following:

> (1) Mary the mother of the Lord; (2) Mary the wife of Cleophas or Alphaeus, who was the mother of James the bishop and apostle, and of Simon and Thaddeus, and of one Joseph; (3) Mary Salome, wife of Zebedee, mother of John the evangelist and James; (4) Mary Magdalene. These four are found in the Gospels. James and Judas and Joseph were sons of an aunt (2) of the Lord's. James also, and John were sons of another aunt (3) of the Lord's. Mary (2), mother of James the Less [Younger] and Joseph, wife of Alphaeus was the sister of Mary the mother of the Lord, whom John names of Cleophas.[4]

This attempt to unravel all the Marys is interesting and it generally confirms that at least as early as the Middle Ages something like the relationships we have suggested were taught. It raises the possibility that Salome was actually the sister of Jesus' mother, and so Cleopas was the Lord's uncle not because he was Joseph's brother but by marriage. If so, then Eusebius was right in reporting Hegesippus as saying that Clopas was the Lord's uncle, but wrong in his interpretation of this. Though we have preferred to keep Cleopas as Joseph's brother for our interpretation, if this other version of relationships is correct, it would alter nothing of importance.

Early Fathers such as Augustine[5] took Mary of Bethany to

be the 'sinner' of Luke 7:36–8 (AV), and Wenham adds to this strong early tradition citation of twenty-one other scholars in modern times who have argued this.[6] The anointing in Matthew 26:6–13, Mark 14:3–9 and John 12:1–8 is seen as a re-enactment and completion of the first — by the same woman identified as such by John in 11:2 in a reference back to the earlier rather than forward to the later act. By the time of Gregory the Great in the early 600s he could assume that the 'sinner', Mary of Bethany and Mary Magdalene were all the same person as this became accepted in the West.[7]

Our own reasons for accepting the early church teaching are as follows: firstly, we may note how the two Marys, though both centrally and intensely involved with Jesus, never appear together in the accounts. Thus we find:

1. The 'sinner', in Luke 7:36–8 (AV), anoints him.
2. Magdalene, healed by Jesus, joins his women supporters who travel with him (Lk 8:2).
3. Coming to Bethany 'Martha opened her home to him' (Lk 10:38). We find her sister Mary present (10:39), though it is apparently Martha's home not hers.
4. Jesus heals their brother Lazarus (Jn 11).
5. Mary of Bethany anoints Jesus' feet (Mt 26:6–13; Mk 14:3–9; Jn 12:1–8) and is told to keep ointment for his burial (Jn 12:7).
6. Mary Magdalene stands at the cross (Mt 27:56; Mk 15:40; Jn 19:25).
7. Mary Magdalene visits the tomb to anoint Jesus for burial, and is the first to see Jesus (Mt 28:1–10; Mk 16:9; Jn 20:10–18).

If they are not the same person, it would be a real mystery why Mary of Bethany (who seems to have so deep an understanding of and devotion to the Lord) would be nowhere mentioned in the accounts of his crucifixion and

Resurrection, even though Bethany is only about 1.5 miles from Jerusalem.

There is, of course, no reason why someone could not have one nickname in one circle and a different one in another. It would have been odd to have said 'Mary Magdalene' in the immediate context of her home town of Bethany. On the other hand, with so many Marys around, 'Mary of Magdala' may well have come to be the name later used in the church, identifying her with the key part of her life which had indirectly brought her into contact with Jesus. There is no great significance in the fact that the Gospel writers do not make it explicit that the two Marys are the same. Other relationships, for example, Jesus' relationship to Salome, James and John, are not made explicit either. When the Gospels were written, many of the church may well have known about such relationships, and the writers may not have thought it necessary or relevant to be explicit.

Some moderns reject the identification on the grounds of some evident sympathy with the scepticism of Simon the Pharisee that Jesus could transform a 'sinner' into a 'saintly' woman like Mary of Bethany (thus the *Illustrated Bible Dictionary*[8]). We believe this sadly in error. In actual fact, the identification of Mary of Bethany, Magdalene, and the 'sinner' makes an excellent overall coherent picture. Mary, unsatisfied with the kind of domestic preoccupations of her sister Martha, fell into a dissolute life style in the delectable, but immoral resort of Magdala. But, as so often happens, Mary failed to find the 'real life' she sought in this way, instead adding mental oppression and fragmentation to her moral decline. In this sorry state Jesus found her, bringing her (as we have seen in some modern lives) reality, mental and spiritual healing, and forgiveness and cleansing of her sins. Owing him much, as Jesus himself testified (Lk 7:47), she developed an intense love and devotion to him, joining the women who followed and supported him, and so coming to understand more of his mission than many others.

Naturally, Jesus would now be a welcome guest in the home of Martha, her sister (and note Lk 10:38–9 seems to imply that it was Martha's, but no longer Mary's house). Mary, as might be expected, expressed the intense love of the redeemed sinner by drinking in his every word. Martha (giving us perhaps a glimpse of why Mary had run off in the first place) mistakenly thought that Jesus had redeemed Mary simply to restore her to domesticity. But Jesus' reply, 'Mary has chosen what is better' (Lk 10:42), refers not merely to one occasion, but to her whole place as a member of his itinerant group of followers, with increasingly deep understanding of his mission. In her anointing of him, Jesus saw a deeper spiritual intuition, and spoke of her later role in anointing him for burial (Jn 12:7). Thus she appears both at the cross and the tomb, returning with the other ladies to complete the burial anointing. To her, then, Jesus chooses first to appear after his Resurrection. She is a central character in the whole drama.

## Parallel listing of verses

In reading our reconstruction of the Resurrection appearances, it may help to have the four actual Gospel accounts placed side by side. This is done in Appendix 2, with text taken from the NIV.

It must, of course, be remembered that it cannot be possible strictly to arrange the events of the accounts in chronological order. We have shown in Chapter 6 how some of the incidents concerning different people were happening at the same time. This kind of parallel setting out therefore has limited value in itself, but is useful to consult in reading the reconstruction.

## Notes

1.　A Edersheim, *The Life and Times of Jesus the Messiah* (1900), vol ii, p 603.

2. Eusebius, *Ecclesiastical History*, vol xxii (*Nic & Pos Nic Fath*, 2, i, 199).
3. Eusebius, *Ecclesiastical History*, vol xi (*Nic & Pos Nic Fath*, 2, i, 146).
4. *Ant Nic Fath*, 1, 155.
5. Augustine, *Harmony of the Gospels*, 2, lxxviii (*Nic & Pos Nic Fath*, 1, vi, 172).
6. John Wenham, *Easter Enigma*, p 24.
7. Gregory, *Epistle to Gregoria*, vol xxv (*Nic & Pos Nic Fath*, 2, xii, 219).
8. *The Illustrated Bible Dictionary* (1980) vol 2, p 959.

# APPENDIX 2

| MATTHEW | MARK | LUKE | JOHN |
|---|---|---|---|
| 27:59–61 Joseph took the body, wrapped it in a clean linen cloth, and placed it in his own new tomb ... Mary Magdalene and the other Mary were sitting there opposite the tomb. | 15:46–7 Joseph bought some linen cloth, took down the body, wrapped it in the linen, and placed it in a tomb cut out of rock ... Mary Magdalene and Mary the mother of Joses saw where he was laid. | 23:53–5 ... he took it down, wrapped it in linen cloth, and placed it in a tomb cut in the rock ... The women who had come with Jesus from Galilee followed Joseph and saw how his body was laid in it. | 19:38–42 Joseph ... came and took the body ... Nicodemus brought a mixture of myrrh and aloes ... Taking Jesus' body, the two of them wrapped it, with the spices, in strips of linen ... since the tomb was nearby, they laid Jesus there. |
| 27:62–5 The next day [the chief priests etc asked for a guard which Pilate granted]. | | 23:56 Then they went home and prepared spices and perfumes. But they rested on the Sabbath in obedience to the commandment. | |
| 28:1 After the Sabbath, at dawn on the first day of the week, Mary Magdalene and the other Mary went to look at the tomb. | 16:1–2 When the Sabbath was over, Mary Magdalene, Mary the mother of James, and Salome bought spices so that they might go to anoint Jesus' body. Very early on the first day of the week, just after sunrise, they were on their way to the tomb ... | 24:1 On the first day of the week, very early in the morning, the women took the spices they had prepared and went to the tomb. | 20:1 Early on the first day of the week, while it was still dark, Mary Magdalene went to the tomb. |

| | | | |
|---|---|---|---|
| 28:2-4 There was a violent earthquake, for an angel of the Lord came down from heaven and, going to the tomb, rolled back the stone and sat upon it . . . The guards were so afraid of him that they shook and became like dead men. | | | |
| | 16:3 and they asked each other, 'Who will roll the stone away from the entrance of the tomb?' | 24:2 They found the stone rolled away from the tomb, | 20:1 and saw that the stone had been removed from the entrance. |
| | 16:4 But when they looked up, they saw that the stone, which was very large, had been rolled away. | | |
| | | | 20:2 So she came running to Simon Peter and the other disciple . . . and said, 'They have taken the Lord out of the tomb, and we don't know where they have put him!' |

| MATTHEW | MARK | LUKE | JOHN |
|---|---|---|---|
| | 16:5 As they entered the tomb, | 24:3 but when they entered, they did not find the body . . . | |
| | 16:5 they saw a young man dressed in a white robe sitting on the right side, and they were alarmed. | 24:4-5 While they were wondering about this, suddenly two men in clothes that gleamed like lightning stood beside them. In their fright the women bowed down with their faces to the ground, | |
| 28:5 The angel said to the women, 'Do not be afraid . . .' | 16:6 'Don't be alarmed,' he said. | 24:5 but the men said to them, | |
| 28:5 '. . . for I know that you are looking for Jesus, who was crucified . . .', | 16:6 'You are looking for Jesus the Nazarene, who was crucified.' | | |
| | | 24:5 'Why do you look for the living among the dead?' | |
| 28:6 'He is not here; he has risen,' | 16:6 'He has risen! He is not here.' | 24:6 'He is not here; he has risen!' | |

told you, while he was still with you in Galilee: The Son of Man must be delivered into the hands of sinful men, be crucified and on the third day be raised again.'

28:6 'Come and see the place where he lay.'

16:6 See the place where they laid him.

28:7 'Then go quickly and tell his disciples: "He has risen from the dead and is going ahead of you into Galilee. There you will see him." Now I have told you.'

16:7 But go, tell his disciples and Peter, 'He is going ahead of you into Galilee. There you will see him, just as he told you.'

28:8 So the women hurried away from the tomb, afraid, yet filled with joy, and ran to tell his disciples.

16:8 Trembling and bewildered, the women went out and fled from the tomb.

16:8 They said nothing to anyone, because they were afraid.

| MATTHEW | MARK | LUKE | JOHN |
|---------|------|------|------|
| | | 24:9-11 When they came back from the tomb, they told all these things to the Eleven and to all the others. It was Mary Magdalene, Joanna, Mary the mother of James, and the others with them who told this to the apostles. But they did not believe the women ... | |
| | | 24:12 Peter, however, got up and ran to the tomb. Bending over, he saw strips of linen lying by themselves, and he went away, wondering to himself what had happened. | 20:3 So Peter and the other disciple [John] started for the tomb ... [John arrived first, looked in but did not enter. Peter entered, saw the strips of linen and, lying separately, the folded-up burial headcloth. Then John entered — and believed.] |
| | | | 20:10 Then the disciples went back to their homes, |

20:11-12 but Mary stood outside the tomb crying. As she wept, she bent over to look into the tomb and saw two angels in white, seated where Jesus' body had been ... [there follows her speech with the angels.]

20:14-17 ... she turned round and saw Jesus ... Jesus said to her ... 'Go ... to my brothers and tell them ...'

16:9 he appeared first to Mary Magdalene, out of whom he had driven seven demons.

28:9-10 Suddenly Jesus met them. 'Greetings,' he said. They came to him, clasped his feet and worshipped him. Then Jesus said to them, 'Do not be afraid. Go and tell my brothers to go to Galilee; there they will see me.'

| MATTHEW | MARK | LUKE | JOHN |
|---|---|---|---|
| | | | 20:18 Mary Magdalene went to the disciples with the news: 'I have seen the Lord!' And she told them that he had said these things to her. |
| | 16:10–11 She went and told those who had been with him and who were mourning and weeping. When they heard that Jesus was alive and that she had seen him, they did not believe it. | | |
| | 16:12 Afterwards Jesus appeared in a different form to two of them while they were walking in the country. | 24:13–15 Now that same day two of them were going to a village called Emmaus … As they talked … Jesus himself came up … | |
| | | 24:22–3 '… some of our women amazed us. They went to the tomb early this morning, but didn't find his body. They came and told us that they had seen a vision of angels, who said he was alive.' | |

companions went to the tomb and found it just as the women had said, but him they did not see.'

| | | |
|---|---|---|
| 16:13 These returned and reported it to the rest; but they did not believe them either. | 24:33–5 They got up and returned at once to Jerusalem. There they found the Eleven and those with them, assembled together and saying, 'It is true! The Lord has risen and has appeared to Simon.' Then the two told what happened on the way, and how Jesus was recognised by them when he broke the bread. | 20:19 On the evening of that first day of the week, when the disciples were together, with the doors locked for fear of the Jews, Jesus came and stood among them and said, 'Peace be with you!' After he said this, he showed them his hands and side ... |
| 16:14 Later Jesus appeared to the Eleven as they were eating; he rebuked them for their lack of faith ... | 24:36–9 While they were still talking about this, Jesus himself stood among them and said to them, 'Peace be with you.' ... 'Look at my hands and my feet. It is I myself! ...' | |

# BIBLIOGRAPHY

Aardsma, G E and Humphreys, D R. 'Has the Speed of Light Decayed Recently?' *Creation Research Society Quarterly*. Vol 25 (1988): pp 36–45.

Albright, W F. *The Christian Century*. November 1958.

Allegro, John. *The Sacred Mushroom and the Cross*. Sphere Books: London, 1973.

Ambrose. *Hexameron* in *The Fathers of the Church* (translated by J J Savage). Catholic University of America Press: Washington, 1961.

Andrews, E H. *Is Evolution Scientific?* Evangelical Press: Welwyn, 1977.

Andrews, E H. *From Nothing to Nature*. Evangelical Press: Welwyn, 1978.

Andrews, E H. *God, Science and Evolution*. Evangelical Press: Welwyn, 1980.

Andrews, E H. *Christ and the Cosmos*. Evangelical Press: Welwyn, 1986.

Andrews, E H, Gitt W, and Ouweneel, W J (eds). *Concepts in Creationism*. Evangelical Press: Welwyn, 1986.

Ashwell, A. *Life of Samuel Wilberforce*. Two volumes. Murray: London, 1880–2.

Atkins, P. *The Creation*. W H Freeman: Oxford, 1981.

Augustine. *De Genesi Ad Litterum*. c 401–15.

Ayer, A J. *Language, Truth and Logic*. Twentieth Impression. Gollancz: London, 1964 (first edition, 1936; second edition, 1946).

Ayer, A J. *The Problem of Knowledge*. Pelican: London, 1956.

Bacon, Francis. *Of The Advancement of Learning*. 1605

Bacon, Francis. *Novum Organum*. 1620.

Bacon, Francis. *Valerius Terminus* (1734) in *Philosophical Works of Francis Bacon* (ed, J Robertson). George Routledge: London, 1905.

Baker, Sylvia. *Bone of Contention*. Evangelical Press: Welwyn, 1976.

Balleine, G R. *A History of the Evangelical Party in the Church of England*. Longmans: London, 1908.

Barbour, Ian G. *Issues in Science and Religion*. SCM Press: London, 1966.

Barbour, Ian G. *Myths, Models and Paradigms*. SCM Press: London, 1974.

Barnes, Thomas. *Origin and Destiny of the Earth's Magnetic Field*. Creation Life: San Diego, 1973.

Barnett, Paul. *Is the New Testament History?* Hodder: London, 1986.

Bartholomew, D J. *God of Chance*. SCM Press: London, 1984.

Bartholomew, M. 'Lyell and Evolution.' *British Journal for the History of Science*. Vol 6:23 (1973): p 266.

Bartholomew, M. 'The Singularity of Lyell.' *History of Science*. (1980): pp 276–93.

Bede. *Hexameron*.

Bell, A E. *Christian Huygens*. Arnold: London, 1947.

Berry, R J. *Neo-Darwinism*. Edward Arnold: London, 1982.

Berry, R J. *God and Evolution*. Hodder: London, 1988.

Beveridge, W I. *The Art of Scientific Investigation*. Heinemann: London, 1968.

Black, Max. *A Companion to Wittgenstein's Tractatus*. Cambridge University Press: Cambridge, 1971.

Blackmore, Vernon and Page, Andrew. *Evolution The Great Debate*. Lion: Oxford, 1989.

Blaiklock, E M. *Man or Myth*. Anzea: Australia, 1983.

Blake, R M, et al. *Theories of Scientific Method*. University of Washington Press: Washington, 1960.

Blocher, Henri. *In The Beginning*. Inter-Varsity Press: Leicester, 1984 (translated by D G Preston from 1979 french edition).

Blomberg, Craig. *The Historical Reliability of the Gospels*. Inter-Varsity Press: Leicester, 1987.

Bloor, D. *Knowledge and Social Imagery*. Routledge, 1976.

Bonino, Jose Miguez. *Christians and Marxists*. Hodder: London, 1976.

Born, M. *The Natural Philosophy of Cause and Chance*. Oxford University Press: Oxford, 1949 (second edition, Dover: New York, 1964).

Bowden, M. *The Rise of the Evolution Fraud*. Sovereign: Kent, 1982.

Bowler, Peter J. *Fossils and Progress*. Science History Publications: New York, 1976.

Bowler, Peter J. *Evolution: The History of an Idea*. University of California Press: Berkeley, 1984.

Boyle, Robert. *The Christian Virtuoso*. London, 1690.

Boyle, Robert. *Works*. Miller: London, 1744 (and many later editions).

Braithwaite, R B. *Scientific Explanation*. Harper: New York, 1953.

*British Regional Geology: North Wales*. Third Edition. HMSO: London, 1961.

Brooke, J H. 'Natural Theology and the Plurality of Worlds.' *Annals of Science*. Vol 34 (1977): pp 221–86.

Brooks, Jim. *Origins of Life*. Lion: Hertfordshire, 1985.

Brown, Colin. *Miracles and the Critical Mind*. Paternoster: Exeter, 1984.

Brown, Colin. *That You May Believe*. Paternoster: Exeter, 1985.

Brown, Colin (ed). *The New International Dictionary of New Testament Theology*, Three Vols. Paternoster: Exeter, 1975–85.

Brown, Colin. *History & Faith*, Inter-Varsity Press: Leicester, 1987.

Brown, F K. *Fathers of the Victorians*. Cambridge University Press: Cambridge, 1961.

Brown, Harold I. *Perception, Theory and Commitment*. University of Chicago: Chicago, 1979.

Brown, Harold I. *Observation and Objectivity*. Oxford University Press: Oxford, 1987.

Bruce, F F. *The Canon of Scripture*. Chapter House: Glasgow, 1988. (US edition by IVP used.)

Bruce, F F. *The New Testament Documents: Are They Reliable?* Revised edition. Inter-Varsity Press: Leicester, 1961.

Bruce, F F. *Jesus and Christian Origins Outside the New Testament*. Hodder: London, 1974.

Bruce, F F. *The Spreading Flame*. Revised edition. Paternoster: Exeter, 1982.

Bruce, F F. *The Books and the Parchments*. Revised edition. Pickering & Inglis: London, 1984.

Buckland, William. *Vindiciae Geologicae*. Oxford University Press: Oxford, 1820.

Buckland, William. *Reliquiae Diluvianae*. John Murray: London, 1823.

Buckland, William. *Geology and Mineralogy Considered With Reference to Natural Theology*. Pickering: London, 1836.

Buffon, G L. *Époques de la Nature*. 1778.

Buridan, Jean. *Quaestiones Super Octo Physicorum*.

Burke, Derek (ed). *Creation and Evolution*. Inter-Varsity Press: Leicester, 1985.

Burnett, D. *Unearthly Powers*. MARC: Eastbourne, 1988.

Butterfield, H. *The Whig Interpretation of History*. G Bell and Sons: London, 1931.

Caird, G B. *The Language and Imagery of the Bible*. Westminster: Philadelphia, 1980.

Calvin, J. *Commentary on Genesis*. Banner of Truth: Edinburgh, 1965 (translated by J King).

Cannon, Susan Faye. *Science in Culture: The Early Victorian Period*. Dawson: Folkestone, 1978.

Carr, E H. *What is History?* Second edition. Penguin: London, 1987 (first edition, 1961).

Chalmers, A F. *What is this thing called Science?* Second edition. Open University: Milton Keynes, 1982.

Chalmers, Thomas. *The Evidence and Authority of the Christian Revelation.* Blackwood: Edinburgh, 1814.

Chrysostom, *Homilies on Genesis* in *The Fathers of the Church* (translated by R C Hill). Catholic University of America Press: Washington, 1985.

Cicero. *The Nature of the Gods.* c 45 BC.

Clark, Robert E D. *Christian Belief and Science.* Second impression. English Universities Press: London, 1961. (First published 1960.)

Clark, J W and Hughes, T M. *The Life and Letters of Adam Sedgwick.* Two volumes. Cambridge University Press: Cambridge, 1890.

Collingwood, R G. *The Idea of History.* Oxford University Press: London, 1936.

Copernicus. *Revolutions of the Heavenly Spheres.* 1543.

Coppleston, F. *A History of Philosophy.* Vol 4. Image Books: New York, 1960.

Cranfield, C E B. *Romans.* Two volumes. T & T Clark: Edinburgh, 1980.

Crick, F. *Life Itself.* Macdonald: London, 1982.

Crick, Francis. *Of Molecules and Man.* University of Washington Press: London, 1966.

Croft, L R. *How Life Began.* Evangelical Press: Welwyn, 1988.

Cunningham, L. *St Francis of Assisi.* Twayne/Holts: Eastbourne, 1977.

Cupitt, Don. *The Sea of Faith.* BBC: London, 1984.

Darwin, Charles. *The Origin of Species.* Murray: London, 1859.

Darwin, Francis (ed). *The Life and Letters of Charles Darwin.* Two volumes. John Murray: London, 1887.

Davies, Paul. *Other Worlds.* Dent: London, 1980.

Davies, Paul. *God and the New Physics.* Pelican: Middlesex, 1983.

Dawkins, Richard. *The Selfish Gene.* Granada: London, 1978.

Dawkins, Richard. *The Blind Watchmaker.* Penguin: London, 1986.

Dawson, J W. *The Origin of the World According to Revelation and Science.* Second edition. Hodder and Stoughton: London, 1880.

Dawson, J W. *Modern Ideas of Evolution.* Watson: Reseda, 1977.

Dawson, J W. *The Meeting Place of Geology and History.* Religious Tract Society: London, 1894.

Del Ratzsch. *Philosophy of Science.* Inter-Varsity Press: Leicester, 1986.

Delitzsch, F. *A New Commentary on Genesis.* Two volumes. 1888–9 (translated by S Taylor).

Deluc, A. *An Elementary Treatise on Geology.* 1809.

Denton, Michael. *Evolution: A Theory in Crisis.* Burnett: London, 1985.

Descartes, René. *Meditations*. 1641.

Descartes, René. *Discourse on Method*. 1637.

Desmond, A. *Archetypes and Ancestors*. Blond & Briggs: London, 1982.

Dijksterhuis, E J. *The Mechanisation of the World Picture*. Oxford University Press: Oxford, 1961.

Douglas, J D (ed). *The Illustrated Bible Dictionary*. IVP: Leicester, 1980.

Drake, Ellen T. 'The Hooke Imprint on the Huttonian Theory.' *American Journal of Science*. Vol 281 (1981): pp 963–73.

Drake, Stillman. *Galileo*. Oxford University Press: Oxford, 1980.

Drake, Stillman. *Galileo at Work*. New edition. University of Chicago Press: London, 1981.

Draper, John William. *History of the Conflict Between Religion and Science*. Henry S King: London, 1875.

Dray, William. *Philosophy of History*. Prentice-Hall: Englewood Cliffs, 1964.

Duhem, P. *The Aim and Structure of Physical Theory*. Princeton: Oxford, 1954 (first edition 1906).

Durant, John (ed). *Darwinism and Divinity*. Blackwell: Oxford, 1985.

Eccles, John C. *The Human Psyche*. Springer-Verlag: New York, 1980.

Eccles, John C, and Popper, Karl. *The Self and Its Brain*. Springer-Verlag: New York, 1977.

Eddington, Arthur Stanley. *The Nature of the Physical World*. Cambridge University Press: Cambridge, 1928.

Edersheim, Alfred. *The Life and Times of Jesus the Messiah*. Two volumes. Tenth Impression. Longman's Green: London, 1900.

Eigen, Manfred and Winkler, Ruthild. *Laws of the Game*. Penguin: London, 1982.

Einstein, Albert. *Ideas and Opinions*. Dell: New York, 1973 (first published, 1954).

Elton, G R. *The Practice of History*. Paperback edition. Fontana: London, 1969.

Ernest, V. *I Talked with Spirits*. Coverdale House: Eastbourne.

Faber, G S. *Genius and Object*. 1823.

Fauvel, J et al. *Let Newton Be*. Oxford University Press: Oxford, 1988.

Feigl, H. *The Mental and the Physical*. University of Minnesota Press: Minneapolis, 1967.

Filby, F A. *Creation Revealed*. Pickering and Inglis: London, 1964.

Filby, Fredk A. *The Flood Reconsidered*. Pickering and Inglis: London, 1970.

Fleming, Ambrose. *Evolution or Creation?* Marshall: London.

Forster, Roger T and Marston, V Paul. *God's Strategy in Human History*. Tyndale House: Illinois, 1973.

Fraser, A. 'Radiometric Dating.' *Christian Graduate*. Vol 30:4 (1977): p 120.

Gale, B. *Evolution Without Evidence*. University of New Mexico Press: Albuquerque, 1982.

Galileo, Galilei. *Letter to the Grand Duchess Christina*. 1615.

Galileo, Galilei. *Dialogue on the Two World Systems*. 1632.

Galton, Francis. *English Men of Science: Their Nature and Nurture*. Macmillan: London, 1874.

Gandhi, M K. *An Autobiography*. Housmans: London, 1972.

Gardiner, Patrick. *The Nature of Historical Explanation*. Oxford University Press: Oxford, 1968.

Gardiner, Patrick (ed). *The Philosophy of History*. Oxford University Press: Oxford, 1974.

Gardner, Martin. *Fads and Fallacies in the Name of Science*. Dover edition. Dover: New York, 1957 (first edition 1952).

Gardner, Rex. *Healing Miracles: A Doctor Investigates*.

Gasson, R. *The Challenging Counterfeit*. AOG Publishers: London, 1958.

Geach, Peter T. *Providence and Evil*. Cambridge University Press: Cambridge, 1977.

Geikie, xxxxxxxxx, 1882.

Geisler, Norman L. *Christian Apologetics* Baker: Grand Rapids, 1976.

Geisler, Norman L. *Miracles and Modern Thought*. Zondervan: Grand Rapids, 1979.

Gillispi, Charles Coulston. *Genesis and Geology*. Harper & Row, New York, 1951.

Godfrey, Laurie R (ed). *Scientists Confront Creationism*. W W Norton: London, 1983.

Gordon, E O (ed), *The Life and Correspondence of William Buckland, DD, FRS*. 1894.

Gosse, P H. *Omphalos*. 1857.

Gould, S J and Eldredge N. 'Punctuated Equilibria: The Tempo and Mode of Evolution Reconsidered.' *Paleobiology*. Vol 3 (1977): pp 115–51.

Gray, Asa. *Natural Selection ...* Trubner: London, 1861.

Gray, Asa. *Natural Science and Religion*. Scribner: New York, 1880.

Green, Michael. *Evangelism in the Early Church*. New edition. Highland: Stockport, 1984.

Greene, J C. 'The History of Ideas Revisited.' *Revue De Synthese* (1986), pp 201–27.

Greenlee, J H. *Introduction to New Testament Textual Criticism*. Eerdmans: Grand Rapids, 1964.

Greenlee, J Harold. *Scribes, Scrolls and Scripture*. Eerdmans: Grand Rapids, 1985.

Grieve, Val. *Your Verdict on the Empty Tomb of Jesus*. STL/IVP: Leicester, 1988.

Guthrie, Donald. *New Testament Introduction*. New edition. Tyndale Press: London, 1974.

Habig, M. *St Francis of Assisi*. SPCK: London, 1980.

Hacking, I. *Representing and Intervening*. Cambridge University Press: Cambridge, 1983.

Hall, D H. *History of Earth Sciences During the Scientific and Industrial Revolutions*. Elsevier: Barking, 1976.

Hall, Robert. *Works of Robert Hall* (ed: O Gregory). 1832.

Hallam, A. *Great Geological Controversies*. Oxford University Press: Oxford, 1983.

Hanson, N R. *Patterns of Discovery*. Cambridge University Press: Cambridge, 1958.

Hawking, Stephen. 'The Direction of Time.' *New Scientist* 9 July 1987, pp 46–9.

Hawking, Stephen. *A Brief History of Time*. Bantam: London, 1988.

Hawthorne, Tim. *Windows of Science and Faith*. Inter-Varsity Press: Leicester, 1987.

Hayward, Alan. *Creation and Evolution*. SPCK: London, 1985.

Heaton, E W. *Everyday Life in Old Testament Times*. Batsford: London, 1956.

Heidel, Alexander. *The Babylonian Genesis*. Second edition. University of Chicago Press: London, 1963 (first edition, 1951).

Heidel, Alexander. *The Gilgamesh Epic and Old Testament Parallels*. Second edition. University of Chicago Press: London, 1963.

Heisenberg, W. *Physics and Philosophy*. Allen and Unwin: London, 1971.

Helm, Paul. *Objective Knowledge*. Inter-Varsity Press: Leicester, 1987.

Henbest, N. 'Brightest Supernova for Four Centuries.' *J Brit Astron Assoc*. Vol 97:3 (1987): pp 130–2.

Herbert, Lord Edward. *On Truth (De Veritate)*. Paris, 1624 (first London edition, 1645).

Hesse, Mary. Models and Analogies in Science. xxxxxxx, 1966.

Himmelfarb, Gertrude. *Darwin and the Darwinian Revolution*. Second edition. Norton: New York, 1962, (first edition, 1959).

Hodge, Charles. *What is Darwinism?* Scribner's: New York, 1874.

Hooke, R. *Micrographia*. London, 1665.

Hooykaas, R. *Natural Law and Divine Miracle: The Principle of Uniformity in Geology, Biology and Theology*. E J Brill: Leiden, 1963.

Hooykaas, R. *Religion and the Rise of Modern Science*. Scottish Academic Press: Edinburgh, 1972.

Houghton, John. *Does God Play Dice?* Inter-Varsity Press: Leicester, 1988.

Hoyle, Fred and Wickramasinghe, Chandra. *Evolution from Space*. Dent: London, 1981.

Hull D. *Darwin and His Critics*. Harvard University Press: Massachusetts, 1973.

Hume, David. *A Treatise of Human Nature*, 1739.

Hume, David. *An Enquiry Concerning Human Understanding* 1748.

Huxley, T H. *Collected Essays*. 1898. Two volumes. MacMillan: London (1894, 1898).

Irvine, W. *Apes, Angels and Victorians*. McGraw-Hill: New York, 1955.

Ito, Yushi. 'Hooke's Cyclic Theory of the Earth in the Context of Seventeenth Century England.' *British Journal for the History of Science*. Vol 21 (1988): pp 295–314.

Jacobs, J A. *The Earth's Core*. Academic Press: New York, 1975 (and also 1962).

Jaki, Stanley. *Brain, Mind and Computers*. Herder & Herder: New York, 1969.

Jaki, Stanley. *The Road of Science and the Ways of God*. Scottish Academic Press: Edinburgh, 1978.

Jeeves, Malcolm A. *The Scientific Enterprise and Christian Faith*. Tyndale Press: London, 1969.

Jenkins, D E. *God, Miracle and the Church of England*. SCM: London, 1987.

Jensen, J V. 'The X-Club.' *British Journal for the History of Science*. Vol 5, 17 (1970): pp 63–72.

Jensen, J V. 'Return to the Wilberforce-Huxley Debate.' *British Journal for the History of Science*. Vol 21, 2, 69 (1988): pp 161–80.

Joad, C E M. *Recovery of Belief*. Faber: London, 1952.

Joad, C E M. *Returning to the Church*. Abridged edition. Churchman Publishing: Worthing, 1984.

Jones, D Gareth. *Our Fragile Brains*. IVP: Leicester, 1981.

Josephus, Flavius. *The Antiquities of the Jews* in *Complete Works* (translated by W Whiston). Pickering and Inglis: London, 1960. Also Loeb edition (translated by R Marcus): London, 1937.

Kenyon, F. *Our Bible and the Ancient Manuscripts*. Fourth edition. Eyre & Spottiswoode: London, 1939.

Kenyon, F. *The Bible and Archaeology*. Harrap: London, 1940.

Kenyon, F. *The Text of the Greek Bible*. Revised edition (ed: A W Adams). Duckworth: Gloucester, 1975.

Keynes, J M. *A Treatise on Probability*. Macmillan: London, 1921.

Kidner, Derek. *Proverbs*. Tyndale Press: London, 1964.

Kidner, Derek. *Genesis*. Tyndale Press: London, 1967.

Kitcher, P. *Abusing Science: The Case Against Creationism*. MIT Press: Cambridge, 1982.

Kittel, G. *Theological Dictionary of the New Testament*. Paternoster: Exeter, 1964–74.

Kłausner, J. *Jesus of Nazareth*. Allen and Unwin: London, 1925.

Kline, M. 'Because It Had Not Rained.' *Westminster Theological Journal*. Vol 20 (1958): p 15.

Kline, M. *The Structure of Biblical Authority*. Eerdmans: Grand Rapids, 1975.

Koch, K E. *Christian Counselling and Occultism*. Kregel: Grand Rapids, 1972.

Koenigsberger, L. *Herman Von Helmholtz*. Dover: New York, 1965 (first edition, 1906).

Koestler, Arthur. *The Act of Creation*. Hutchinson: London, 1964.

Koestler, Arthur. *The Sleepwalkers*. Penguin: London, 1968.

Koestler, Arthur. *The Roots of Coincidence*. Hutchinson: London, 1972.

Kuhlman, Kathryn. *I Believe in Miracles*. Revell: New Jersey, 1968.

Kuhn, T S. *The Structure of Scientific Revolutions*. Second edition. University of Chicago Press: Chicago, 1970 (first edition, 1962).

Kurtz, J H. *Bible and Astronomy*. Third edition. 1857 (first edition, 1842).

Laplace, P S. *Analytic Theory of Probability*. 1812.

Laplace, P S. *A Philosophical Essay on Probability*. 1814.

Lasslet, P. *The Physical Basis of Mind*. Blackwell: Oxford, 1950.

Latourette, Kenneth Scott. *A History of Christianity*. New edition. Two volumes. Harper & Row: New York, 1976.

Laudan, R. *Science and Values*. University of California Press: Berkeley, 1984.

Laudan, R. *From Mineralogy to Geology: The Foundations of a Science 1650–1830*. University of Chicago Press: Chicago, 1987.

Lawrence, D H. *The Rainbow*. Phoenix edition. Heinemann: London, 1954 (first edition 1915).

Leakey, Richard. *The Making of Mankind*. Michael Joseph: London, 1981.

Leplin, J (ed). *Scientific Realism*. University of California Press: London, 1984.

Levine, J M. *Dr Woodward's Shield*. University of California Press: California, 1977.

Lewin, R. 'The Unmasking of Mitochondrial Eve.' *Science*. Vol 238 (2nd October 1987): pp 24–8.

Lewis, C S. *Miracles*. Paperback edition. Fontana: London, 1960 (first edition, 1947).

Lewis, C S. *Mere Christianity*. Ninth impression. Fontana: London, 1962 (first edition, 1952).

Lhwyd, E. *Lithophylacii Britannici Ichnograpia*. London, 1699.

Lindberg, D C. *Science in the Middle Ages*. University of Chicago: London, 1978.

Livingstone, David N. *Darwin's Forgotten Defenders*. Eerdmans/Scottish Academic Press: Edinburgh, 1987.

Lucas, R J. 'Wilberforce and Huxley: A Legendary Encounter.' *The Historical Journal*. Vol 22 (1979): pp 313–30.

MacKay, Donald M. *Science and Christian Faith Today*. Falcon: London, 1963.

MacKay, Donald M (ed). *Christianity in a Mechanistic Universe*. Inter-Varsity Press: Leicester, 1965.

MacKay, Donald M. *The Clockwork Image*. Inter-Varsity Press: Leicester, 1974.

MacKay, Donald M. *Science, Chance and Providence*. Oxford University Press: Oxford, 1978.

MacKay, Donald M. 'Selves and Brains.' *Neurosciences*. Vol 3 (1978): pp 599–606.

MacKay, Donald M. *Brains, Machines and Persons*. Collins: London, 1980.

MacKay, Donald M. 'Review of *God of Chance*.' *Religious Studies*. Vol 21 (1986): pp 622–4.

Mae-Wan, Ho, Saunders, Peter and Fox, Sidney. 'A New Paradigm for Evolution.' *New Scientist*. 27th February 1986.

Manuel, F E. *The Religion of Isaac Newton*. Oxford University Press: Oxford, 1974.

Marcus Aurelius. *Meditations* (translated by M Staniforth). Penguin: London, 1964 (original c 167–80 AD).

Marczmar, A G and Eccles, John C (eds). *Brain and Human Behaviours*, Springer-Verlag: New York, 1972.

Marsden, G M. 'Creation Versus Evolution.' *Nature*. Vol 305 (1983): pp 571–4.

Marsden, George M. *Fundamentalism and American Culture: The Shaping of Twentieth Century Evangelicalism, 1870–1925*. Oxford University Press: Oxford, 1980.

Marshall, I Howard (ed). *New Testament Interpretation*. Paternoster: Exeter, 1979.

Marston, V Paul. *God and the Family*. Kingsway: Eastbourne, 1984 (first edition, *The Biblical Family*. Cornerstone: Illinois, 1980.)

Marston, V Paul and Forster, Roger T. *God's Strategy in Human History*. Tyndale House: Illinois, 1973.

Marx, Karl. *The Economic and Philosophic Manuscripts of 1844* (translated by M Milligan). International Publishers: New York, 1964.

Marx, Karl. *The German Ideology* (ed R Pascal). International Publishers: New York, 1947 (original written in 1845–6, unpublished).

Marx, Karl. *The Grundrisse* (translated by M Nicolaus). Penguin: London, 1973 (original written in 1857–8, unpublished).

Marx, Karl. *Das Kapital*. 1867.

McCluhan, Marshall and Fiore, Quentin. *The Medium is the Message*. Allan Lane: London, 1967.

McDonald, H D. *Ideas of Revelation*. Macmillan: London, 1959.

McDowell, Josh. *Evidence that Demands a Verdict*. Revised edition. Here's Life: San Bernardino, 1979.

McDowell, Josh. *More Evidence that Demands a Verdict*. Revised edition. Here's Life: San Bernardino, 1981.

McDowell, Josh. *The Resurrection Proven Beyond Doubt!* Scripture Press: Bucks, 1988.

McKie, D. *Antoine Lavoisier*. Constable: London, 1962 (first edition, 1952).

Medawar, P. *Induction and Intuition in Scientific Thought*. Methuen: London, 1969.

Metzger, Bruce M. *The Canon of the New Testament*. Oxford University Press: Oxford 1987.

Metzger, Bruce M. *The Text of the New Testament*. Oxford University Press: Oxford, 1968.

Metzger, Bruce M. *Manuscripts of the Greek Bible*. Oxford University Press: Oxford, 1981.

Midgley, Mary. *Evolution as a Religion*. Methuen: London, 1985.

Mill, John Stuart. *A System of Logic*. Longman: London, 1961 (first edition, 1843).

Mill, John Stuart. *Essay on Theism*. 1874.

Miller, Hugh. *Footprints of the Creator; or the Asterolepis of Stromness*. W P Ninno: Edinburgh, 1849.

Miller, Hugh. *The Testimony of the Rocks*. 1857 (first edition, 1849).

Moltmann, Jurgen. *God in Creation: An Ecological Doctrine of Creation*. SCM Press: London, 1985.

Monod, Jacques. *Chance and Necessity*. Fontana: London, 1971 (translated by Knopf, 1970).

Montagu, Ashley (ed). *Science and Creationism*. Oxford University Press: Oxford, 1984.

Moore, James R. *The Post Darwinian Controversies*. Cambridge University Press: Cambridge, 1979.

Morison, F. *Who Moved the Stone?* Faber: London, 1930.

Morris, Henry M. *Many Infallible Proofs*. Creation Life: San Deigo, 1974.

Morris, Henry M. *The Genesis Record*. Baker: Grand Rapids, 1976.

Morris, Henry M. *Evolution and the Modern Christian*. Second edition. Baker: Grand Rapids, 1977.

Morris, Henry M. *The Beginning of the World*. Second edition. Accent Books: Denver, 1977.

Morris, Henry. *Men of Science, Men of God*. Master Book Publishers: San Diego, 1982.

Morris, Henry M. *The Biblical Basis for Modern Science*. Baker: Grand Rapids, 1984.

Morris, Henry M. *A History of Modern Creationism*. Master Book Publishers: San Diego, 1984.

Morris, Henry M. *Science and the Bible*. Revised edition. Scripture Press: Bucks, 1988.

Morris, Henry M and Whitcomb, J. *The Genesis Flood*. Baker: Grand Rapids, 1961.

Moule, C F D. *The Phenomenon of the New Testament*. A & C Black: London, 1967.

Muggeridge, Malcolm. *Another King*. St Andrews Press: Edinburgh, 1968.

Muggeridge, Malcolm. *Jesus Rediscovered*. Fontana: London, 1969.

Muggeridge, Malcolm. *Christ and the Media*. Hodder: London, 1971.

Muggeridge, Malcolm. *Something Beautiful for God*. Seventh impression. Fontana: London, 1976.

Neve, M and Porter R. 'Alexander Catcott.' *British Journal for the History of Science*. Vol x: i (1977): pp 37–60.

Newman, R C and Eckelman, H. *Genesis One and the Origin of the Earth*. Baker: Grand Rapids, 1981.

Newton-Smith, W. *The Rationality of Science*. Routledge and Kegan Paul: London, 1981.

Nickles, T (ed). *Scientific Discovery, Logic and Rationality*. Reidel: London, 1980.

Nidditch, P H (ed). *The Philosophy of Science*. Oxford University Press: Oxford, 1968.

Nietzsche, F. *Thus Spoke Zarathustra*. 1883–4. (Translated by R J Hollingdale) Penguin, 1961.

O'Connor, J (ed). *Modern Materialism: Readings on Mind-Body Identity* (general editor: J Fogelin). Harcourt Brace and World: New York, 1969.

Oresme, N. *Le Livre du Ciel*. 1377.

Origen, *First Principles* (translated by G W Butterworth). SPCK: London, 1936.

Orr, James. *Science and Christian Faith* and *The Early Narratives of Genesis* (Volumes 4 and 6 in *The Fundamentals*). Testimony Publishing Company: Chicago, 1910–15.

Paley, William. *Horae Paulinae*. 1790.

Paley, William. *A View of the Evidences of Christianity*. 1794.

Paley, William. *Natural Theology*. 1802.

Payne, D F. *Genesis One Reconsidered*. Tyndale Press: London, 1964.

Peacocke, A R. *Creation and the World of Science*. Clarendon: Oxford, 1979.

Peacocke, Arthur (ed). *Reductionism in Academic Disciplines*. SRFE and NFER-Nelson: Guildford, 1985.

Peacocke, Arthur. *God and the New Biology*. Dent: London, 1986.

Pearce, E K Victor. *Who Was Adam?* Second edition. Paternoster: Exeter, 1969.

Pearce, E K Victor. 'The Flood and Archaeology.' *Faith and Thought*. Vol 101 (1974): pp 228–41; Vol 102 (1975): pp 18–21.

Pember, G H. *Earth's Earliest Ages*. 1876.

Penfield, W. *The Mystery of the Mind*. Princeton University Press: Princeton, 1975.

Pfeiffer, John E. *The Emergence of Man*. Third edition. Harper and Row: London, 1978.

Phillips, J B. *Ring of Truth*. Hodder: London, 1970.

Pitman, Michael. *Adam and Evolution*. Rider: London, 1984.

Planck, Max. *The Universe in the Light of Modern Physics*. Second edition. Unwin: London, 1937.

Polanyi, Michael. *Personal Knowledge: Towards a Post-Critical Philosophy*. Routledge: London, 1958.

Polkinghorne, J. *The Quantum World*. Longman: Essex, 1984.

Polkinghorne, J. *Science and Creation*. SPCK Press: London, 1988.

Polkinghorne, J. *Science and Providence*. SPCK Press: London, 1989.

Pollard, W G. *Chance and Providence*. Faber and Faber: London, 1958.

Poole, M W and Wenham, J Gordon. *Creation or Evolution — A False Antithesis?* Latimer House: Oxford, 1987.

Popper, Karl. *The Logic of Scientific Discovery*. Hutchinson: London, 1956 (Original in German, 1934).

Popper, Karl. *Conjectures and Refutations*. Second edition. Routledge and Kegan Paul: London, 1965 (first edition 1963).

Porter, R. 'Charles Lyell and the Principles of the History of Geology.' *British Journal for the History of Science*. ix, 2, 32 (1976), pp 91–103.

Porter, R. *The Making of Geology*. Cambridge University Press: Cambridge, 1977.

Postman, Neil. *Amusing Ourselves to Death*. Heinemann: London, 1986.

Powell, Graham and Shirley. *Christian Set Yourself Free*. New Wine: Chichester, 1983.

Powers, J. *Philosophy and the New Physics*. Methuen: London, 1982.

Price, Roger. *The Age of the Earth*. 1979.

Quine, W V. *Word and Object*. Wiley: New York, 1960.

Qur'an (translated by N J Dawood). Penguin: London, 1970.

Ramm, Bernard. *The Christian View of Science and Scripture*. Second impression. Paternoster: Exeter, 1961 (first published, 1954).

Ramsay, W M. *St Paul the Traveller and the Roman Citizen*. Hodder & Stoughton: London, 1895.

Ramsay, W M. *The Bearing of Recent Discovery*. 1915.

Rattray-Taylor, G. *The Great Evolution Mystery*. Secker & Warburg: London, 1983.

Rautsch, Del. *Philosophy of Science*. IVP: Leicester, 1986.

Ray, J. *Reflections on the Study of Nature* (translated by Smith). 1876.

Ray, J. *The Wisdom of God Manifested in the Works of Creation*. 1691.

Reader, John. *Missing Links*. Collins: London, 1981.

Renan, J E. *Life of Jesus*. 1863.

Rhappaport, R. 'Geology and Orthodoxy.' *British Journal for the History of Science*. x, 1 (1977), pp 37–60.

Rheticus. *Narratio Prima*. 1540.

Ridley, M. *The Problems of Evolution*. Oxford University Press: Oxford, 1985.

Roberts, A and Donaldson, J (eds). *Writing of the Fathers*. Eerdmans: Grand Rapids, 1985.

Roberts, M B. 'The Roots of Creationism.' *Faith and Thought*. Vol 112: 1 (1986): pp 21–36.

Robertson, J (ed). *The Philosophical Works of Francis Bacon*. George Routledge: London, 1905.

Robinson, John A T. *Redating the New Testament*. SCM Press: London, 1976.

Robinson, John A T. *Can we trust the New Testament?* Mowbrays: London, 1977.

Romer, J. *Testament*. Michael O'Mara Books: London, 1988.

Rudwick, M. *The Meaning of Fossils*. Macdonald: London, 1972.

Rudwick, M. 'Charles Lyell and his London Lectures on Geology.' *Royal Society Notes and Records*. Vol 29 (1974): pp 231–63.

Rudwick, M. 'Lyell's Chronological Model.' *ISIS*. Vol 243 (1977): pp 440–3.

Rudwick, M. 'Charles Darwin in London: The Integration of Public and Private Science.' *ISIS*. Vol 73 (1982): p 190, etc.

Russell, Colin A. *Science and Social Change 1700–1900*. Macmillan: London, 1983.

Russell, Colin A. *Crosscurrents*. Inter-Varsity Press: Leicester, 1985.

Russell, Colin A, Hooykaas, R and Goodman, David C. *The Conflict Thesis and Cosmology*. Open University Press: Milton Keynes, 1974.

Ryle, Gilbert. *The Concept of Mind*. Hutchinson: London, 1949.

Sabritsky, Bill. *Demons Defeated*. Sovereign World: Chichester, 1985.

Sanday, W and Headlam, A C. *A Critical and Exegetical Commentary on the Epistle to the Romans*. Fifth edition. T & T Clark: Edinburgh, 1902.

Sartre, Jean-Paul. *Existentialism and Humanism*. Methuen: London, 1948.

Sartre, Jean-Paul. *Words*. Hamilton: London, 1964.

Savage, L J. *Foundations of Statistics*. Wiley: New York, 1954.

Schaeffer, Francis A. *Genesis in Space and Time*. Inter-Varsity Press: Illinois, 1972.

Schwartz, J H. *The Red Ape*. Hamilton: London, 1987.

Schweitzer, Albert. *The Quest for the Historical Jesus: A Critical Study of its Progress from Reimarus to Wrede*. 1910.

Searle, John. *Minds, Brains and Science*. BBC: London, 1984.

Seneca. *Epistulae Morales. Ad Lucilium*. 63–5 AD (translated by R M Gummere in three volumes. Loeb: London, 1917–25).

Setterfield, B. *The Atomic Constants, Light and Time*. Stanford Research Institute International: Stanford, 1987.

Sherrington, C S. *The Brain and Its Mechanism*. Cambridge University Press: Cambridge, 1933.

Sherrington, C S. *Man on his Nature*. Cambridge University Press: Cambridge, 1940.

Sherwood, E R and Stern, Curt. *The Origin of Genetics: A Mendel Source Book*. Freeman: London, 1966.

Smart, Ninian. *Concept and Empathy*. Macmillan: London, 1986.

Smith, John Pye. *Relation Between the Holy Scriptures and Some Parts of Geological Science*. 1839 (final version, 1854).

Spanner, Douglas. *Biblical Creation and the Theory of Evolution*. Paternoster: Exeter, 1987.

Sperry, R W. 'Forebrain Commissurotomy and Conscious Awareness.' *J Med Phil*. Vol 2 (1977): pp 101–26

Sperry, R W et al. 'Self Recognition and Social Awareness ...' *Neuropsychologia*. Vol 17 (1979): pp 156–66.

Stanesby, Derek. *Science, Reason and Religion*. Croom Helm: London, 1985.

Stannard, Russell. *Science and the Renewal of Belief*. SCM Press: London, 1982.

Steneck, N. *Science and Creation in the Middle Ages*. Notre Dame: London, 1976.

Stillingfleet, E. *Origines Sacrae*. 1662.

Stock, E. *The History of the Church Missionary Society* 1899–1916.

Stoner, Peter. *Science Speaks*. Moody: Chicago, 1963.

Strauss, D F. *Life of Jesus*. 1835–6 (translated in 1846).

Suetonius. *Life of Claudius*. 120 AD (translated by J C Rolfe. Loeb: London, 1914).

Suppe, Frederick (ed). *The Structure of Scientific Theories*. Second edition. University of Illinois Press: London, 1977.

Talcott, R. 'A Burst of Discovery: The First Days of Supernova 1987a.' *Astronomy*. June 1987.

Thackray, A. and Morrell F J. *Gentlemen of Science*. Clarendon: Oxford, 1981.

Thorpe, W H. *Animal Nature and Human Nature*. Methuen: London, 1974.

Thorpe, W H. *Purpose in a World of Chance*. Oxford University Press: Oxford, 1978.

Tindale, Matthew. *Christianity as Old as Creation*. 1730.

Toland, John. *Christianity Not Mysterious*. 1696.

Toon, P. *Evangelical Theology 1833–1856*. Marshall, Morgan and Scott: Basingstoke, 1979.

Torrens, Hugh. 'Hawking History — a Vital Future for Geology's Past.' *Modern Geology*. Vol 13 (1988): pp 83–93.

Torrey, R A. *Difficulties in the Bible*. Moody: Chicago, 1907.

Torrey, R A. *The Fundamentals*. Baker Book House reprint (1988) of 1917 Bible Institute edition. Four volumes. Original twelve volumes issued by Testimony Publishing House: Chicago, 1910–1915.

Tournier, Paul. *The Whole Person in a Broken World*. Collins: London, 1965.

Tucker, R A. *Philosophy and Myth in Karl Marx*. Cambridge University Press: Cambridge, 1961.

Turner, F M. 'Victorian Conflict Between Science and Religion.' *ISIS*. Vol 69 (1978): pp 356–76.

Van De Fliert, R. 'Fundamentalism and the Fundamentals of Geology.' *ASA Journal*, 'Origins and Change' (1978).

Van Leeuwen, Mary Stewart. *The Person in Psychology*. Inter-Varsity Press/Eerdmans: Leicester, 1985.

Van Till, Howard J. *The Fourth Day*. Eerdmans: Grand Rapids, 1986.

Vermes, G. 'Biblical Studies and the Dead Sea Scrolls 1947–1987.' *Journal for the Study of the Old Testament*. Vol 38 (1987): pp 113–28.

Vesalius, *Anatomy of the Human Body*. 1543.

Von Mises, R. *Probability, Statistics and Truth*. Revised edition. Allen and Unwin: London, 1957 (first edition, 1939).

Von Rad, G. *Commentary on Genesis*. SCM Press: London, 1961.

Walker, Benjamin. *Gnosticism*. Aquarian Press: Northamptonshire, 1983.

Ward, Keith. *Rational Theology and the Creativity of God*. Blackwell: Oxford, 1982.

Ward, Keith. *The Battle for the Soul*. Hodder: London, 1985.

Warfield, Benjamin. *Counterfeit Miracles*. 1918.

Wells, H G. *Mind at the End of its Tether*. Heinemann: London, 1945.

Wenham, J Gordon. *Genesis 1–15*. Word Bible Commentary: 1987.

Wenham, John. *Easter Enigma*. Paternoster: Exeter, 1984.

Wesley, John. *A Clear and Concise Demonstration of the Divine Inspiration of Holy Scripture* in Wesley's *Works*. Hendrickson's Publishers: Massachusetts, 1986 printing (third edition, 1872).

Wesley, John. *Journals* in Wesley's *Works*. Hendrickson's Publishers: Massachusetts, 1986 printing.

Westermann, G. *Genesis 1–11*. SPCK: London, 1984.

Westfall, Richard S. *Science and Religion in Seventeenth Century England* Paperback edition. University of Michigan Press: Michigan, 1973.

Whewell, William. *The Philosophy of the Inductive Sciences*. Two volumes. 1840 and 1847.

Whitcomb, John C. *The Early Earth*.

Whitcomb, John C and DeYoung, Donald B. *The Moon: Its Creation, Form and Significance*. BMH Books: Indiana, 1978.

White, A. *A History of the Warfare of Science with Theology in Christendom*. Two volumes. Macmillan: London, 1896.

Wilder-Smith A E. *Man's Origin, Man's Destiny*. Telos/Marshall, Morgan and Scott: London, 1974.

Wilson, E O. *Sociobiology: The New Synthesis*. Belknap, Harvard University Press: Cambridge, Massachusetts, 1975.

Wink, Walter. *Naming the Powers*. Fortress Press: Philadelphia, 1984.

Wink, Walter. *Unmasking the Powers*. Fortress Press: Philadelphia, 1986.

Wiseman, P J. *Creation Revealed in Six Days*. Marshall, Morgan and Scott: Basingstoke, 1949.

Wittgenstein, Ludwig. *Tractatus Logico-Philosophicus* (translated by D F Pears and B F McGuiness). Routledge: London, 1961 (first English edition, 1922).

Wittgenstein, Ludwig. 'Lectures on Religious Belief' in C Barrett (ed), *Lectures and Conversations in Aesthetics, Psychology and Religious Belief*. Blackwell: Oxford, 1966.

Wolfe, David L. *Epistemology*. Inter-Varsity Press: Illinois, 1982.

Wood, B A. *Human Evolution*. Chapman and Hall: London, 1978.

Woodward, J. *Essay Toward a Natural History of the Earth*. London, 1695.

Wright, G F. *Studies in Science and Religion*. 1882.

Wright, G F. *Scientific Confirmations of Old Testament History*. 1896.

Wright, G F. *Scientific Aspects of Christian Evidences*. 1898.

Wright, J Stafford. *What is Man?* Paternoster: Exeter, 1976.

Young, Davis A. *Creation and the Flood*. Baker: Grand Rapids, 1977.

Young, Davis A. *Christianity and the Age of the Earth*. Zondervan, Grand Rapids, 1982.

Young, Davis A. 'Scripture in the Hands of the Geologists.' *Westminster Theological Journal*. Vol 49, 1–34 (1987): pp 257–304.

Young, E J. *Studies in Genesis One*. Presbyterian and Reformed Publishing Co: New Jersey, 1964.

Young, E J. *Genesis 3*. Banner of Truth: Edinburgh, 1966.

Young, E J. *In the Beginning*. Banner of Truth: Edinburgh, 1976.

Yule, J D. *The Impact of British Religious Thought in the Second Quarter of the Nineteenth Century*. Cambridge, PhD thesis, 1976.

# Index

# Index of Bible References